NATIONAL CURRICULUM EDITION

UNDERSTANDING MATHEMATICS

Second Edition

3

C. J. Cox & D. Bell

JOHN MURRAY

Acknowledgements

The authors have been delighted with the enthusiastic reception given to the Understanding Mathematics series and wish to thank their publishers, reviewers, and all who have written with encouraging comments and helpful suggestions, especially Sue Jennings (Exeter University School of Education), the Devon Users' Group, and the pupils and teachers who have written (from as far away as Kuwait!) in response to the 'challenges'.

We are also grateful for advice given during preparation of the first edition from:

Kath Hart, Brian Bolt (Exeter University), Andrew Rothery (Worcester College of Education), Alec Penfold, Martyn Dunford (Huish Episcopi School), Jacqueline Gilday (Wells Blue School), Hazel Bevan (Millfield School), John Wishlade (Uffculme School), John Halsall, David Symes, Simon Goodenough, Mary Mears.

Thanks are also due to the editorial and production staff at John Murray, Sue Glover, and to all the many teachers and pupils who have helped in the testing and revising of the course.

Illustrations by Tony Langham and Technical Art Services

Photographs by permission of: Science Photo Library (p.7); Philip Harris Education (p.8); United Nations (p.27); James Davis Photography (p.98); Egyptian Tourist Board (p.111); Colorsport (p.116); G. A. Macdonald, U.S. Geological Survey 1975 (p.157); Marc Henrie ASC (p.171)

© C. J. Cox and D. Bell 1990

First published 1985
by John Murray (Publishers) Ltd
50 Albemarle Street, London W1X 4BD

Reprinted 1986, 1987, 1989

Second edition 1990

Reprinted 1992 (twice) with revisions

Typeset by Blackpool Typesetting Services Ltd., Blackpool
Printed in Great Britain at the University Press, Cambridge

British Library Cataloguing in Publication Data

Cox, Christopher J.
   Understanding mathematics 3. — 2nd ed.
   Pupils' book
   1. Mathematics
   I. Title   II. Bell, D. (David), *1942–*
   510

ISBN 0-7195-4756-3

Preface

Understanding Mathematics is a complete course of five books for secondary pupils in the 11–16 age range. This is the third of a three-book course covering Key Stage 3 of the National Curriculum Programme to Level 8. The parallel series, **Steps in Understanding Mathematics**, covers up to Level 6 with some extension to Level 7.

The development of each topic was planned with reference to the findings of the research project *Concepts in Secondary Mathematics and Science* (CSMS), resulting in 'common core' exercises with a less steep incline of difficulty than other texts. In both series, pupils are stretched by extension (boxed) activities, while the common core allows easy transfer between sets, and between the two series. The emphasis on constant revision within the exercises (an approach that is echoed in the National Mathematics Curriculum), together with the Summaries, the Glossary, and the weekly revision Papers, has proved a very successful confidence-building approach.

The **Teachers' Resource Books** have teaching notes and demonstration examples; transparency masters; answers, including diagrams; aural (mental) tests; practical worksheet masters; assessment tests; computer teaching programs.

Two further publications supplement the main course: **Aural Tests in Mathematics** (Books 1–5) provide essential practice in life-skills, and **Mathematics Coursework 1–3** encourages pupils to explore mathematical ideas – to say 'What if . . .?'

Notes on this National Curriculum edition

The many improvements in this edition make using it alongside the first edition inadvisable, though not impossible. The Teachers' Resource Book contains full details of the changes made, but the major ones are:

- the reordering of topics to facilitate preparation for Standard Assessment at the end of Key Stage 3;

- the expansion of some topics to cover the National Curriculum more thoroughly;

- extra chapters at Level 8 for the ablest pupils.

Contents

About this book

This is the third book of Understanding Mathematics, which completes the course leading to assessment at the end of Key Stage 3.

Each chapter is concerned with a mathematical topic, and is divided into **exercises. New ideas** are clearly explained, and **discussion starters** give you the chance to talk about the mathematics and to see how it links with everyday life. **Computer programs** are included; the BASIC used will work on all the popular micros.

Almost all the exercises have four kinds of question:

- **Introductory questions** are for everyone.
- **Starred questions** are optional for those who find the introductory questions very easy.
- **Further questions** follow. These continue the topic to a higher level.
- **Boxed questions** challenge those who are keen and quick, and give lots of ideas for investigations and practical work.

This structure helps you learn at your own pace, and builds up your confidence.

The book also includes:

- **Using your calculator** exercises
- **Projects**
- **Papers** – for homework and revision
- **Summaries** of the ideas met in each chapter, to help you study and revise.
- **Glossary**, giving the meaning of mathematical words which you will meet in the course.

Your teacher will also give you **worksheets** during the course for projects, practical work and assessment.

1 Transformations: enlargement

A Scale factor

1 : 6.

Fig. 1:1

For Discussion

What is happening in Figure 1:1?
What instruments make objects look a different size?

In Figure 1:2, ABCD and A'B'C'D' are **similar**, that is, they are the same shape but not the same size. The sides of A'B'C'D' are twice as long as the sides of ABCD. ABCD has been **enlarged by scale factor 2** to give A'B'C'D'.

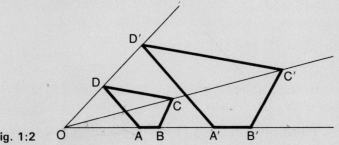

Fig. 1:2

(a) Measure OA and OA', OB and OB', OC and OC', and OD and OD'. Discuss your answers.

(b) If you wished to enlarge ABCD by **scale factor 3** from the same centre to give A"B"C"D", how long would you make OA", OB", OC" and OD"?

1 Copy Figure 1:2 exactly. (Start at O, leaving about 6 cm above it and 9 cm on its right. Make ∠AOC = 30° and ∠AOD = 45°.) Enlarge ABCD by scale factor 3 from centre O.

2 In Figure 1:3 the sides of P'Q'R'S' are half the length of the sides of PQRS. Check this. PQRS has been reduced in size, but in mathematics we say PQRS has been **enlarged by scale factor** $\frac{1}{2}$ to give P'Q'R'S'.

(a) If you wished to 'enlarge' PQRS by scale factor $\frac{1}{3}$ to give P"Q"R"S", how long should you make OP", OQ", OR", and OS"?

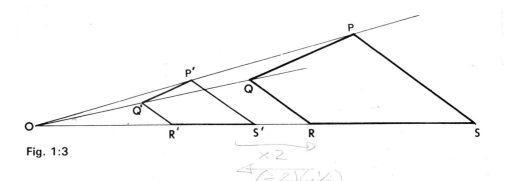

Fig. 1:3

(b) Draw any large irregular pentagon and 'enlarge' it by scale factor $\frac{1}{2}$ using a centre of enlargement somewhere inside the pentagon, as in Figure 1:4. Measure distances carefully, correct to the nearest millimetre.

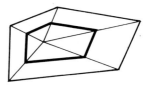

Fig. 1:4

(c) Check the accuracy of your enlarged pentagon by measuring the sides and comparing these with the original lengths.

3 (a) On 1 cm squared paper draw x- and y-axes from 0 to 12 each.

(b) Plot A (3, 0), B (4, 0), C (4, 2) and D (3, 4).
Join them to make a trapezium.

(c) Use rays from the origin, O, to enlarge ABCD by scale factor 2 to give A'B'C'D'. State the co-ordinates of A', B', C' and D'.

(d) Taking a new centre of enlargement, E, at (11, 8), enlarge A'B'C'D' (not ABCD) by scale factor $\frac{1}{2}$ to give A"B"C"D". State the co-ordinates of A", B", C" and D". (This will involve half co-ordinates.)

(e) What scale factor 'enlarges' ABCD to A"B"C"D"?

4 A rectangle 2 cm by 1 cm is enlarged. What is its new size if the scale factor of the enlargement is:

(a) 10   (b) $\frac{1}{2}$ (c) $2\frac{1}{2}$ (d) $\frac{1}{10}$?

5 State the scale factor for each diagram in Figure 1:5, then state the lengths w, x, y and z. (The diagrams are not drawn to scale.)

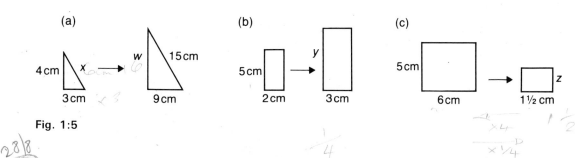

(a)

4cm · 3cm · x → w · 15cm · 9cm

(b)

5cm · 2cm → y · 3cm

(c)

5cm · 6cm → z · 1½ cm

Fig. 1:5

28/8

6 (a) On 1 cm squared paper, draw x- and y-axes: x from 0 to 15, y from 0 to 10.

(b) Join (6, 0) to (6, 4) and join (6, 4) to (0, 4) to make a rectangle. Using the origin as the centre of enlargement, draw similar rectangles of scale factors 1.5, 2, 2.5 and 0.5.

7 Investigate what happens to co-ordinates of points when shapes are enlarged using the centre as origin. What if a different centre is used?

8 Figure 1:6 shows a pantograph. You could use four strips of fairly stiff card, each about 15 cm by 2 cm, and five drawing pins. The fixed pivot can be made by a pin pushed through from behind the drawing paper.

When AB = BC = CD = DA the pantograph enlarges by scale factor 2.

Experiment with other positions of A, B and C.

If made of wood or perspex the pantograph will work much better.

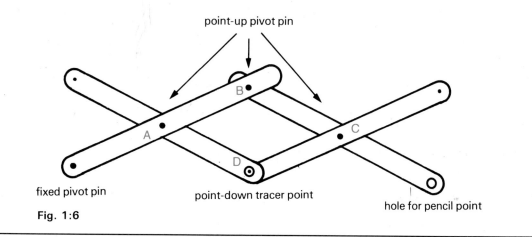

point-up pivot pin

fixed pivot pin

point-down tracer point

hole for pencil point

Fig. 1:6

B   Negative scale factor

Figure 1:7 shows △ABC enlarged by scale factor 2 to give A'B'C'. It also shows △ABC enlarged to give A"B"C" with the centre of enlargement between the two triangles. △A"B"C" is the same size as △A'B'C', but to distinguish it we say it has been **enlarged by scale factor − 2** (a negative enlargement).

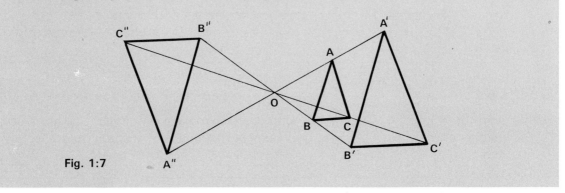

Fig. 1:7

1 (a) Copy Figures 1:8 and 1:9 carefully onto squared paper (1 cm squared is best).

 (b) Figure 1:8 shows a small triangle enlarged by scale factor 2. Find the centre of enlargement by drawing rays joining the corresponding corners on each triangle and finding where the rays meet. You should find it is at (0, 2).

 (c) Figure 1:9 shows the same small triangle enlarged to make its sides three times as long, but the larger triangle is upside-down. Join corresponding corners to find the centre of the enlargement. You should find it is between the two triangles at (2, 3).

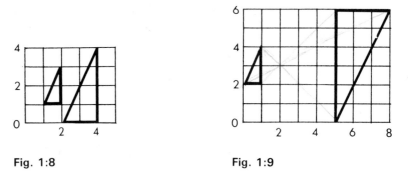

Fig. 1:8   Fig. 1:9

2 Draw any simple small shape and enlarge it, both by scale factor 2 and by scale factor − 2, using the same centre for both. (Take the centre *outside* the shape, and be careful to leave enough space on each side of it.)

3 Repeat question 2 for scale factors $\frac{1}{2}$ and $-\frac{1}{2}$.

4 Draw a diagram like Figure 1:10, then draw rays through O to give A'B'C' where AO = OA', BO = OB', and CO = OC'. You should find the triangle is inverted but not enlarged. Mathematicians call this an enlargement by scale factor − 1.

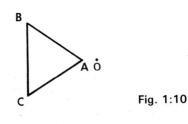

Fig. 1:10

5 Copy and complete this table for the co-ordinates of the images of the given points A, B, C, and D, using the origin as centre. (Draw the points on a grid if it helps you.)

Scale factor	A (3, 0)	B (0, 2)	C (3, 2)	D (− 1, 2)
2				
$\frac{1}{2}$				
− 1				
− 2				
$-\frac{1}{2}$				

6 In Figure 1:11 a shadow is cast on the screen.
In Figure 1:12 a slide is projected through a lens to give an image on a screen.

(a) Suggest a possible scale factor for each enlargement.

(b) In Figure 1:11 how far from the lamp must the object be to cast an image of enlargement factor 5 on the screen 5 metres from the lamp?

(c) You have a slide with THE END on it. What must THE END look like when you put it in the projector, looking from behind it?

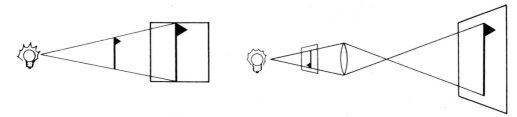

Fig. 1:11   Fig. 1:12

7 Use a lens to make images of windows on a wall. Measure distances to find if the rules of enlargement apply.

For Discussion

Use a calculator to find:
$300\,000 \times 20\,000$
$0.0006 \div 20\,000$

Positive powers of ten

10^2 is short for 10×10 = a hundred

10^3 is short for $10 \times 10 \times 10$ = a thousand

10^6 is short for $10 \times 10 \times 10 \times 10 \times 10 \times 10$ = a million

10^9 is short for $10 \times 10 \times 10 \times 10 \times 10 \times 10 \times 10 \times 10 \times 10$ = a billion

Negative powers of ten

10^{-1} is short for $\frac{1}{10} = 0.1$ = a tenth

10^{-2} is short for $\frac{1}{100} = 0.01$ = a hundredth

10^{-3} is short for $\frac{1}{1000} = 0.001$ = a thousandth

Note that 10^0 is 1, not 0.

Standard form

Number	On paper	On calculator	On computer
3100	3.1×10^3	3.1 03	3.1E3
462 000	4.62×10^5	4.62 05	4.62E5
0.36	3.6×10^{-1}	3.6 -01	3.6E-1
0.0005	5×10^{-4}	5. -04	5E-4

The index (raised) figure tells you how many columns the figures should be moved to convert from standard form to an ordinary number, moving to the left for a positive index, and to the right for a negative index.

1 Write as a power of 10:
  (a) 100   (b) 100 000   (c) $\frac{1}{10}$ (d) $\frac{1}{1000}$ (e) 1.

2 Write as an ordinary decimal number:
  (a) 3×10 (b) 4×10^2 (c) 1×10^3 (d) 1×10^5 (e) 4.6×10^2
  (f) 3.1×10^3 (g) 6.81×10^2.

3 Write as an ordinary decimal number:

(a) 4×10^{-1} (b) 1×10^{-2} (c) 7×10^{-3} (d) 3.1×10^{-1}

(e) 5.6×10^{-2} (f) 3.08×10^{-2}.

4 Write in standard form:

(a) 3000   (b) 400   (c) 3600   (d) 87 000   (e) 6100   (f) 821 000

(g) 10 000 000.

5 Write in standard form:

(a) 0.05   (b) 0.4   (c) 0.0001   (d) 0.067   (e) 0.081   (f) 0.0056

*6 Write as an ordinary decimal number:

(a) 1.63×10 (b) 4.91×10^2 (c) 3.03×10^3 (d) 4.44×10^4

(e) 7.6×10^{-1} (f) 3.15×10^{-2} (g) 9.87×10^{-3}.

*7 Write in standard form:

(a) 14 000   (b) 380 000   (c) 760   (d) 101 000   (e) 0.071

(f) 0.33   (g) 0.001 23

8 Using a scientific calculator, evaluate the following, writing your answers both in standard form and as ordinary decimal numbers.

(a) 23 000 × 45 000 × 36 000

(b) 140 561 × 9507.91

(c) 0.002 ÷ 356 501

(d) 2 ÷ 4560 ÷ 7135

9 ● Light travels at 5.8×10^{12} miles per year. This distance is called a light-year.

● The Sun is 8.65×10^5 miles in diameter.

● The centre of the Sun is at $1.3 \times 10^7\,°C$. The centre of a coal fire is $8 \times 10^2\,°C$.

● A 200 inch telescope can 'see' about 7×10^9 light-years.

● The Sun is 1.6×10^{-5} light-years away from Earth.

● The nearest star after the Sun is Proxima Centaurus. It is 4.2×10^0 light-years away.

● Our galaxy is called the Milky Way. It is about 1×10^5 light-years across and contains at least 1×10^{11} stars.

- The next galaxies to ours are the Magellanic Clouds. They are 1.6×10^5 light-years away.

Rewrite these facts giving the numbers as ordinary decimals. You could organise your answer as a table.

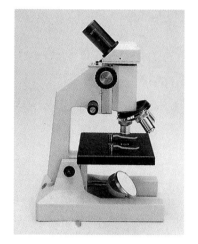

10
- An atom has a radius of 10^{-9} mm.

- The best ordinary microscope can see objects as small as 5×10^{-4} mm across.

- A micron is 1×10^{-3} mm.

- An electron microscope can 'see' down to 2×10^{-3} microns.

- A human hair has a radius of between 3×10^{-2} mm and 7.5×10^{-2} mm.

- A red blood cell has a diameter of 7×10^{-3} mm.

Rewrite these facts giving the numbers as ordinary decimals. You could organise your answer as a table.

11
- Earth was formed 5 000 000 000 years ago.

- The first sea life appeared about 600 000 000 years ago.

- The first land life (plants) appeared about 400 000 000 years ago.

- The first land animals appeared about 350 000 000 years ago.

- The first mammals and reptiles appeared about 270 000 000 years ago.

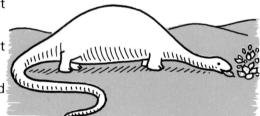

- The first dinosaurs appeared about 225 000 000 years ago. Most dinosaurs died out about 135 000 000 years ago.

- The first humans appeared about 1 000 000 years ago.

Rewrite these facts giving the numbers in standard form. You could organise your answer as a table.

12 On a scientific calculator, numbers in standard form can be keyed in using the EXP or EE key.

To enter 8.36×10^{-4}, key 8.36 EXP 4 +/−

This enables calculations with numbers in standard form. Find in standard form correct to 3 decimal places:

(a) $(3.16 \times 10^3) + (7.36 \times 10^{-2})$

(b) $(4.25 \times 10^5) \div (1.26 \times 10^{-3})$

(c) $(8.8 \times 10^{-6}) \times (4.1 \times 10^5)$

(d) $\dfrac{(3.5 \times 10^4) \times (5.3 \times 10^{-1})}{(7.6 \times 10)}$

(e) $\dfrac{(4.1 \times 10^{-5}) + (3 \times 10^3)}{(7.9 \times 10^{-1})}$

13 Use the information in questions 9 and 10 to answer these.

(a) How long does it take in minutes for light to travel from the Sun to Earth?

(b) If a spacecraft could travel at a quarter of the speed of light, how long would it take to reach:
(i) the Sun   (ii) Proxima Centaurus   (iii) the Magellanic Clouds?

(c) How many atoms are on the surface of the head of a pin of radius 1 mm?

14 Make a scale model to illustrate the facts given in question 9 and/or question 11.

15 What numbers can you make using 23 000, 45 000, and 0.002? Write your answers using standard form.

A Prime factors

```
  5 REM "PRIFACT"
 10 LET C = Ø
 20 LET A = 1
 30 PRINT "Type number."
 40 INPUT N
 50 IF INT(N) < > N OR N < = 1 THEN
    GOTO 4Ø
 55 IF N = 2 THEN GOTO 21Ø
 60 CLS     (Clear screen)
 70 PRINT; N; "ˆ=ˆ";
 80 LET M = N
 90 LET P = 2
100 IF M/P = INT(M/P) THEN GOTO 14Ø
110 IF P > N/2 THEN GOTO 21Ø
120 LET P = P + 1
130 GOTO 1ØØ
140 IF C = 1 THEN PRINT "ˆXˆ";
150 LET C = 1
160 PRINT; P;
170 LET A = A*P
180 IF A = N THEN GOTO 22Ø
190 LET M = M/P
200 GOTO 1ØØ
210 IF C = Ø THEN PRINT "Prime
    Factors are 1 and ˆ";N
220 PRINT
230 GOTO 1Ø
```

Notes

When the program is run, line 1ØØ finds if the number divides by 2. If it does, the 2 is printed on the screen at line 16Ø, the number is divided by 2 at line 19Ø, and the process starts again.

When the answer will no longer divide by 2, line 12Ø increases the divisor by 1 (to 3) and so on.

INT gives the integral part of a positive number, so INT(3.6) is 3. Line 5Ø finds out if N is a whole number, and line 1ØØ finds whether M divides exactly by P.

For Discussion

1 Why is there a semi-colon at the end of line 7Ø?

2 Which line tells the computer to stop dividing?

3 C is a 'flag' which is either set to 0 or 1. Find out why it is needed.

4 Draw up a table to show the factors of various numbers. Look for patterns in your table. For example, which numbers have an odd number of factors?

5 What numbers are represented by the letters in Figure 3:1? Make up your own factor puzzles.

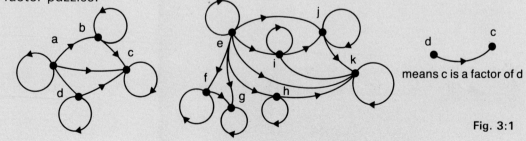

means c is a factor of d

Fig. 3:1

1 Work out:

(a) $2 \times 3 \times 3$ (b) $2 \times 3 \times 5$ (c) $2 \times 5 \times 5$ (d) $2 \times 2 \times 2 \times 2$

(e) $2 \times 3 \times 3 \times 3$ (f) $2 \times 3 \times 5 \times 5$.

2 List the prime numbers from 2 to 41 in order. Check that you have written thirteen numbers.

3 The flow-chart in Figure 3:2 expresses numbers as the product of primes.

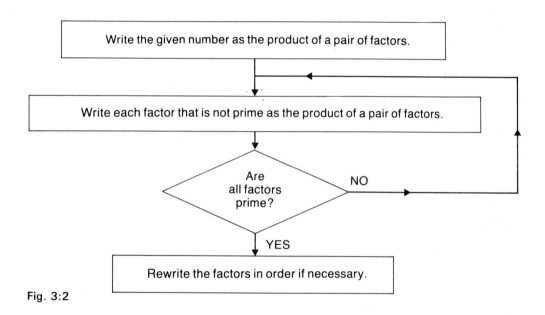

Fig. 3:2

Follow this flow-chart method to express 48 as the product of prime numbers:

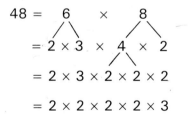

$48 = 6 \times 8$

$= 2 \times 3 \times 4 \times 2$

$= 2 \times 3 \times 2 \times 2 \times 2$

$= 2 \times 2 \times 2 \times 2 \times 3$

Write as the product of prime factors:

(a) 6   (b) 12   (c) 16   (d) 45   (e) 100   (f) 81   (g) 180.

4 The PRIFACT program expresses the number as a product of primes by dividing by the lowest possible number until the number reduces to 1. In fact, only prime numbers need be used as the divisors.

Examples   For 36   For 252

2	36
2	18
3	9
3	3
	1

2	252
2	126
3	63
3	21
7	7
	1

or, failing to divide in order:

2	252
3	126
7	42
2	6
3	3
	1

$$36 = 2 \times 2 \times 3 \times 3 \qquad\qquad 252 = 2 \times 2 \times 3 \times 3 \times 7$$

Use the division method to express the following numbers as a product of prime numbers.
(a) 90   (b) 420   (c) 378   (d) 726   (e) 945.

*5 Use either the flow-chart or the division method to reduce to a product of prime factors:
(a) 42   (b) 65   (c) 72   (d) 196   (e) 2625.

6 Example $a^3 = a \times a \times a$
$2^3 = 2 \times 2 \times 2$
$24 = 2 \times 2 \times 2 \times 3 = 2^3 \times 3$

Note: The raised figures are called 'indices'.

Rewrite your answers to question 4 using indices.

7 Small numbers can be factorised 'in your head' using either the flow-chart or the division method.

Without written working, write as the product of prime factors:
(a) 32   (b) 63   (c) 35   (d) 40   (e) 54   (f) 136   (g) 240   (h) 252.

8 Example $a^3 = a \times a \times a$ and $b^2 = b \times b$

so $a^3 b^2 = a \times a \times a \times b \times b$

and $12a^3 b^2 = 2 \times 2 \times 3 \times a \times a \times a \times b \times b$

Note that a and b need not be prime numbers.

Split into as many factors as possible:
(a) $6a^2$ (b) $2b^2$ (c) $4b^2$ (d) $2a^2 b$ (e) $24a^5 b^2 c$.

---

9 Draw a Sieve of Eratosthenes from 1 to 120, arranging the numbers in rows of six, starting   1   2   3   4   5   6.

Look for patterns in it and write about them.

See Book 1, Chapter 30.

10 Write a computer program which illustrates the Sieve of Eratosthenes.

11 Using each of the figures 1 to 9 once only, write correct multiplication examples. You will need to think very carefully about what placings are possible. We think there are nine answers; two have the answer 5346 and two have the answer 5796. All the examples have one of the two multiplying numbers starting with a 1.

Example   This shows the idea, but is not a correct answer:

$432 \times 78 = 1659$

B   Highest Common Factor

The Highest Common Factor (H.C.F.) of a set of numbers is the biggest number that divides exactly into all of them.

Example

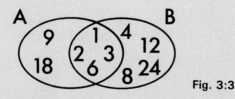

Fig. 3:3

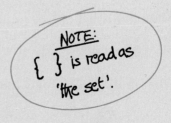
NOTE:
{ } is read as 'the set'.

A = {factors of 18} = {1, 2, 3, 6, 9, 18}
B = {factors of 24} = {1, 2, 3, 4, 6, 8, 12, 24}
{common factors of 18 and 24} = {1, 2, 3, 6}
The **Highest** Common Factor of 18 and 24 is 6.

```
  5 REM "HCF1"; HCF by division
 1Ø PRINT "How many numbers?"
 2Ø INPUT N
 3Ø CLS     (Clear screen)
 4Ø PRINT "Type 1st number."
 5Ø INPUT A
 6Ø PRINT A     (May be omitted)
 7Ø FOR L = 2 TO N
 8Ø PRINT "Type number ‸";L
 9Ø INPUT B
1ØØ PRINT B     (May be omitted)
11Ø IF A < > B THEN GOTO 14Ø
12Ø LET C = B
13Ø GOTO 21Ø
14Ø IF A > B THEN GOTO 18Ø
15Ø LET T = A
16Ø LET A = B
17Ø LET B = T
18Ø LET C = B
19Ø IF A/C = INT(A/C) AND
       B/C = INT(B/C) THEN GOTO 22Ø
2ØØ LET C = C − 1
21Ø IF C > Ø THEN GOTO 19Ø
22Ø LET A = C
23Ø NEXT L
24Ø PRINT "HCF is ‸";C
25Ø GOTO 1Ø
```

To find the H.C.F. of two numbers, called A and B, line 11Ø checks for both numbers being the same, then lines 14Ø to 17Ø make sure that A is the bigger number and B the smaller. Line 18Ø lets C equal B, and lines 19Ø to 21Ø divide A and B by numbers from C down to 1 until a number is found that divides exactly into both of them; their H.C.F.

For more than two numbers the H.C.F. of the first two is found, then A becomes this H.C.F. at line 22Ø, a new B is taken in, and the process is repeated.

Try to write the stores table for the H.C.F. of 6, 9 and 12. Start:

L	2					
A	6	9				
B	9	6				
T	6					
C		6	5	4	3	

1 List the factors and the common factors of the following pairs of numbers, then state their H.C.F.
  (a) 12 and 15   (b) 20 and 25   (c) 8 and 16   (d) 14 and 42   (e) 24 and 36

2 State the H.C.F. of the following without any written working.
  (a) 4 and 6   (b) 8 and 12   (c) 16 and 32   (d) 25 and 35   (e) 27 and 30
  (f) 21 and 49   (g) 20 and 40   (h) 100 and 125

*3 State the H.C.F. of:
  (a) 5 and 20   (b) 8 and 28   (c) 9 and 15   (d) 28 and 42   (e) 18 and 36
  (f) 18 and 45   (g) 9 and 42   (h) 26 and 65   (i) 42 and 56.

*4 What is the H.C.F. of 2 and 3?

*5 Make up a pair of numbers like those in question 2 such that their H.C.F. is:
  (a) 2   (b) 3   (c) 4   (d) 5   (e) 6   (f) 7   (g) 1.

6 Example Find the H.C.F. of 16, 24 and 36.

The H.C.F. of 16 and 24 is 8.
The H.C.F. of 8 and 36 is 4.
Answer: The H.C.F. of 16, 24 and 36 is 4.

NOTE:
It doesn't matter which two numbers you start with.

Find the H.C.F. of:
(a) 6, 18 and 20   (b) 6, 15 and 18   (c) 15, 25 and 30   (d) 1, 5 and 10
(e) 2, 26 and 118   (f) 3, 21 and 47   (g) 27, 36 and 54   (h) 26, 39 and 65.

7 Prime factors are useful for the H.C.F. of larger numbers.

Example Find the H.C.F. of 168 and 180.

$$168 = 2 \times 2 \times 2 \times 3 \times 7$$
$$180 = 2 \times 2 \times 3 \times 3 \times 5$$

H.C.F. $= 2 \times 2 \times 3 = 12$

Use this method for the H.C.F. of:
(a) 90 and 108   (b) 98 and 343   (c) 363, 495 and 165.

8 Example
$$a^2 = a \times a$$
$$a^3 = a \times a \times a$$

The H.C.F. of a^2 and a^3 is $a \times a = a^2$.

Example
$$b^4c^2 = b \times b \times b \times b \times c \times c$$
$$b^3cd = b \times b \times b \times c \times d$$

The H.C.F. of b^4c^2 and b^3cd is b^3c.

Find the H.C.F. of:
(a) x^2 and x (b) x^3 and x^4 (c) $2x$ and $4x$ (d) $2a$ and $4a^2$
(e) $2a^2$ and $5a^3$ (f) b^3 and b^4d (g) $2x^2$ and $6xy$.

9 Can you spot an easy way to find the H.C.F. of algebraic expressions? Try before you read the next line!

Take the lowest power of each common letter.

Example The H.C.F. of $12a^2b^3$, $6a^3b^2c$ and $9a^2b$ is $3a^2b$.

State the H.C.F. of:
(a) $2cd^2$ and $3c^2$ (b) $6a^2g$ and $15ag^2$ (c) $4a^2st$, $2a^2s$ and $2ast$
(d) $4a^3sy^2$, $6a^2y^3$ and $12ay^4$ (e) $2x$ and y (f) $3ab$ and $2ab^2$
(g) $6x$, $7ab$ and $14ab$.

10 What is the smallest number that:
  (a) divided by 2 has remainder 1, and divided by 3 has remainder 2
  (b) divided by 2, 3 or 4 has remainder 1, but divided by 5 has no remainder
  (c) divided by 2, 3, 4 or 6 has remainder 1, but divided by 7 has no remainder?
  Make up some more questions like these.

11 Here is another program which finds H.C.F.s. The method used is rather clever.
  Can you work out how and why it works?

```
  5  REM ''HCF2''
 1Ø  PRINT ''How many numbers?''
 2Ø  INPUT N
 3Ø  CLS      (Clear screen)
 4Ø  PRINT ''Type 1st number.''
 5Ø  INPUT A
 6Ø  PRINT A      (May be omitted)
 7Ø  FOR L = 2 TO N
 8Ø  PRINT ''Type number ˄'';L
 9Ø  INPUT B
1ØØ  PRINT B      (May be omitted)
11Ø  IF A = B THEN GOTO 16Ø
12Ø  LET C = ABS (A − B)
```

```
13Ø  IF A < B THEN LET B = A
14Ø  LET A = C
15Ø  GOTO 11Ø
16Ø  NEXT L
17Ø  PRINT ''HCF is ˄'';A
18Ø  GOTO 1Ø
```

Note

ABS in line 12Ø finds the difference
between A and B as a positive number, e.g.
ABS(6 − 2) and ABS(2 − 6) are both 4.

C Lowest Common Multiple

The Lowest Common Multiple (L.C.M.) of a set of numbers is the smallest number
that all of them divide into exactly.

Example   {multiples of 6} = {6, 12, 18, 24, 30, 36, 42, 48, . . .}
          {multiples of 8} = {8, 16, 24, 32, 40, 48, 56, 64, . . .}
          {common multiples of 6 and 8} = {24, 48, . . .}
          The **Lowest** Common Multiple of 6 and 8 is 24.

The following computer program calculates the L.C.M. of two or more numbers.

```
  5  REM ''LCM''
     LCM by multiples of largest
 1Ø  PRINT ''How many numbers?''
 2Ø  INPUT N
 3Ø  CLS      (Clear screen)
 4Ø  PRINT ''Type 1st number.''
 5Ø  INPUT A
 6Ø  PRINT A      (May be omitted)
```

```
 7Ø  FOR L = 2 TO N
 8Ø  PRINT ''Type number ˄'';L
 9Ø  INPUT B
1ØØ  PRINT B      (May be omitted)
11Ø  IF A > B THEN GOTO 15Ø
12Ø  LET T = A
13Ø  LET A = B
14Ø  LET B = T
```

```
15Ø  LET C = A                 18Ø  GOTO 16Ø
16Ø  IF A/B = INT (A/B) THEN   19Ø  NEXT L
       GOTO 19Ø                2ØØ  PRINT "LCM is ‿";A
17Ø  LET A = A + C             21Ø  GOTO 1Ø
```

Notes

Lines 1Ø and 1ØØ are the same as in program HCF1. To find out how the program works write a stores table for L, A, B and C for the numbers 3, 4 and 6.

1 List the first eight multiples, then the common multiples, and finally the Lowest Common Multiple, as in the example, for:
  (a) 3 and 7   (b) 8 and 12   (c) 6 and 9.

2 Without written working state the L.C.M. of:
  (a) 3 and 6   (b) 4 and 6   (c) 7 and 9   (d) 15 and 20   (e) 16 and 24
  (f) 3, 4 and 5   (g) 2, 3 and 5   (h) 5, 7 and 10.

*3 Repeat question 2 for:
  (a) 2 and 3   (b) 2 and 5   (c) 3 and 5   (d) 3 and 7   (e) 3 and 9
  (f) 2, 3 and 8   (g) 2, 3 and 7   (h) 3, 7 and 9   (i) 2, 3, 6 and 9
  (j) 2, 3, 5 and 9   (k) 6, 12 and 48.

*4 State the H.C.F. for the numbers in question 2.

5 Prime factors help to find the L.C.M. of large numbers (see exercise 3B, question 7).

  Example   Find the L.C.M. of 18, 30 and 36.

$$18 = 2 \times 3 \times 3$$
$$30 = 2 \times 3 \times 5$$
$$36 = 2 \times 2 \times 3 \times 3$$

We can see that the L.C.M. must be made up of 2s, 3s and 5s.
But $2 \times 3 \times 5$ would not be large enough as 2×2 is needed for 36 and 3×3 is needed for 36.
The L.C.M. is therefore $2 \times 2 \times 3 \times 3 \times 5 = 4 \times 9 \times 5 = 36 \times 5 = 180$.

Note that you can think of this method as a 'printing outfit' where you need enough of each number to be able to print the prime factor product for each in turn.

Use the prime factor method to find the L.C.M. of:
  (a) 12 and 27   (b) 6, 9 and 12   (c) 15, 18 and 30   (d) 9, 45 and 75.

6 Example $3a^2b = 3 \times a \times a \times b$
$12ab^2c = 2 \times 2 \times 3 \times a \times b \times b \times c$
The L.C.M. needs 2s, 3s, as, bs and cs.
Two each are needed of 2s, as and bs.
The L.C.M. is $2 \times 2 \times 3 \times a \times a \times b \times b \times c = 12a^2b^2c$.

Find the L.C.M. of:
(a) $4a^2b$ and $6ab^2$ (b) xy^2 and xyz (c) $3st$ and $9s^2t$
(d) $12a^2b^2$ and $6ab^2c$.

7 Look at the questions and answers for question 6. Can you see a quick way to find the powers of each letter in the L.C.M., similar to that in exercise 3B, question 9?

Write the H.C.F. and the L.C.M. of:
(a) a^3bc^2, a^2b and $2abc$ (b) $3a^2b$, $2xy$ and ax^2 (c) $4ab$, $3xy$ and $2by$
(d) $15a^2bx^3$, $20abx^2$ and $5a^4bx^2$.

---

8 Take any two numbers. Find their L.C.M. and H.C.F. Multiply the numbers. Multiply the L.C.M. by the H.C.F. Surprised? Investigate! Could you use this to find the L.C.M. of two numbers once you know their H.C.F.?

9 What is the size of the smallest box that can be completely filled with 6 cm cubes, or 8 cm cubes, or 10 cm cubes? Make models to illustrate your answer.

10 Write a computer program to add together any two fractions, giving the answer as a simplified common fraction.

4 Probability: review

Probability of an outcome = $\dfrac{\text{number of ways the outcome can happen}}{\text{number of possible outcomes}}$

Note that this rule only applies if all possible outcomes are equally likely; e.g. for a loaded die the probabilities of scoring each number from 1 to 6 are not all $\frac{1}{6}$.

1 State as a fraction the probability of each of the following.
  (a) A stranger having a birthday on a Sunday in a year when Jan. 1 is a Monday.
  (b) A heart card being on top of a shuffled pack.
  (c) A black ball being picked from a bag of 8 black and 7 green balls.
  (d) A number from 1 to 10, picked at random, being a triangular number.
  (e) A number from 1 to 10, picked at random, being a prime number.
  (f) A number from 1 to 10, picked at random, being a factor of 36.

2 State whether you consider the probability of each of the following events to be:
0;   less than $\frac{1}{2}$; $\frac{1}{2}$;   more than $\frac{1}{2}$;   1;   or if you need more information before you can decide. Justify your choice.
  (a) A tossed coin landing heads.
  (b) It snowing in September in London.
  (c) It snowing in February in London.
  (d) You visiting the moon.

  (e) A new electric light bulb not working.
  (f) A twenty-year-old woman living to be thirty.
  (g) A triangle having an interior angle sum of 180°.
  (h) A square having an interior angle sum of 180°.
  (i) A calculator battery going flat during an examination.
  (j) A certain man running a four-minute mile.

3 Some probabilities can be calculated, some found by researching past records, some by random testing of a large sample, and some can be changed by your own actions.

Give examples of each of the above, and discuss the situations in question 2 with reference to these statements.

4 Two dice are thrown and their scores added. Copy and complete the following table to show the results.

Second die

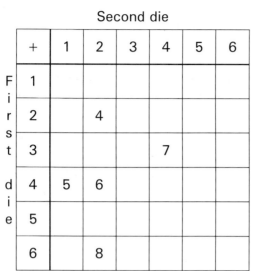

+	1	2	3	4	5	6
F i r s t 　 1							
2		4				
t 　 3				7		
d i 　 4	5	6				
e 　 5						
6		8				

The table of all possible outcomes is sometimes called the possibility space.

State as simply as possible the probability of each total from 2 to 12 in order.

Comment on, and try to explain, the pattern of your answer.

5 Dominic and Ivan have to pass through four sets of traffic lights on their way to school. They want to calculate the chance of having to stop at the lights once, twice, thrice, or all four times. They count a stop (S) if the lights are red or amber, and a go (G) if they are green, or red and amber, and assume stop and go are equally likely. Copy and complete the tree diagram and find the chances. What connection does your answer have with page 118?

1st   2nd   3rd   4th

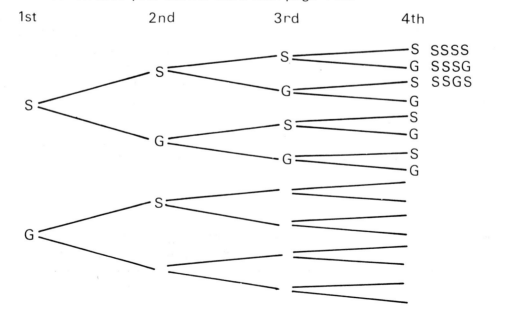

6 Justin has a biased coin which has a 0.8 chance of landing heads. Explain why the chance of it landing tails must be 0.2.

7 Three pupils each throw a fair die four times. The outcomes are:

Camilla 3, 3, 3, 3   Gill 1, 2, 3, 4   Robin 2, 6, 3, 4

John says he will give you £5 if you can repeat one of these outcomes in four throws of the same die. Whose outcome would you choose to try to repeat? Why? Discuss your reasoning with your classmates.

8 Class 9G, of 15 boys and 15 girls, are holding a quiz. Each pupil has to answer one question, the order being selected by the teacher drawing their names from a hat.

Explain why:

(a) the probability that the first pupil chosen is a boy is 0.5

(b) the probability that the last pupil chosen is a boy is not 0.5

(c) the probability that the first person chosen will answer correctly is not 0.5.

At half-lesson bell 12 boys and 8 girls have been chosen, and ten of them answered correctly. Now what is the probability that the next pupil chosen will be a boy? Is the next answer more likely to be correct, more likely to be wrong, evens, or can you not give a probability for this?

9 Write a program to simulate the throwing of two dice as in question 4. Make sure your program prints out the final results, perhaps as a bar-chart.

10 Jane and Penny are playing a dice game. They have two cubic dice, each numbered from 1 to 6, which they throw together. If the total score (e.g. 3 + 5 = 8) is a prime number, then Penny moves the counter. Otherwise Jane moves the counter. The winner is the one who moves the counter off the end of the board (Figure 4:1).

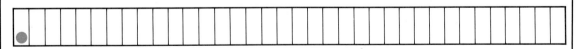

Fig. 4:1

Investigate this game.

You could look at similar games, perhaps changing the length of the board, or finding the score in a different way, e.g. by subtracting the two numbers.

5 Fractions: × and ÷ by fractions

A Multiplication of fractions

For Discussion

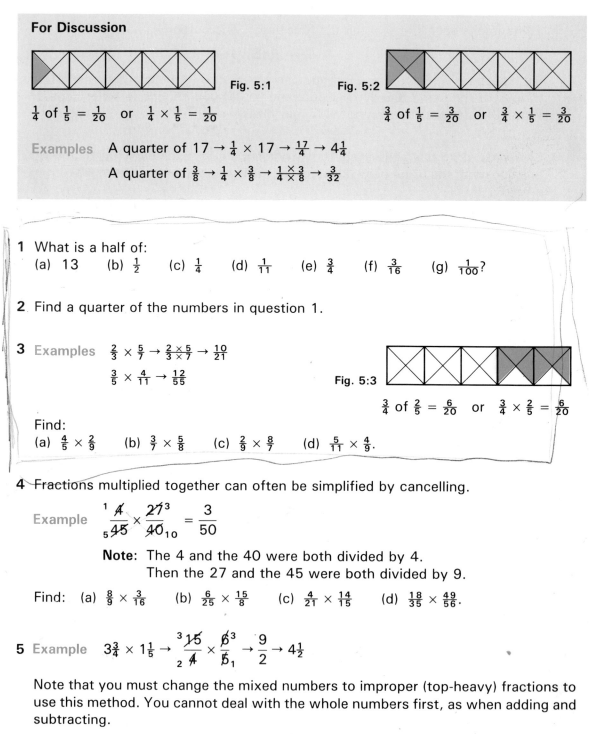

Fig. 5:1

$\frac{1}{4}$ of $\frac{1}{5} = \frac{1}{20}$ or $\frac{1}{4} \times \frac{1}{5} = \frac{1}{20}$

Fig. 5:2

$\frac{3}{4}$ of $\frac{1}{5} = \frac{3}{20}$ or $\frac{3}{4} \times \frac{1}{5} = \frac{3}{20}$

Examples A quarter of $17 \to \frac{1}{4} \times 17 \to \frac{17}{4} \to 4\frac{1}{4}$

A quarter of $\frac{3}{8} \to \frac{1}{4} \times \frac{3}{8} \to \frac{1 \times 3}{4 \times 8} \to \frac{3}{32}$

1 What is a half of:
   (a) 13   (b) $\frac{1}{2}$ (c) $\frac{1}{4}$ (d) $\frac{1}{11}$ (e) $\frac{3}{4}$ (f) $\frac{3}{16}$ (g) $\frac{1}{100}$?

2 Find a quarter of the numbers in question 1.

3 Examples $\frac{2}{3} \times \frac{5}{7} \to \frac{2 \times 5}{3 \times 7} \to \frac{10}{21}$

$\frac{3}{5} \times \frac{4}{11} \to \frac{12}{55}$

Fig. 5:3

$\frac{3}{4}$ of $\frac{2}{5} = \frac{6}{20}$ or $\frac{3}{4} \times \frac{2}{5} = \frac{6}{20}$

Find:
   (a) $\frac{4}{5} \times \frac{2}{9}$ (b) $\frac{3}{7} \times \frac{5}{8}$ (c) $\frac{2}{9} \times \frac{8}{7}$ (d) $\frac{5}{11} \times \frac{4}{9}$.

4 Fractions multiplied together can often be simplified by cancelling.

   Example $\dfrac{^1\cancel{4}}{_5\cancel{45}} \times \dfrac{\cancel{27}^3}{\cancel{40}_{10}} = \dfrac{3}{50}$

   Note: The 4 and the 40 were both divided by 4.
   Then the 27 and the 45 were both divided by 9.

   Find: (a) $\frac{8}{9} \times \frac{3}{16}$ (b) $\frac{6}{25} \times \frac{15}{8}$ (c) $\frac{4}{21} \times \frac{14}{15}$ (d) $\frac{18}{35} \times \frac{49}{56}$.

5 Example $3\frac{3}{4} \times 1\frac{1}{5} \to \dfrac{^3\cancel{15}}{_2\cancel{4}} \times \dfrac{\cancel{6}^3}{\cancel{5}_1} \to \dfrac{9}{2} \to 4\frac{1}{2}$

   Note that you must change the mixed numbers to improper (top-heavy) fractions to use this method. You cannot deal with the whole numbers first, as when adding and subtracting.

   Find: (a) $4\frac{1}{6} \times \frac{4}{15}$ (b) $2\frac{4}{7} \times 1\frac{11}{24}$ (c) $1\frac{2}{3} \times \frac{12}{25}$ (d) $1\frac{5}{6} \times 1\frac{9}{33}$.

22

*6 (a) Add $\frac{1}{2}$ to $\frac{1}{4}$. (b) Multiply $\frac{1}{2}$ by $\frac{1}{4}$.
(c) Find the difference between your two answers.

*7 Repeat question 6, first for $\frac{2}{3}$ and $\frac{3}{4}$, and then for $\frac{5}{8}$ and $1\frac{3}{5}$.

8 $a = 5\frac{1}{4}$; $b = 1\frac{1}{2}$; $c = \frac{5}{12}$.

Find: (a) $a + b$ (b) ab (c) $b - c$ (d) $3c$ (e) ac
(f) c^2 (g) $6a$ (h) $a - c$ (i) b^2.

9 Four-fifths of a $3\frac{1}{4}$ kg bag of potatoes are starting to sprout. How many grams of potatoes are not starting to sprout?

10 Jim spent $\frac{3}{4}$ of his money on a present, $\frac{2}{3}$ of *the remainder* on a magazine, and had 16p left. What did he have to start with, and how much did he spend on the present and the magazine?

11 Two-fifths of a class are boys and two-fifths of the girls can swim. Nine girls cannot swim. How many boys are there?

12 Reciprocals

The reciprocal of x is $\dfrac{1}{x}$.

The reciprocal key of a calculator is usually marked $\boxed{1/x}$.

Examples The reciprocal of 2 is $\frac{1}{2}$ or 0.5
The reciprocal of 9 is $\frac{1}{9}$ or $0.\dot{1}$

(a) Investigate 4 $\boxed{1/x}$ $\boxed{1/x}$ $\boxed{1/x}$ $\boxed{1/x}$.

(b) Use the $\boxed{1/x}$ key to find f if $\dfrac{1}{f} = \dfrac{1}{3} + \dfrac{1}{5}$.

13 (a) Find one-third of $(\frac{1}{4} + \frac{1}{2} + \frac{1}{6})$. (b) Find the mean of $\frac{1}{4}$, $\frac{1}{2}$ and $\frac{1}{6}$.
(c) Find the mean of $\frac{1}{3}$, $\frac{1}{2}$ and $\frac{2}{9}$. (d) Find the mean of 1, $\frac{1}{2}$, $\frac{2}{3}$ and $\frac{3}{4}$.

14 Find the fractions that multiply together to make 1.

5

B Division by a fraction

To divide by a fraction, multiply by its inverse.

Examples $3 \div \frac{1}{4} \to 3 \times \frac{4}{1} \to 12$

Note that $\frac{4}{1}$ is the inverse of $\frac{1}{4}$.

$2\frac{1}{2} \div 1\frac{2}{3} \to \frac{5}{2} \div \frac{5}{3} \to \frac{1\cancel{5}}{2} \times \frac{3}{\cancel{5}_1} \to \frac{3}{2} \to 1\frac{1}{2}$

The reciprocal of a fraction is its inverse.

Example   The reciprocal of $\frac{3}{4}$ is $\frac{1}{\frac{3}{4}}$. $\frac{1}{\frac{3}{4}} \to 1 \div \frac{3}{4} \to 1 \times \frac{4}{3} \to \frac{4}{3}$.

1 Find: (a) $6 \div \frac{1}{2}$ (b) $4 \div \frac{3}{4}$ (c) $3 \div 1\frac{2}{3}$ (d) $\frac{1}{18} \div \frac{2}{3}$ (e) $1\frac{1}{3} \div 2\frac{2}{5}$.

*2 Find: (a) $\frac{1}{4} \div \frac{1}{4}$ (b) $\frac{1}{3} \div \frac{1}{2}$ (c) $\frac{3}{5} \div \frac{2}{5}$.

*3 Find: (a) $\frac{2}{3} \div 1\frac{1}{4}$ (b) $\frac{4}{5} \div 2\frac{2}{3}$ (c) $5 \div 2\frac{2}{3}$ (d) $2 \div \frac{3}{5}$ (e) $\frac{1}{2} \div 2\frac{1}{3}$.

4 Find: (a) $2\frac{1}{2} \div 1\frac{1}{3}$ (b) $1\frac{3}{4} \div 2\frac{1}{7}$ (c) $2\frac{1}{2} \div 3\frac{3}{4}$ (d) $3\frac{3}{8} \div 2\frac{1}{4}$ (e) $2\frac{6}{11} \div 2\frac{7}{22}$.

5 A ferry crosses in $\frac{3}{4}$ of an hour. How many crossings could it make in 12 hours?

6 How many small cakes can cook make from a 3 kg bag of flour if $\frac{3}{5}$ kg makes 24?

7 How many $\frac{3}{16}$ litre glasses can be filled from a $4\frac{1}{2}$-litre container?

8 Eight pints are about $4\frac{1}{2}$ litres. About how many pints is 1 litre?

---

9 Use a calculator to find answers to the following as decimal fractions. Remember the rule of BODMAS, that is **Brackets; Of; Divide; Multiply; Add; Subtract,** in that order.

Find:
(a) $\frac{2}{5}$ of $\frac{5}{8} + \frac{1}{4}$ (b) $\frac{3}{4} - 1\frac{1}{2} \div 4\frac{1}{2}$ (c) $\frac{3}{4} - \frac{5}{8} \div 1\frac{1}{5}$ (d) $(\frac{3}{4} - \frac{5}{8}) \div 1\frac{1}{5}$
(e) $6\frac{2}{3} \times 1\frac{1}{5} + 2\frac{4}{5}$ (f) $6\frac{2}{3} \times (1\frac{1}{5} + 2\frac{4}{5})$ (g) $3\frac{1}{4} - 2\frac{1}{3} \times 3$
(h) $(3\frac{1}{4} - 2\frac{1}{3}) \times 3$.

10 Draw diagrams to illustrate that $\frac{1}{4} \div \frac{3}{4} = \frac{1}{3}$.

For Discussion

Figure 6:1 illustrates that 4 increased in the ratio 3:2 becomes 6.

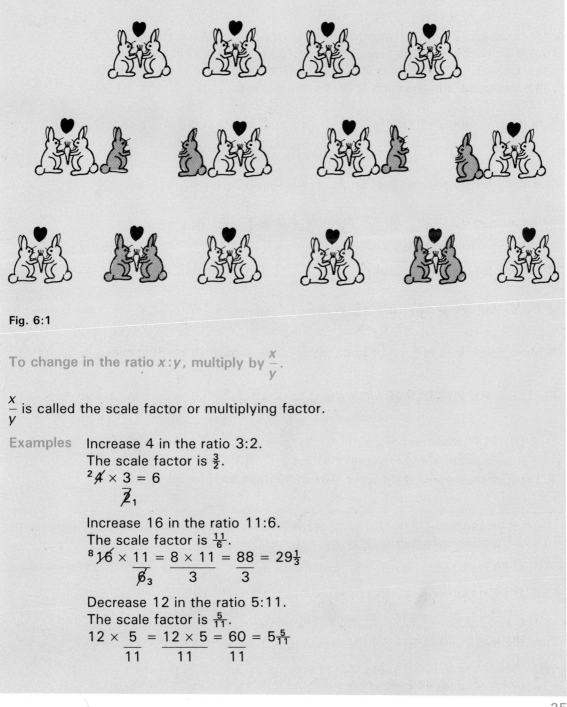

Fig. 6:1

To change in the ratio $x:y$, multiply by $\dfrac{x}{y}$.

$\dfrac{x}{y}$ is called the scale factor or multiplying factor.

Examples Increase 4 in the ratio 3:2.
The scale factor is $\frac{3}{2}$.
$$\frac{{}^2\!\!\!\not4 \times 3}{\not2_1} = 6$$

Increase 16 in the ratio 11:6.
The scale factor is $\frac{11}{6}$.
$$\frac{{}^8\!\!\!\not{16} \times 11}{\not6_3} = \frac{8 \times 11}{3} = \frac{88}{3} = 29\tfrac{1}{3}$$

Decrease 12 in the ratio 5:11.
The scale factor is $\frac{5}{11}$.
$$12 \times \frac{5}{11} = \frac{12 \times 5}{11} = \frac{60}{11} = 5\tfrac{5}{11}$$

6

1 State the scale factor:
   (a) to increase in the ratio 7:5   (b) to decrease in the ratio 5:7.

2 (a) Increase 9 in the ratio 11:3.   (b) Increase 8 in the ratio 7:6.
   (c) Decrease 14 in the ratio 2:3.   (d) Decrease 11 in the ratio 3:10.

*3 (a) Increase 20 in the ratio 5:4.   (b) Increase 100 in the ratio 7:2.
   (c) Decrease 13 in the ratio 1:13.   (d) Increase 10 in the ratio 13:2.
   (e) Increase 9 in the ratio 7:6.   (f) Decrease 15 in the ratio 3:10.
   (g) Decrease 9 in the ratio 4:7.   (h) Increase 7 in the ratio 13:9.

*Worksheet 6 may be used here.

4 **Example**   What scale factor changes 12 to 15?

It is an increase, so put the larger on top: $\dfrac{15}{12} \xrightarrow{\text{cancel}} \dfrac{5}{4}$.

Example   What scale factor changes 3.5 kg to 650 g?

The units are different; change them both to the smaller unit (grams).

It is a decrease, hence $\dfrac{650}{3500} \xrightarrow{\text{cancel}} \dfrac{13}{70}$.

What scale factor changes:

   (a) 18 to 45   (b) 93 to 36   (c) 4p to £0.24   (d) £2.40 to 90p
   (e) 200 cm to 2.5 m   (f) 85 m to 0.3 km   (g) 9.8 cl to 14 ml
   (h) 5 mm to 0.035 m?

5 **Example**   6 painters can paint a school in 46 days. How long should 8 painters take?

The number of painters has increased in the ratio 8:6, so the time taken should *decrease* in the ratio 6:8. The scale factor is $\frac{6}{8}$.

Answer: 46 days $\times \dfrac{6}{8} \to {}^{23}\cancel{46}$ days $\times \dfrac{\cancel{6}^3}{\cancel{8}_{4\,2}} \to \dfrac{69}{2} \to 34\frac{1}{2}$ days.

Just state the scale factor for each of the following. Do not work out the answers yet. Think carefully whether it is an increase or a decrease.

   (a) If 24 dollars are worth £5, how many dollars are worth £8?

   (b) If 24 dollars are worth £5, how many £'s are $18?

   (c) 8 km/h is about 5 m.p.h. How many km/h is 28 m.p.h.?

   (d) 8 km/h is about 5 m.p.h. How many m.p.h. is 50 km/h?

   (e) When a man is 30 years old he weighs 80 kg.
      What should his weight be when he is 40 years old?

BEWARE!
Several questions
are not sensible
and cannot be
answered.

26

(f) A cyclist takes $1\frac{1}{2}$ hours to cycle home at 10 m.p.h. How long would she have taken at 12 m.p.h.?

(g) 18 km/h is about 5 cm/s. How many km/h is 12 cm/s?

(h) A train with 6 coaches has 180 passengers. How many passengers are there on an 8-coach train?

(i) An aeroplane completes a journey in 44 minutes at an average speed of 350 knots. How long would the same journey take at 400 knots?

(j) A woman's annual salary brings her £8 712.50 in 7 months. What is her annual salary?

(k) Fifty maths books cost £295. What will 115 of them cost?

6 Mark your answers to question 5, correct them as necessary, then use them to find the answers to the questions.

7 60 000 locusts can devastate 5 hectares a week. How many locusts would devastate 8 hectares a week? How long would it take 80 000 locusts to devastate 5 hectares? How many hectares could 1 000 000 locusts devastate in a week?

8 600 men have provisions for 27 days. 120 men join them. How many days will the provisions now last? If the rations are then reduced by a quarter, how many days will they last?

9 A line is divided in the ratio 3:8:11. The middle length is 12 cm. How long is the line and what are the other two lengths?

10 Use two multiplying factors in the following.

(a) 11 workers can pick 660 mangel-wurzels in 3 hours. How many mangel-wurzels could 9 workers pick in 10 hours?

(b) A house-extension 7.2 metres by 3.5 metres costs £2158. What would you estimate to be the cost of a similar extension 6 metres by 4 metres?

A One-journey graphs

For Discussion   Fig. 7:1

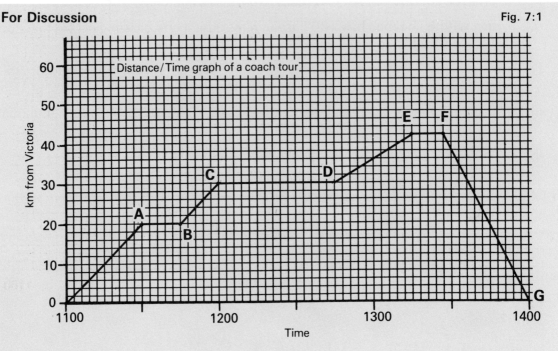

1 In Figure 7:1

   (a) Why is the graph line flat between A and B?

   (b) Why does the line FG slope the other way to line OA?

   (c) Can you tell how many hills were climbed on the journey?

   (d) How many minutes are represented by six small squares?

   (e) How many kilometres are represented by six small squares?

   (f) State how far A, B, C, D, E, F and G are from Victoria, giving your answers as ordered pairs, e.g. (X, 35 km).

   (g) State the time at the points A to G. Give your answers as ordered pairs.

   (h) Between O and A the coach went 20 km in half an hour. The mean (average) speed of the coach between O and A is therefore 40 km/h.
        Find the mean speed between B and C, and between D and E.

   (i) How far was the whole journey?

   (j) Calculate the mean speed for the whole journey using the formula:

        $$\text{Mean speed} = \frac{\text{Total distance}}{\text{Total time}}$$

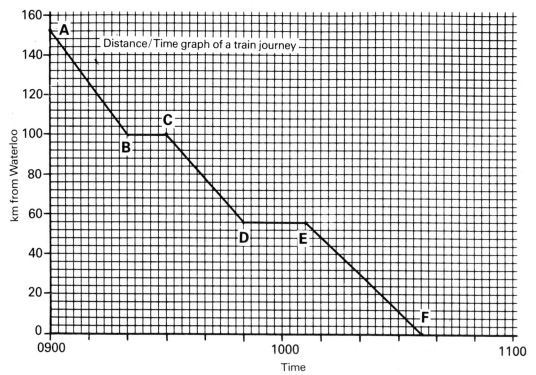

Fig. 7:2

2 In Figure 7:2

(a) How far is the train from Waterloo at 0900?

(b) How many times does the train stop on the journey (excluding Waterloo)?

(c) For how long is the train stationary at the station which is 100 km from Waterloo?

(d) State the time at the points B, C, D, E and F.

(e) How far from Waterloo is the train at 0920, 0940, 1000 and 1010?

(f) Which of the three journeys between stops is the slowest?

(g) Find the mean speed of the train between A and B, between C and D, and between E and F.

3 Draw a distance/time graph, like Figures 7:1 and 7:2, for the following cycle ride.
Scales Horizontal: Time, 1500 to 1900; 4 cm to 1 hour.
Vertical: Miles from Langport, 0 to 20 miles; 2 cm to 5 miles.

The journey starts from Langport at 1500 at a mean speed of 10 m.p.h. for the first hour. After a rest of half an hour the journey continues at 10 m.p.h. for another 10 miles. Then the cyclist returns to Langport at 15 m.p.h. without stopping.
(a) At what time was the cyclist 20 miles from Langport?

(b) At what time did the cyclist reach Langport on the return journey?

4 Draw a distance/time graph for the following journey.
Scales Horizontal: Time, 1600 to 1900; 6 cm to 1 hour.
Vertical: Miles from home, 0 to 10; 1 cm to 1 mile.

Neil starts from school, 10 miles from his home, at 4:20 p.m. The school bus has a mean speed of 10 m.p.h. The nearest it comes to Neil's home is 2 miles, and Neil gets off the bus there.

He stays at the bus-stop for 10 minutes until his friend arrives and they walk to her house, in the opposite direction to Neil's, for 20 minutes at 3 m.p.h. Neil then turns round and runs home at 6 m.p.h.

(a) At what time does he arrive home?

(b) At what time would he have arrived home if he had started walking home at 4 m.p.h. as soon as he got off the bus?

5 Comment fully on the journeys represented by Figures 7:3, 7:4 and 7:5.

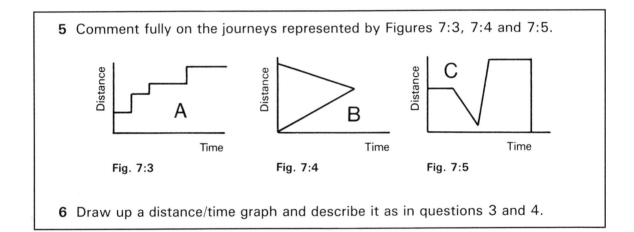

Fig. 7:3   Fig. 7:4   Fig. 7:5

6 Draw up a distance/time graph and describe it as in questions 3 and 4.

B Two-journey graphs

For Discussion

Two tramps are approaching each other along a road. Both are walking at 2 km/h. At 2 p.m. the first tramp had just left a farm and the second tramp was 4 km away.

A fly leaves the first tramp at 2 p.m. and flies at 5 km/h to the other tramp, then returns and flies back to the first, and so on until the tramps meet.

Where is the fly at 2:45 p.m.?

Figure 7:6 shows a graphical solution to this question.

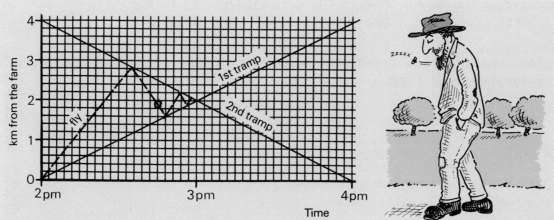

Fig. 7:6

Further examples

(a) Using the scales for question 1 below, draw journey lines for:

Leave home at 1000; travel at 10 km/h for $\frac{1}{2}$ h; continue away from home at 30 km/h for $\frac{1}{2}$ h; return home at 40 km/h.

Start 35 km from home at 1015 and travel towards home at 50 km/h.

(b) Using the scales for question 3 on page 32, draw journey lines for:

Leave Bridgwater at 1215; travel at 55 m.p.h. for 1 h; return towards Bridgwater for $1\frac{1}{2}$ h at 20 m.p.h.

Someone stationary 40 miles from Bridgwater.

1 Draw axes: Horizontal: Time, 1000 to 1130; 4 cm to 30 min.
                 Vertical: km from home, 0 to 40; 2 cm to 10 km.

Draw a line to represent Jane leaving home at 1000 and cycling at 20 km/h.

Draw another line to represent Bill leaving his house, 40 km from Jane's home, at 1000, and cycling towards Jane at 20 km/h.

(a) At what time does Jane meet Bill?
(b) How far apart are they at 1030?

2 Draw axes as in question 1.

'Mum leaves home at 1000 and drives at an average speed of 40 km/h to meet dad. Dad leaves work, 30 km from home, at 1000 and starts walking home at 5 km/h.'

Draw two lines to find when and where they meet.

*3 Draw axes: Horizontal: Time, 1200 to 1500; 4 cm to 1 hour.
                 Vertical: Miles from Bridgwater, 0 to 80; 2 cm to 20 miles.

Draw a line to represent a train leaving Bridgwater at 1200 at 40 m.p.h.
Draw a line to represent a train coming towards Bridgwater at 60 m.p.h. if it is 60 miles
from Bridgwater at 1300 (be careful: *not* 1200).

How far from Bridgwater and at what time do the trains pass each other?

*4 Draw a pair of axes as in question 3.
Draw a line to represent a car leaving Bridgwater at 1200 at 40 m.p.h.
Draw a line to represent another car leaving Bridgwater at 1230, chasing the first car
at 70 m.p.h.

Where and when will the second car catch up the first?

*Worksheet 7 may be used here.

5 Draw a pair of axes as in question 3.
Find where and when a train which leaves Bridgwater at 1300 at 80 m.p.h. passes
another train coming towards Bridgwater at 60 m.p.h. and reaching there at 1500.

6 Draw axes: Horizontal: Time, 1600 to 1900; 6 cm to 1 hour.
                Vertical: Miles from Taunton, 0 to 25; 2 cm to 5 miles.

A bus leaves Taunton at 1600 and travels at a mean speed of 24 m.p.h. to Minehead,
24 miles away. It stays at Minehead for 20 minutes then returns to Taunton at
24 m.p.h. On the same day a cyclist leaves Minehead for Taunton at 1630 at a mean
speed of 10 m.p.h. Where and when does the bus pass the cyclist?

---

7 Draw axes: Horizontal: Time in minutes, 0 to 15; 4 cm to 5 min.
                Vertical: Metres from the start, 0 to 1000; 1 cm to 100 m.

A donkey and a mule set out on a 1000-metre race. The donkey runs at 20 km/h
(how many minutes to cover 1 km?), but every 400 metres it stops for 5 min to
eat a carrot. The mule keeps on going at 5 km/h.

(a) Who wins and by how many seconds?
(b) At what time does the donkey pass the mule?
(c) At what time does the mule pass the donkey?

8 At 0800 a man leaves Wearne to walk to Upton. He gets there at 1600. The next
day he leaves Upton at 0800 and returns to Wearne. He arrives at 1600.

Is there a point between Upton and Wearne where he was at the same time on
both days? If so, where is it?

8 Statistics: displaying information

A Scatter graphs

Scatter graphs are drawn when a statistician suspects that there is a link, or 'correlation', between two measures of data. For example, a pupil's achievement in English and in History.

Figure 8:1 shows how to draw a scatter graph from the data given in the table for 26 pupils' marks in English and History.

Pupil	A	B	C	D	E	F	G	H	I	J	K	L	M
English/50	12	23	26	12	30	8	33	26	10	31	22	32	16
History/50	12	11	26	20	31	8	10	18	2	23	20	36	13

	N	O	P	Q	R	S	T	U	V	W	X	Y	Z
	39	27	41	31	10	41	26	44	39	20	48	44	23
	33	35	21	43	30	42	50	38	39	20	46	50	26

Conclusion

Figure 8:1 shows some evidence of correlation – the dots are mainly in a band sloping across the graph. This is illustrated in Figure 8:2. The 'line of best fit' is drawn by eye so that as many dots as possible are on it, or equally spaced each side of it.

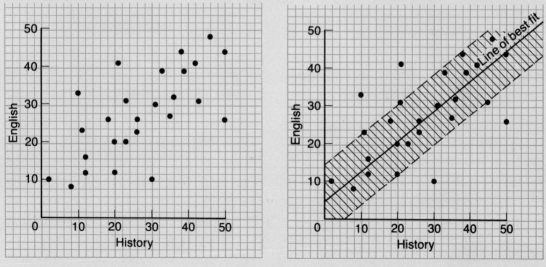

Fig. 8:1

Fig. 8:2

33

Notes:
- For measures to show correlation the line of best fit does not have to be straight; it could be a continuous smooth curve.
- Some data give exact correlation, as in a conversion graph where, say, the number of German Marks obtained from an Exchange Bureau is directly proportional to the number of Pounds Sterling. In this case all the dots will lie on the line of best fit.

  Other data will give a negative correlation – the trend is for one measure to decrease as the other increases; for example, the value of a car and its age.
- A problem arises in putting in the dots when several pairs of data are the same. You can slightly misplace the dots, or instead use squares, not lines, to represent each score. Several dots may then be placed in the same square.

For Discussion

Do you think the following will give positive correlation (like Figure 8:1), negative correlation (see the second note above), or no correlation?
(a) birth rate – number of prams sold
(b) intelligence – beauty
(c) number of cigarettes sold – deaths from lung cancer
(d) membership of the Conservative Party – number of sunny days in August.
(e) number of score draws – pools dividend size
(f) car engine size – miles per gallon
(g) number of days a pupil is absent from school – marks in end-of-year assessment
(h) number of pupils in a school – number of teachers in the same school
(i) size of a detergent packet – cost per gram of the powder in the packet

1 A psychologist is investigating the connection, if any, between Intelligence Quotient and the number of books read by a person in a year. She records the following data:

IQ	80	80	85	85	90	90	90	95	95	95	95
No. of books	8	10	4	12	10	16	20	12	15	4	30

100	100	100	100	100	100	100	105	105	105	105
20	25	35	40	26	18	50	40	10	40	45

110	110	110	110	115	115	120	120	125	130
36	40	50	48	30	50	40	50	45	45

Draw a scatter graph to illustrate the data.
Scales: Horizontal: IQ, 80 to 130; 5 points to 1 cm.
Vertical: Books, 0 to 50; 5 books to 1 cm.
If you consider that there is correlation then draw the line of best fit.

2 The table shows the result of a survey. Draw a scatter graph to decide if there is correlation between the amount of pocket money received and the number of children in a family. If there is correlation drawn the line of best fit.

Scales: Horizontal: Number of children, 0 to 7; 2 cm divisions.
Vertical: Pocket money, £0 to £4; 1 cm to 25 pence.

No. of children in family	1	2	3	4	5	6	7
Amount of pocket money per week	£2 £3.50 £3.75 £4	£3 £2.50 £2 £3 £1 £1.50 £1 £1.25	£3 £2 £1 £1.50 £1 £1.25	£2 £1.75 £1 £0.50 £1.25 £1.50	£1.50 £1 £0.75 £0.50	£1 £0.50	£0.75

*3 In 1983 a survey was conducted in various regions of the UK. Some of the findings are given in this table.

Centre of area	Miles from London	% of households with two cars	a computer
Newcastle	300	8	11
Leeds	200	12	13
Liverpool	210	12	15
Birmingham	120	15	15
Northampton	70	15	14
Norwich	120	18	11
Dover	80	18	15
Greater London	0	13	13
Exeter	170	20	15
Cardiff	160	14	16
Glasgow	400	10	13
Belfast	300	14	5

Using scatter graphs, investigate the truth of the statement that the further you lived from London the less likely you were to have:

(a) a second car (b) a computer.

Suggested scales:
Miles from London, 0 to 400; 1 cm to 25 miles.
% cars or computers, 5 to 20; 2 cm to 5%.

4 This table shows road traffic accident statistics in Northern Ireland from 1931 to 1988, and the number of licensed vehicles in the province.

	Deaths (nearest 10)	Vehicles (10 000s)		Deaths (nearest 10)	Vehicles (10 000s)		Deaths (nearest 10)	Vehicles (10 000s)
1931	110	3	1941	280	6	1951	170	11
1932	120	4	1942	230	5	1952	130	12
1933	140	4	1943	160	4	1953	160	13
1934	130	4	1944	150	4	1954	160	14
1935	120	4	1945	120	6	1955	160	16
1936	130	5	1946	120	7	1956	140	17
1937	130	5	1947	110	7	1957	170	18
1938	120	6	1948	130	8	1958	140	19
1939	150	6	1949	150	10	1959	160	21
1940	180	5	1950	140	10	1960	170	23

	Deaths (nearest 10)	Vehicles (10 000s)		Deaths (nearest 10)	Vehicles (10 000s)		Deaths (nearest 10)	Vehicles (10 000s)
1961	170	24	1971	300	38	1981	220	44
1962	160	26	1972	370	38	1982	220	46
1963	180	28	1973	340	38	1983	170	48
1964	220	30	1974	320	38	1984	190	51
1965	190	32	1975	310	38	1985	177	47
1966	250	33	1976	300	40	1986	236	47
1967	220	35	1977	360	42	1987	214	48
1968	220	36	1978	290	43	1988	178	50
1969	260	37	1979	290	44			
1970	270	37	1980	230	44			

Investigate, using a scatter graph, the correlation, if any, between the number of vehicles on the road and the number of people killed in road traffic accidents. Explain your findings.

Suggested scales: Deaths, 100 to 350; 2 cm to 50
Vehicles (10 000s), 0 to 50; 1 cm to 50 000

5 Carry out a survey, then investigate your results for correlation. Some ideas:
  (a) Number of children in a family – number of pets in a family.
  (b) Number of cigarettes smoked daily – length of time person can hold their breath.
  (c) Head circumference – score on a maths test.
  (d) Length of middle finger – ability at art (1 = very good, 5 = hopeless).
  (e) The suggestions in the 'For Discussion' section.
  (f) Something else.

B Decision trees

Decision trees are special flow charts which are used to identify objects. Figure 8:3 is a decision tree which can be used to try to identify a tree!

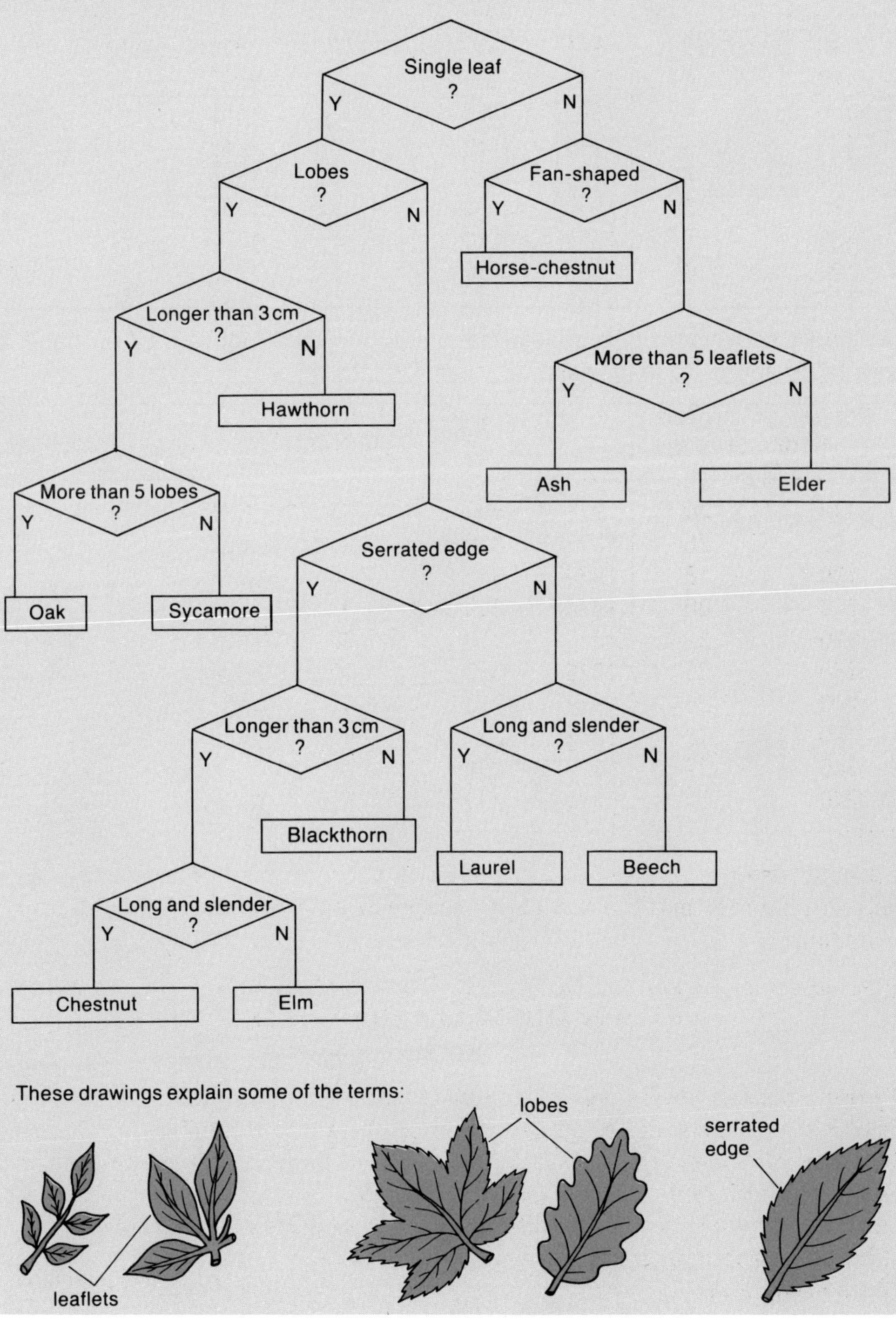

Single leaf?
Y / N

Lobes?
Y / N

Fan-shaped?
Y / N

Horse-chestnut

Longer than 3 cm?
Y / N

Hawthorn

More than 5 leaflets?
Y / N

Ash

Elder

More than 5 lobes?
Y / N

Oak

Sycamore

Serrated edge?
Y / N

Longer than 3 cm?
Y / N

Blackthorn

Long and slender?
Y / N

Laurel

Beech

Long and slender?
Y / N

Chestnut

Elm

These drawings explain some of the terms:

lobes

serrated edge

leaflets

Fig. 8:3

1 Here is a tree route! Identify the tree!

Y   N   N   Y

2 Draw up a decision tree to identify the shapes in Figure 8:4. Your questions should be:

Green?   Straight sides?   Three sides?   Grey?

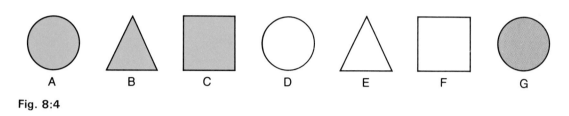

Fig. 8:4

---

3 Design a tree to identify a special parallelogram (see Figure S17 on page 239) from facts about its diagonals.

C   Networks

We considered networks as line patterns in Book 1. Now we consider their use in planning routes.

Fig. 8:5

Figure 8:5 shows a map of part of England and Wales, with some important towns and roads marked. Figure 8:6 is a topological map, or network. It shows how the roads link the towns, and the distances between the towns in miles, but neither the road lengths nor the town positions are to scale.

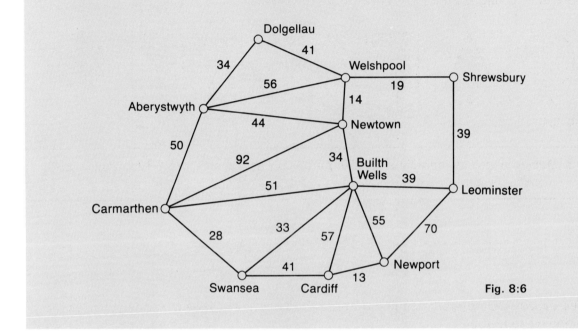

Fig. 8:6

Refer to Figure 8:6 to answer questions 1 to 3. You will need to copy the network several times.

1 The following towns are to be linked by landlines laid along the roadsides so that a bank's branches can exchange computer data: Builth Wells, Cardiff, Swansea, Carmarthen, Aberystwyth, Newtown, Welshpool. Find the shortest possible way to do this.

2 The Welsh Electricity Board wishes to inspect all its lights along the roads given in Figure 8:6, starting from its head office in Cardiff. Plan out the shortest route, stating which roads will be covered twice.

3 Eli is sponsored to have a drink in each town on the topological map. What is the shortest route for Eli's taxi driver so that Eli revisits as few towns as possible, and the route is as short as it can be?

Figure 8:7 shows France, with some important towns and roads marked. Figure 8:8 is a network made from this map. The distances are in kilometres. Use Figure 8:8 to answer questions 4 to 6.

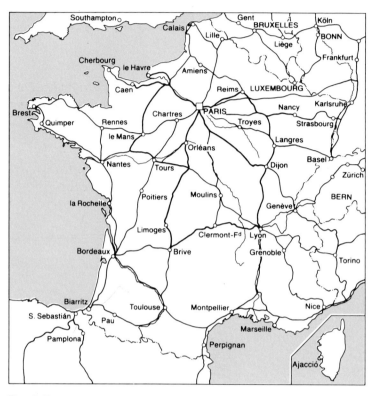

Fig. 8:7

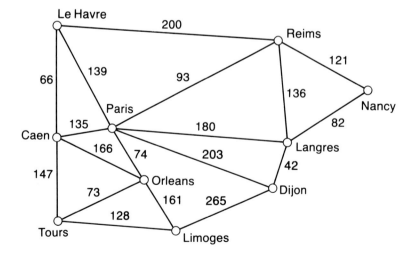

Fig. 8:8

4 A cable TV company wishes to link all the towns to Paris with cables running alongside main roads. Find the shortest possible route.

5 The French Department of Transport (Le Ministère de Transport) wishes to inspect all the roads shown on the network map, starting and ending at Paris. Find the shortest distance in which it is possible to do this.

6 Janice is a courier based in Paris. She has to visit clients in hotels in every town on the network, staying overnight as necessary. Plan out her shortest route.

7 You probably did the above questions by trial and improvement, but there are various rules which can help you find the shortest routes. By designing simpler networks of your own try to find some rules, then try them on the Welsh and French networks.

Using your calculator

Your skin

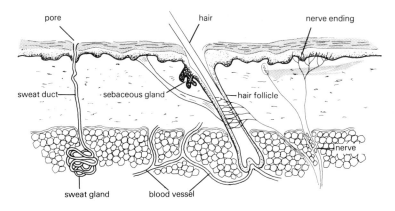

Every day your body creates many millions of skin cells to replace those that you wash or rub away. Every 27 days you get a complete new outer skin.

The whole adult body has a skin area of about $1\frac{1}{2}$ square metres. A square centimetre of average skin contains 100 sweat glands, each connected to the surface by ducts 5 mm long, 350 cm of nerves, hundreds of nerve endings, 10 hair follicles, 15 sebaceous glands and 1 metre of blood vessels.

The sweat glands keep your body at the correct temperature; on a normal day they will excrete $\frac{1}{3}$ litre of water. Playing tennis for an afternoon on a hot day will increase this to about $7\frac{1}{2}$ litres.

The hair follicles in a man's beard produce about 15 cm of hair a year for at least 3 years before slowing down for a rest.

Use your calculator to help you answer the following questions.

1 One square metre is the area of a square side 1 metre (or 100 cm). Therefore $1\,m^2 = 100 \times 100\,cm^2 = 10\,000\,cm^2$.

In the skin of the whole adult body, about how many:
(a) sweat glands   (b) kilometres of nerves   (c) hair follicles
(d) sebaceous glands   (e) kilometres of blood vessels
(f) kilometres of sweat gland ducts?

2 If a tennis player plays every afternoon for seven hot days, about how many gallons of water will she lose through her sweat glands? (Take 4.55 litres = 1 gallon.)

3 For a man's beard follicle, about how many:
(a) mm of growth per day   (b) cm of growth per month
(c) cm of growth in 3 years?

9 Vectors: notation

Vectors may be written as $\overrightarrow{AB}$ or as $\underset{\sim}{a}$. Sometimes you will see a vector printed 'bold' as **a**. You should replace this by $\underset{\sim}{a}$ when writing it yourself.

Vectors that use the same letters *must* be parallel (or in one straight line).

For Discussion

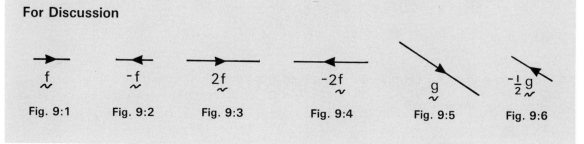

| Fig. 9:1 | Fig. 9:2 | Fig. 9:3 | Fig. 9:4 | Fig. 9:5 | Fig. 9:6 |

1 In Figure 9:7, $\overrightarrow{AB} = \begin{pmatrix} 0 \\ -2 \end{pmatrix}$; $\overrightarrow{BC} = \begin{pmatrix} 2 \\ -2 \end{pmatrix}$; $\overrightarrow{CD} = \begin{pmatrix} 4 \\ 0 \end{pmatrix}$.

Write vectors $\overrightarrow{DE}$ to $\overrightarrow{NO}$ in the same way.

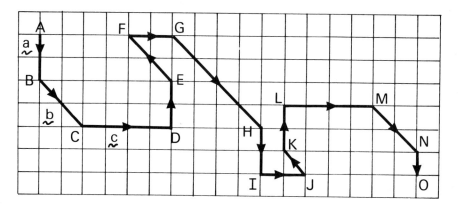

Fig. 9:7

2 In Figure 9:7, $\overrightarrow{AB}$ has been named as vector $\underset{\sim}{a}$; $\overrightarrow{BC}$ has been named as vector $\underset{\sim}{b}$; $\overrightarrow{CD}$ has been named as vector $\underset{\sim}{c}$.

As vector $\overrightarrow{JK}$ is parallel to vector $\overrightarrow{BC}$, but half as long and going in the opposite direction, we can say that vector $\overrightarrow{JK} = -\frac{1}{2}\underset{\sim}{b}$.

Name all the vectors $\overrightarrow{DE}$ to $\overrightarrow{NO}$ in terms of $\underset{\sim}{a}$, $\underset{\sim}{b}$, or $\underset{\sim}{c}$.

*3 d is a vector 2 squares long and horizontal, that is, $\underset{\sim}{d} = \begin{pmatrix} 2 \\ 0 \end{pmatrix}$.

e is a vector one square long and straight down, that is, $\underset{\sim}{e} = \begin{pmatrix} 0 \\ -1 \end{pmatrix}$.

Draw the following vectors on squared paper. Your answer should look something like the diagram in question 1.

$\overrightarrow{AB} = \underset{\sim}{d}$; $\overrightarrow{BC} = \underset{\sim}{e}$; $\overrightarrow{CD} = \underset{\sim}{d}$; $\overrightarrow{DE} = \underset{\sim}{e}$; $\overrightarrow{EF} = 2\underset{\sim}{d}$; $\overrightarrow{FG} = 2\underset{\sim}{e}$; $\overrightarrow{GH} = 3\underset{\sim}{d}$;

$\overrightarrow{HI} = -\underset{\sim}{e}$; $\overrightarrow{IJ} = -\underset{\sim}{d}$; $\overrightarrow{JK} = -\underset{\sim}{e}$; $\overrightarrow{KL} = -\underset{\sim}{d}$; $\overrightarrow{LM} = -2\underset{\sim}{e}$; $\overrightarrow{MN} = 2\underset{\sim}{d}$.

*4 Write as a 2 by 1 column matrix each of the vectors in question 3.

Start your answer: $\overrightarrow{AB} = \begin{pmatrix} 2 \\ 0 \end{pmatrix}$; $\overrightarrow{BC} = \begin{pmatrix} 0 \\ -1 \end{pmatrix}$; . . .

5 (a) $\underset{\sim}{a} = \begin{pmatrix} 3 \\ -2 \end{pmatrix}$; $\underset{\sim}{b} = \begin{pmatrix} 0 \\ 2 \end{pmatrix}$; $\underset{\sim}{c} = \begin{pmatrix} 2 \\ 0 \end{pmatrix}$

Plot and label (remembering the arrows) the following vectors, each one following on from the end of the previous one.

$\underset{\sim}{a}$; $\underset{\sim}{b}$; $2\underset{\sim}{a}$; $-3\underset{\sim}{c}$; $-\underset{\sim}{b}$; $4\underset{\sim}{c}$; $2\underset{\sim}{b}$; $-\underset{\sim}{a}$; $3\underset{\sim}{c}$; $-\underset{\sim}{b}$; $\underset{\sim}{c}$; $\underset{\sim}{a}$; $-\underset{\sim}{b}$

(b) Write all the above vectors as column matrices, then calculate the final sum.

Start your answer: $\begin{pmatrix} 3 \\ -2 \end{pmatrix} + \begin{pmatrix} 0 \\ 2 \end{pmatrix} + \begin{pmatrix} 6 \\ -4 \end{pmatrix} + . . .$

(c) Check that the vector calculated as the sum of all the others in part (b) is the one vector that goes straight from the start to the finish of the diagram you drew. It is called the **resultant vector.**

6 Vectors like $\begin{pmatrix} 2 \\ 1 \end{pmatrix}$ are restricted to one plane (two dimensions). By introducing a perpendicular axis, the z-axis, we can extend vectors to three dimensions.

In Figure 9:8 $\underset{\sim}{a}$ is a three-dimensional vector.

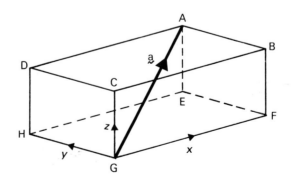

Fig. 9:8

$$\underset{\sim}{a} = \begin{pmatrix} x \\ y \\ z \end{pmatrix} \text{ (} x \text{ from G to F; } y \text{ from F to E; } z \text{ from E to A)}$$

If $x = 5$ units, $y = 4$ units, and $z = 2$ units, then

$$\underset{\sim}{a} = \begin{pmatrix} 5 \\ 4 \\ 2 \end{pmatrix} \text{ or } \overrightarrow{GA} = \begin{pmatrix} 5 \\ 4 \\ 2 \end{pmatrix}$$

Similarly $\overrightarrow{GB} = \begin{pmatrix} 5 \\ 0 \\ 2 \end{pmatrix}$

5 from G to F
0 in the y direction
2 from F to B

and $\overrightarrow{EC} = \begin{pmatrix} -5 \\ -4 \\ 2 \end{pmatrix}$

-5 from E to H
-4 from H to G
2 from G to C

Write as a 3 by 1 column matrix each of these vectors in Figure 9:8.

$\overrightarrow{GD}$; $\overrightarrow{GH}$; $\overrightarrow{HB}$; $\overrightarrow{AG}$; $\overrightarrow{BH}$; $\overrightarrow{FD}$; $\overrightarrow{FA}$; $\overrightarrow{DB}$.

7 Design a game which uses vectors, e.g. a car race, a treasure hunt.

A   Area of a parallelogram

The area of a parallelogram is the length of its base multiplied by its height.

For Discussion

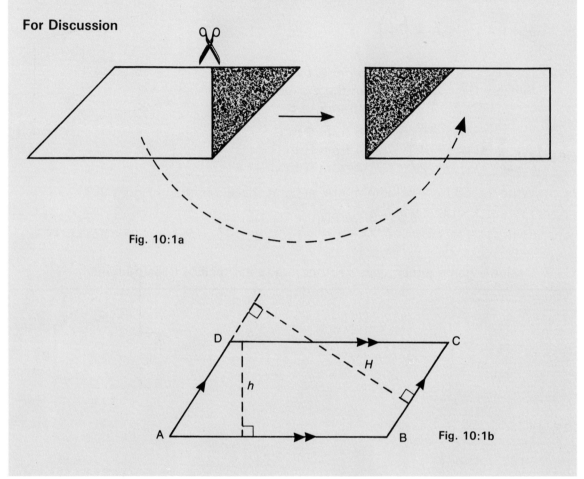

Fig. 10:1a

Fig. 10:1b

1 By making suitable measurements, using the bottom line as base, calculate the area of each parallelogram in Figure 10:2.

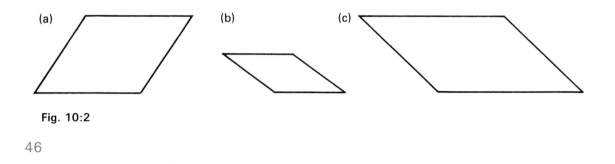

(a)   (b)   (c)

Fig. 10:2

2 Choose the easier base and height measurements to calculate the areas of the parallelograms in Figure 10:3.

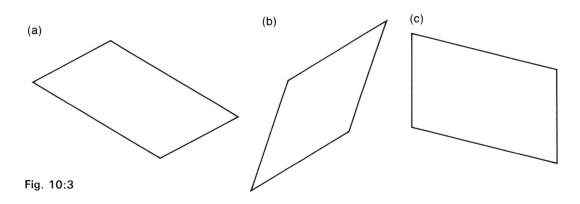

(a)

(b)

(c)

Fig. 10:3

3 Calculate the areas of the parallelograms in Figure 10:4. The diagrams are not to scale.

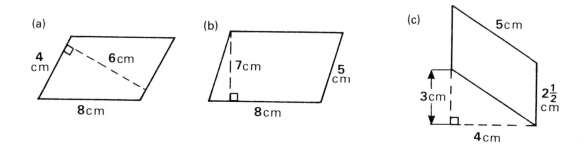

(a)

4 cm
6 cm
8 cm

(b)

7 cm
8 cm
5 cm

(c)

5 cm
3 cm
4 cm
$2\frac{1}{2}$ cm

Fig. 10:4

*4 Calculate the areas of the parallelograms represented in Figure 10:5.

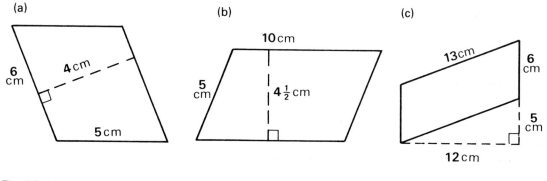

(a)

6 cm
4 cm
5 cm

(b)

10 cm
5 cm
$4\frac{1}{2}$ cm

(c)

13 cm
6 cm
5 cm
12 cm

Fig. 10:5

*5 By making suitable measurements find the true areas of the shapes drawn in Figure 10:6.

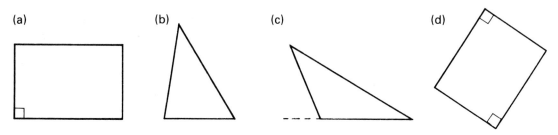

(a)　　　　　　　　(b)　　　　　　　　(c)　　　　　　　　(d)

　　Fig. 10:6

6 Calculate the height of a parallelogram of base 8 cm if its area is 72 cm².

7 In Figure 10:4a, the perpendicular distance between the 4 cm sides is 6 cm. From this the area may be calculated, then using the method of question 6 the other perpendicular distance may be found.

Find the second perpendicular distance between the parallel sides for each parallelogram in Figures 10:4 and 10:5.

---

8 A parallelepiped is a solid with six parallelogram-shaped faces. Make one and investigate its geometric properties.

B　Area of a trapezium

The area of a trapezium is half the sum of the parallel sides multiplied by the distance between them.

For Figure 10:7 the area is $\frac{1}{2}(a + b) \times h$.

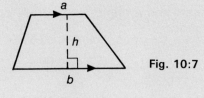

Fig. 10:7

1　Example　For the trapezium in Figure 10:8
Area $= \frac{1}{2}(6 + 11) \times 4$
$= \frac{1}{2} \times 17 \times 4 = 17 \times 2 = 34$ cm².

Note: You can halve the $(a + b)$, or halve the h, or halve the answer to $(a + b) \times h$.

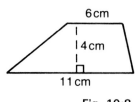

Fig. 10:8

Calculate the area of each trapezium in Figure 10:9. The dimensions are given in centimetres.

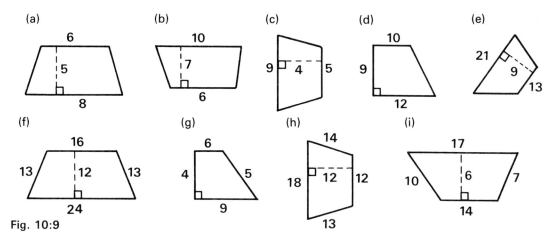

Fig. 10:9

*2 By making suitable measurements find the areas of the trapeziums drawn in Figure 10:10.

(a)   (b)   (c)

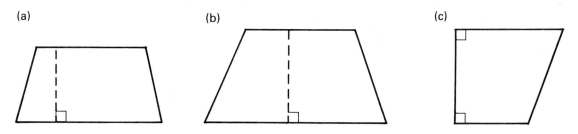

Fig. 10:10

3 Referring to Figure 10:11, state the missing values (a) to (d) and x in the table.

a	1.5 cm	1.4 cm	7 cm	14 cm	2x
b	1.9 cm	1.7 cm	5 cm	(d)	x
h	0.7 cm	0.5 cm	(c)	7 cm	6 cm
Area	(a)	(b)	108 cm²	84 cm²	36 cm²

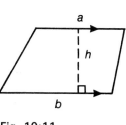

Fig. 10:11

4 Figure 10:12 shows the cross-section of a water tank which has a length of 200 cm. How much water could it hold in (a) cm³ and (b) litres?

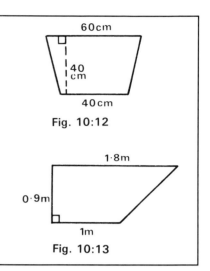

Fig. 10:12

5 Figure 10:13 shows the cross-section of a ditch 100 m long. If 8 m³ of earth can be removed in an hour how long would it take to dig the ditch?

1·8m

0·9m

1m

Fig. 10:13

C Area of a circle

For Discussion

What can you remember about π?

1 The circumference of a circle is $\pi \times d$, where d is the diameter.
The area of a circle is $\pi \times r^2$, where r is the radius.

Taking π as 3.14, calculate the circumference and area of a circle with:
(a) radius 1 cm   (b) radius 2 cm   (c) radius 10 cm   (d) diameter 14 cm.

2 The answers to question 1 are not exact. Why not?

3 Find the coloured area for each shape in Figure 10:14, using the approximation $\pi = \frac{22}{7}$.

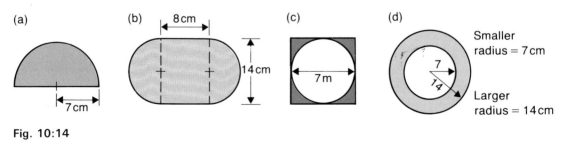

(a)

7cm

(b) 8cm

14cm

(c)

7m

(d) Smaller radius = 7 cm

7

14

Larger radius = 14 cm

Fig. 10:14

*4 Find the area of each shape in Figure 10:15. Take π as 3.14.

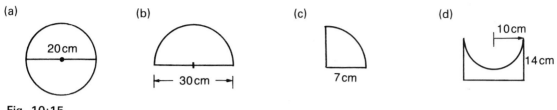

(a) 20 cm

(b) 30 cm

(c) 7 cm

(d) 10 cm 14 cm

Fig. 10:15

5 Emilia's goat is to be tied with a chain 6 metres long to the outside of a barn, 8 metres by 5 metres, in the middle of a 100 metre square field. Where should the chain be fixed to the barn to give the goat the biggest possible grazing area?

6 A circular pond, 38 m in diameter, is to be surrounded by a 2 m wide concrete path, 14 cm thick. How many m³ of 'readymix' concrete should be ordered? (Take $\pi = 3\frac{1}{7}$.)

7 Figure 10:16 represents a concrete pipe of external radius 67.5 cm and internal radius 32.5 cm.
(a) Calculate the coloured area, taking π as $3\frac{1}{7}$.
(b) Calculate in m³ the volume of concrete in a three-metre length of the pipe.

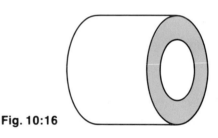

Fig. 10:16

8 The fraction $\frac{22}{7}$ is not a very good approximation for π; a much better one is $\frac{355}{113}$ (easy to remember as 113355).

Compare the decimal values of $\frac{22}{7}$ and $\frac{355}{113}$ with the value for π given by calculators and computers.

Find out what is the most accurate decimal fraction value for π that has yet been calculated.

9 An architect wishes to build a house which encloses the maximum living area within a wall length of 36 m. Investigate the possible plans of the house.

10 Investigate the effect in question 5 of changing the length of the chain and/or repositioning the barn.

11 Percentages: x as a % of y; % change

A One amount as a % of another

Name JASMIN FARDOUM		School Report		SPRING Term

SUBJECT	MARK	MAXIMUM	COMMENTS	
Maths	34	50	Enjoys her work.	CJC
English	105	150	Must learn to spell	BJW
Music	16	80	Sings with enthusiasm	CFG
French	44	132	Must try harder.	L.E.
History	26	39	Good essays.	BC.
Science	84	112	Has an enquiring mind	AMF

Fig. 11:1

Jasmin's teachers have marked her examinations out of different maximum possible scores.

To arrange her results from best to worst she changes each to a percentage.

Example   For maths:

$$34 \text{ out of } 50 \rightarrow \frac{34}{50} \rightarrow \frac{34}{\cancel{50}} \times \cancel{100}^2\% = 68\%.$$

1 (a) On Jasmin's school report, what is her percentage mark in each subject?
   (b) List Jasmin's subjects in order, starting with the one she did best in.

2 Figure 11:2 shows the price list made out by Mr J. Grower when he bought some articles to sell in his shop. It also shows the prices at which he sold them.

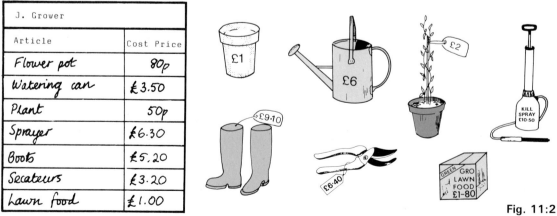

J. Grower	
Article	Cost Price
Flower pot	80p
Watering can	£3.50
Plant	50p
Sprayer	£6.30
Boots	£5.20
Secateurs	£3.20
Lawn food	£1.00

Fig. 11:2

Mr Grower wants to know his profit on each article, expressed as a percentage of his cost price.

Example   For the watering can:
           Cost price = £3.50; Selling price = £6
           Profit = £6 − £3.50 = £2.50
           Profit as a % of cost price = $\dfrac{250}{350} \times 100\%$ → $\dfrac{^5 \cancel{250}}{_7 \cancel{350}} \times 100\%$

$$= \frac{500\%}{7} = 71\tfrac{3}{7}\%.$$

Find the percentage profit on the cost price for each other article in Figure 11:2.

*3 Find:
    (a) 14 as a % of 56   (b) 21 as a % of 168   (c) 12 as a % of 96
    (d) £2 as a % of £10   (e) 400 g as a % of 1600 g.

*4 In each of the following write both amounts in the smaller of the two units before calculating the answer. Find:
    (a) 20p as a % of £1   (b) 40p as a % of £1.60   (c) 3.3 m as a % of 750 cm
    (d) 200 g as a % of 4 kg.

*5 A boutique-owner buys a skirt for £5.60 and sells it for £7. What profit per cent on the cost price does the shop-owner make?

6 Ali buys a book for £2 and later sells it for £1.85. Find his loss as a percentage of his cost price.

7 A factory employs 500 people. During one week the absentee rate was:
   Monday, 50; Tuesday, 10; Wednesday, 15; Thursday, 25; Friday, 40.

   Find for each day the percentage of the work-force who were:
   (a) absent   (b) present.

8 In a box of 40 dozen eggs, eight were bad. What percentage of the box was bad?

With your teacher's permission you may use a calculator for the following.

9 Ann, 72 out of 90;   Sally, 64 out of 80;   Bill, 8 out of 12;
   Janet, 127 out of 144;   Mary, 84 out of 96;   Jill, 92 out of 120.

   (a) Change the above marks to percentages.

   (b) Arrange the pupils' names in order of attainment, from 1st to 6th.

10 Write the first amount as a percentage of the second:
   (a) $17\frac{1}{2}$ $87\frac{1}{2}$ (b) 0.09 0.36   (c) 21 14   (d) 34p £1.36
   (e) 1.2 m 168 cm   (f) 18 ml 1.44 litres   (g) 385 cm² 5 m²

11 Teachers sometimes use one of the following methods to position a class on their results in examinations in different subjects. Investigate these two methods and comment on their fairness.

   Method I   Add up the percentage marks in each subject for each child.
   Method II   Add up the positions in each subject for each child.

B Percentage changes

Change per cent equals change over original, multiplied by 100%

For Discussion

One
Figure 11:3 illustrates the planned net daily expenditure for some council departments.

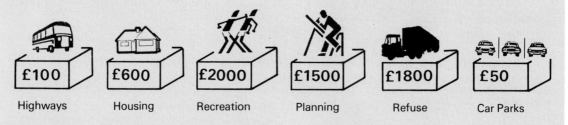

| Highways | Housing | Recreation | Planning | Refuse | Car Parks |
| £100 | £600 | £2000 | £1500 | £1800 | £50 |

Fig. 11:3

Each department is told to cut its planned net daily expenditure by £50.

(a) What percentage cut does this represent for each department?

(b) Which department would suffer the most?

(c) By how much would each department have had to cut their expenditure if a 5% cut had been requested instead of the £50 cut?

(d) Check that both the £50 cut and the 5% cut save the council about £300 a day.

(e) Which method do you think fairer, and why?

Two

John is earning £1000 a month and Hassan is earning £400 a month.

Each is given a £10-a-month pay rise.

What is the percentage change in each man's pay?

1 When the selling price is *more* than the cost price a **profit** has been made.

When the selling price is *less* than the cost price a **loss** has been made.

Both profit and loss represent changes, where the original is the cost price:

Change % = Change × 100% → Profit or Loss % = Profit/Loss × 100%.
$\qquad\qquad\quad$ Original $\qquad\qquad\qquad\qquad\qquad\qquad$ Cost price

Find the percentage profit or loss reckoned on the cost price for the following:

	(a)	(b)	(c)	(d)	(e)
Cost price	£40	32p	96p	£960	£19.20
Selling price	£50	40p	72p	£1080	£12.00

2 *Example*   When washed, a length of material
shrinks from 50 cm to 40 cm. What
percentage change is this?

$\qquad$ Change = 10 cm;
$\qquad$ Original = 50 cm

$\qquad$ Change % = Change × 100%
$\qquad\qquad\qquad\quad$ Original

$\qquad\qquad$ = 10 × 100% = 20%
$\qquad\qquad\quad$ 50

What is the percentage change if a material shrinks from 40 cm to 35 cm?

3 What is the percentage change when a tree grows from 16 m to 20 m?

4 A choir increases in size from eight to fourteen members. What is the percentage change in its size?

5 Another choir increases from 28 to 35 members. Which choir had the bigger percentage increase and by how much?

6 A radio bought for £80 is sold for £66. What is the percentage loss?

7 A car bought for £5200 was sold for £4000. What was the percentage loss?

8 A shop bought bottles of squash at £5.04 a dozen and sold them for 63p each. What was the percentage profit?

9 A tyre costing £18 before tax is sold for £20.70 inclusive of tax. What is the rate of tax per cent?

---

10 Find each of the following changes as a percentage:

	(a)	(b)	(c)	(d)	(e)
Original amount	7.6 cm	1056 cm	1.7 m	1.2 kg	12.960 tonnes
New amount	95 mm	19.8 m	68 cm	2040 g	8100 kg

11 Find out how the percentage key on a calculator works.

12 Using a calculator investigate some percentage changes, e.g. your marks on a series of homeworks; the changing value of the pound against the dollar; the changes in the purchasing power of the pound (Lloyds Bank produce a useful leaflet 'The British Economy in Figures').

C Percentage increase/decrease

Example   Increase 85 by 12%

Method I   12% of 85 → $\frac{12}{100} \times 85$ = 10.2

Answer: 85 + 10.2 = 95.2

Method II   85 increased by 12% → 112% of 85
→ $\frac{112}{100} \times 85$ = 95.2

Method II can be summarised as:

To increase by r% multiply by $\dfrac{100 + r}{100}$.

To decrease by r% multiply by $\dfrac{100 - r}{100}$.

1 The multiplying factor to increase by 12% is 112% or 1.12.
The multiplying factor to decrease by 12% is 88% or 0.88.

State the multiplying factor to:
(a) increase 50 by 4%   (b) decrease 40 by 8%   (c) decrease 90 by 7%
(d) increase 4 by 125%   (e) increase 80 by 220%   (f) decrease 50 by 36%
(g) decrease 450 by 8%   (h) decrease 130 by 7%   (i) increase 140 by 20%.

2 For the changes given in question 1 calculate the changed amount after the given increase or decrease.

3 What you would have to pay for each article in Figure 11:4?

(a)   (b)   (c)

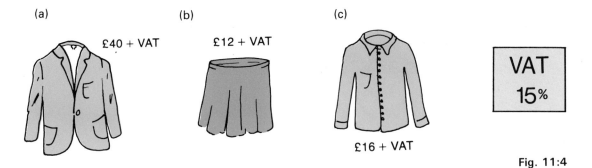

£40 + VAT   £12 + VAT

£16 + VAT

VAT
15%

Fig. 11:4

4 Figure 11:5 shows the front and end elevations of a planned barn. The farmer decides he wants it 30% bigger in all three directions. Draw the elevations of the larger barn, marking on the new dimensions.

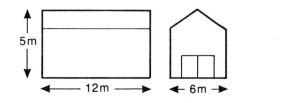

5m

12m   6m

Fig. 11:5

*5 Increase:
(a) 200 by 5%   (b) 80 m by 12%   (c) 250 g by 9%   (d) £90 by 120%.

*6 Decrease:
(a) 400 by 5%   (b) £8 by 30%   (c) 150 m by 7%   (d) 42 cm by 40%.

7 Carla makes 40% profit when she sells a second-hand car which cost her £3000. What did Carla charge for the car?

8 When a piece of material is first washed it shrinks by 5% of its original length of ten metres. What is its new length?

9 Would you rather have an 8% pay rise or a rise of £8 a week? Explain your answer carefully, with examples.

10 In 1986 a club had 600 members. In 1987 its membership increased by 10%. In 1988 its membership dropped by 10%. What was its membership at the start of 1989?

11 Explain your answers to the following questions carefully.
  (a) Can you increase £5 by 200%?   (b) Can you decrease £5 by 200%?

---

12 Ned weeds 20% of his garden every day for a week. He reckons he will have weeded 140% of his garden by the end of the week. Comment on this.

13 Nellie plans to weed 20% of the remaining unweeded portion of her garden every day. How long will it take her to weed her garden?

14 The headmaster boasts at Speech Day that 55% of his fifth year gained a certificate in English and 45% gained a certificate in mathematics, so 100% of the fifth gained at least one of these two subject certificates. Is he correct? Could he possibly be correct?

15 A newspaper reports that Swizzland has the worst unemployment problem in the world, as last year the number of unemployed people rose by 100%. Is the newspaper correct to make this deduction?

16 The rate of inflation in Ardland falls from 35% to 25%. What effect should this have on shop prices?

17 Tonia knows that she charged a customer £7.20 for a watch repair, with VAT at 15% included, but she cannot remember the charge before VAT. Can you help her? Check your answer by adding the VAT back on.

18 Collect examples of percentages from articles in newspapers. Comment on them.

12 Statistics: averages

For Discussion

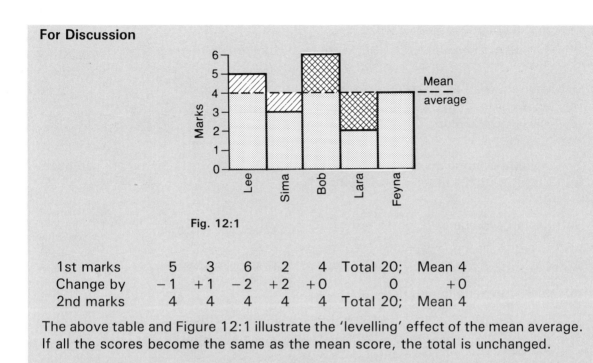

Fig. 12:1

1st marks	5	3	6	2	4	Total 20;	Mean 4
Change by	−1	+1	−2	+2	+0	0	+0
2nd marks	4	4	4	4	4	Total 20;	Mean 4

The above table and Figure 12:1 illustrate the 'levelling' effect of the mean average. If all the scores become the same as the mean score, the total is unchanged.

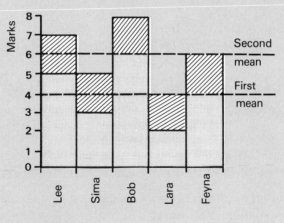

Fig. 12:2

1st marks	5	3	6	2	4	Total 20;	Mean 4
Increase by	+2	+2	+2	+2	+2	+10	+2
2nd marks	7	5	8	4	6	Total 30;	Mean 6

The above table and Figure 12:2 illustrate that the effect of increasing all scores by an amount is to increase the mean by the same amount.

Note: In this exercise 'average' is to be taken as the *mean* average.

1 Find the average of:
   (a) 3, 4, 8   (b) 3, 9, 9   (c) 6, 6, 7, 7, 7, 8, 9, 12.

2 Use your answers to question 1 to write down the average of:
   (a) 13, 14, 18   (b) 23, 24, 28   (c) 53, 54, 58   (d) 83, 89, 89
   (e) 506, 506, 507, 507, 507, 508, 509, 512.

3 The average of some marks is 8. What would the average be if each mark had been:
   (a) 1 less   (b) 1 more   (c) 5 more?

4 Jeff has an average of 8 marks out of 10 in twelve tests. What is his total mark?

5 A car averages 20 km/h for 20 km, then 100 km/h for 900 km.

   (a) How long does the journey take?

   (b) Find the average speed for the journey using the formula:

   $$\text{Average speed} = \frac{\text{Total distance}}{\text{Total time}}$$

6 Repeat question 5(a) and (b) for the following journey:
   A motor-cycle averages 40 km/h for 40 km, then 80 km/h for 240 km.

7 A car travels at 40 km/h for 40 km, then at 60 km/h for 540 km.

   (a) How long does the journey take?

   (b) If the average speed for the journey were taken as being the average of the two
       speeds, that is $\frac{1}{2}(40 + 60) = 50$ km/h, how far would the car go in 10 hours?
   (c) Is your answer to (b) correct for the distance actually travelled in the 10 hours?

   (d) Your answer to (c) should be 'no'. You can *not* find average speed by finding the
       average of the speeds. You must use

   $$\text{Average speed} = \frac{\text{Total distance}}{\text{Total time}}$$

   Find the correct average speed for the car and check that this answer gives the
   correct distance travelled in the ten hours.

*8 Jane has an average mark of 7 after five tests, so we know that she scored 35 marks
   altogether (as 35 ÷ 5 = 7). Find the total score for:
   (a) Ann, average 9 after six texts   (b) John, average 8 after seven tests
   (c) Rashni, average 13 after nine tests   (d) Misa, average 27 after fifteen tests.

*9 For each person in question 8 find the new average after one more test if their scores in this test are: Jane, 13 marks; Ann, 9 marks; John, 9 marks; Misa, 11 marks; Rashni, 11 marks.

Worksheet 12 may be used here.

10 (a) The average of eight numbers is 10. What is their total?
(b) When another number is included the new average is 9. What is the extra number?

11 The average of seven numbers is 8. One of the numbers is 5. What is the average of the other six numbers?

12 The average of six numbers is 10. When another number is included the new average is 9. What is the extra number?

13 Find the average speed for the following journeys. See question 7 if you need help.
(a) 50 km at 25 km/h, then 80 km at 40 km/h.
(b) 65 km at 130 km/h, then 150 km at 100 km/h.

14 Jasmin and Angelo have an average age of 13 y 8 mth.
(a) How old is Jasmin if Angelo is 12 y 7 mth?
(b) Nishi is 13 y 2 mth. What is the average age of Jasmin, Angelo and Nishi?
(c) Jasmin, Angelo, Nishi and Janice have an average age of 14 y 11 mth. How old is Janice?

15 Ann has to travel 120 km in 3 hours. She covers the first 95 km in 2 hours, then is held up for 30 minutes. What speed must she now average if she is not to be late?

16 Marco drives 60 km to an airport in $\frac{3}{4}$ hour, then has to wait $1\frac{1}{2}$ hours for his plane to take off. The plane flies 1500 km in 2 hours. On landing Marco is $\frac{3}{4}$ hour in the airport, then has a 15 minute drive to his hotel, 15 km away. What is his average speed for the whole journey?

17 Find the average speed for:
(a) 36 km at 72 km/h then 1 km at 4 km/h
(b) 25 km at 50 km/h then 2 km at 6 km/h
(c) 60 km at 45 km/h then 1000 km at 750 km/h.

18 The average of some numbers is 12. What are the numbers?

19 Investigate the use of the $\boxed{\bar{x}}$ key on a statistical calculator.

13 Transformations and symmetry: rotations

A Rotations

Figure 13:1 shows the locus (path taken) of a point on the outside circumference of a flanged wheel of a railway engine when the wheel makes one rotation along the railway line. Such a locus is called a **cycloid**.

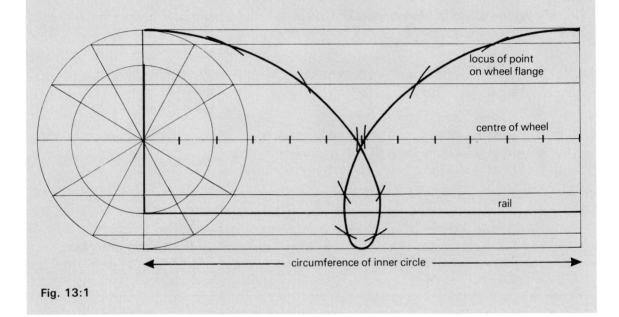

locus of point on wheel flange

centre of wheel

rail

circumference of inner circle

Fig. 13:1

1 Trace or copy accurately flag (a) in Figure 13:2, then draw it in its new position after a rotation of 90° anticlockwise about the marked centre dot.

Repeat for flags (b) to (e).

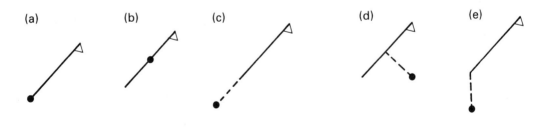

(a)　　　(b)　　　(c)　　　(d)　　　(e)

Fig. 13:2

2 Copy the flags in Figure 13:2 again, but this time rotate them through 180°.

3 In question 2 you should have found that each image flag is either parallel to the object flag or is in the same straight line.

What do you notice about the object and image flags in question 1?

4 Copy the flags again and show on *each* diagram the position of the flag after a 90°, 180° and 270° rotation. (Each diagram will have four flags around its centre point.)

5 Using squared paper copy Figure 13:3 six times. Illustrate the following rotations, one on each diagram. Colour the object and image differently.
  (a) 90° clockwise about (1, 4)
  (b) 90° anticlockwise about (3, 5)
  (c) 180° about (2, 4)
  (d) 180° about (3, 4)
  (e) 180° about (2, 3)
  (f) 90° clockwise about (0, 3)

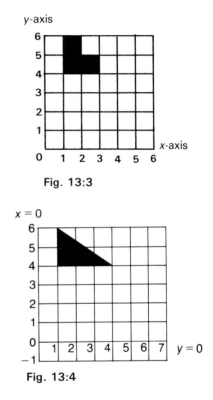

Fig. 13:3

6 Repeat question 5 for Figure 13:4.

Fig. 13:4

7 Design a pattern based on a rotation.

8 Some of the diagrams in Figure 13:5 show a rotation. Copy those that do, and mark the centre of rotation.

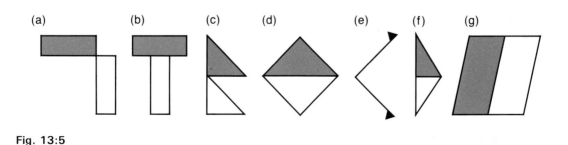

(a)   (b)   (c)   (d)   (e)   (f)   (g)

Fig. 13:5

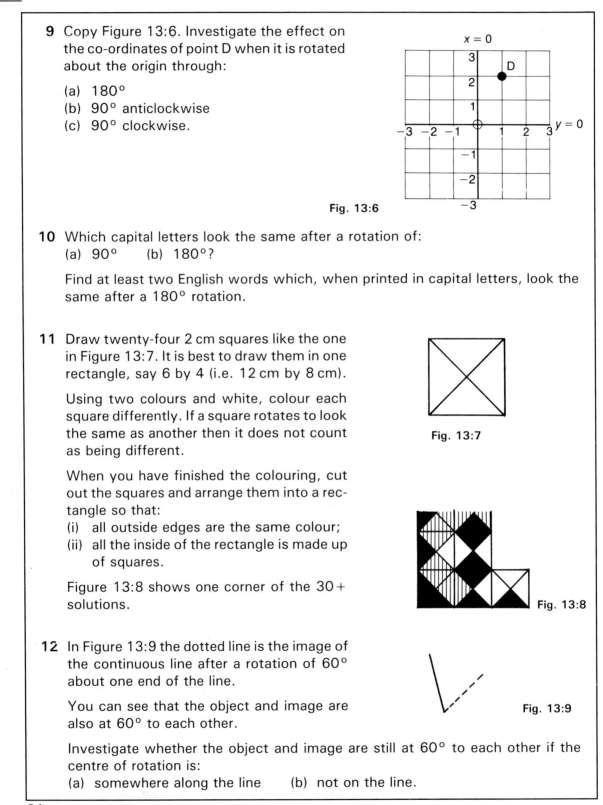

9 Copy Figure 13:6. Investigate the effect on the co-ordinates of point D when it is rotated about the origin through:

(a) 180°
(b) 90° anticlockwise
(c) 90° clockwise.

Fig. 13:6

10 Which capital letters look the same after a rotation of:
(a) 90°   (b) 180°?

Find at least two English words which, when printed in capital letters, look the same after a 180° rotation.

11 Draw twenty-four 2 cm squares like the one in Figure 13:7. It is best to draw them in one rectangle, say 6 by 4 (i.e. 12 cm by 8 cm).

Using two colours and white, colour each square differently. If a square rotates to look the same as another then it does not count as being different.

When you have finished the colouring, cut out the squares and arrange them into a rectangle so that:
(i) all outside edges are the same colour;
(ii) all the inside of the rectangle is made up of squares.

Figure 13:8 shows one corner of the 30 + solutions.

Fig. 13:7

Fig. 13:8

12 In Figure 13:9 the dotted line is the image of the continuous line after a rotation of 60° about one end of the line.

You can see that the object and image are also at 60° to each other.

Fig. 13:9

Investigate whether the object and image are still at 60° to each other if the centre of rotation is:
(a) somewhere along the line   (b) not on the line.

B Rotational symmetry

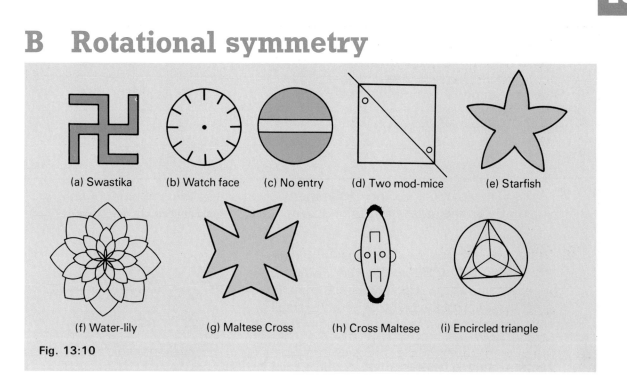

(a) Swastika   (b) Watch face   (c) No entry   (d) Two mod-mice   (e) Starfish

(f) Water-lily   (g) Maltese Cross   (h) Cross Maltese   (i) Encircled triangle

Fig. 13:10

1 Copy and complete this table.

Order of rotational symmetry	Capital letters of the alphabet
1	A, B,
2	H,
3	
4	
infinite	

2 State the order of rotational symmetry for each of the objects in Figure 13:10.

3 Draw a small sketch of each of the following. State under each sketch its order of rotational symmetry.
(a) Isosceles triangle   (b) Equilateral triangle   (c) Rectangle
(d) Parallelogram   (e) Rhombus   (f) Square   (g) Regular hexagon
(h) Regular octagon

4 State the number of lines of symmetry for each shape in Figure 13:10.

5 State the number of lines of symmetry for each shape in question 3.

6 Draw a shape or a pattern to fit the following descriptions:

Shape	(a)	(b)	(c)	(d)	(e)	(f)	(g)	(h)
Order of rotational symmetry	1	1	2	2	3	3	4	4
Number of lines of symmetry	0	1	0	2	0	3	0	4

7 'A diagram either has no line of symmetry *or* it has the same number of lines of symmetry as the order of rotational symmetry.' says Martyn. Is he correct?

8 Draw a set of triangles like those in Figure 13:11, with 2 cm sides. Cut them out and arrange them into one big equilateral triangle such that each of the points where the small triangles meet have the same sign surrounding them.

Hints: (only to be read after you have tried and given up!)

(a) How many signs round the joining points?

(b) How many of each sign are there?

(c) What does this imply about the ● and the ○?

Fig. 13:11

9 The L-shape game

You need: One 1 cm grid of 4 × 4 squares; two 1 cm squares of card; two L-shapes made of card, as in Figure 13:12, coloured differently.

To play: Two players set the pieces as in Figure 13:13. Each player in turn moves their L-shape to a new position. After doing this they may, if they wish, move one neutral square piece too.

The loser is the first to be unable to move their L-shape.

Fig. 13:12

Fig. 13:13

Note: The L-shape may be rotated, translated or reflected. (What will you have to do to the shape to reflect it?)

14 Simplification of algebra: × and ÷

A Review

For Discussion

```
1  FOR N = 1Ø to 5Ø STEP 1Ø
2  LET A = INT(N/9)
3  LET B = A*A
4  IF A < 4 THEN LET B = A*B
5  PRINT B
6  NEXT N
```

(a) Without using a computer, work out what the above program will display on the screen.

(b) Computer algebra has to be written differently from normal handwritten algebra.

How would we normally write:
(i) N/9   (ii) A*A   (iii) A*B?

(c) Why cannot the computer understand A^2 or AB?

1 Simplify:
(a) $a \times a$ (b) $b + b$ (c) $c \times c \times c \times c$ (d) $4 \times d$ (e) $e + e + e$
(f) $4 \times m \times m \times m$ (g) $g + g + g + g$ (h) $4 \times c \times c$.

2 Simplify:
(a) $6 \times a \times a \times c$ (b) $c \times c \times d$ (c) $3 \times c \times c \times d$ (d) $3 \times c \times d \times d$
(e) $4 \times a + 3 \times b \times b$ (f) $2 \times a \times a \times a - 3 \times a \times a$.

3 Write in full, as in questions 1 and 2:
(a) a^3 (b) $3a$ (two ways)   (c) $4a^2$ (d) $3d^2 + 4d$ (e) $4c^3 - 3c$.

4 If $f = 1$, $g = 3$, $h = 2$ and $n = 0$, find the value of:
(a) $2f^2$ (b) $2g^2$ (c) h^3 (d) $2f^3$ (e) $24n^3$ (f) $2gh$ (g) $6fg$
(h) gh^2 (i) g^2h (j) g^2h^2 (k) $h^2 - g^2$.

5 **Example** $3x^2 - x - 2x^2 + 1 - 8 - 4x \rightarrow x^2 - 5x - 7$

Simplify:
(a) $2a + 3a - c$ (b) $5a + 2a^2 - 2a$ (c) $4k + k^2 - 5k$
(d) $3a^2 + a + a^2$ (e) $2 + 2b^2 + 2$ (f) $3a^2b - 2ab - a^2b$
(g) $2x + x^2 - 3x + xy + x^2 + 3x$.

In questions 6, 7 and 8 find the value of the letter a.

6 (a) $5 + a = 3$ (b) $a + 7 = 4$ (c) $a - 7 = 5$ (d) $9a = 54$

7 (a) $4a = -16$ (b) $2a = 5$ (c) $4a = 10$ (d) $8a = -20$

8 (a) $4a + 5 = 21$ (b) $4a - 3 = 9$ (c) $3a - 6 = 12$ (d) $2a + 4 = 2$

---

9 Write an algebraic term (like '$6k$ kilometres') for:
   (a) the cost of 5 pencils at m pence each
   (b) the cost of 8 buns at n pence each
   (c) the cost of n buns at 8 pence each
   (d) the distance gone in 6 hours at d km/h
   (e) the distance gone in m hours at 80 km/h.

10 Find an answer to the following by forming an equation and then solving it.

   (a) Mary has m pence. Joan has twice as much. Together they have 42 pence. How much have they each?

   (b) Jerome is x years old. Hassan is 7 years older. Together their ages total 35 years. Find their ages.

   (c) One boy has 24 marbles more than another boy. If they have 96 marbles altogether how many have they each?

11 The answer is $5a^2 + 4ab$. What is the question?

B Multiplication and division

To multiply: add the indices.

To divide: subtract the indices.

1 **Example**   Simplify $a^2 \times a^3$.

Either: $a^2 \times a^3 \to a \times a \times a \times a \times a \to a^5$

Or: $a^2 \times a^3 \to a^{2+3} \to a^5$

Simplify:
(a) $a^7 \times a^6$ (b) $y^4 \times y^4$ (c) $y^2 \times y^3 \times y^4$ (d) $n^2 \times n^2 \times n^2$.

2 Example   Simplify $2c^2d \times 3c^3d^2$.

Working: $2 \times 3 \to 6$; $c^2 \times c^3 \to c^5$; $d \times d^2 \to d^{1+2} \to d^3$
Therefore $2c^2d \times 3c^3d^2 \to 6c^5d^3$

Simplify:
(a) $3a^2 \times 4a^3$ (b) $2c^2d \times 3cd$ (c) $2a^2b^2 \times 5b^2$ (d) $6c^3 \times 4c^3d^3$.

3 Example   Simplify $c^3 \div c^2$.

$c^3 \div c^2$ can be written as a fraction: $\dfrac{c^3}{c^2}$

Either: $\dfrac{c^3}{c^2} \to \dfrac{\not c \times \not c \times c}{\not c \times \not c} \to c$ Or: $\dfrac{c^3}{c^2} \to c^{3-2} \to c^1 \to c$

Simplify: (a) $\dfrac{a^7}{a^5}$ (b) $\dfrac{a^3}{a^3}$ (c) $c^7 \div c^4$ (d) $g^{15} \div g^5$ (e) $h^3 \div h^3$.

4 Example   Simplify $c^2 \div c^3$.

Answer: $c^2 \div c^3 \to \dfrac{c^2}{c^3} \to \dfrac{1}{c}$

The c is written at the bottom as there was a higher power of c at the bottom in the question.

Simplify: (a) $k^2 \div k^4$ (b) $a^3 \div a^3$ (c) $b \div b^5$
(d) $s^3 \div s^5$ (e) $s^5 \div s^3$.

*5 Simplify:
(a) $a^4 \times a^2$ (b) $a^6 \times a^3$ (c) $m^2 \times m^4$ (d) $f^2 \times f^5$ (e) $8c^2 \times 4c^3$
(f) $3d^4 \times 4d^5$ (g) $3a^2 \times 4d^2$ (h) $5b^2 \times 3c^6$ (i) $2a^3b \times 3ab^2$
(j) $4xy^2 \times 4xy^2$.

*6 Simplify:

(a) $\dfrac{b^4}{b^2}$ (b) $\dfrac{b^7}{b^6}$ (c) $a^7 \div a$ (d) $a^4 \div a^4$ (e) $k^3 \div k^5$ (f) $s^2 \div s^6$

(g) $t \div t$ (h) $t^4 \div t^6$ (i) $t^6 \div t^4$ (j) $s \div s^8$.

7 Example   Simplify $\dfrac{6s^7t}{12s^3t^2}$.

Working: $\dfrac{6}{12} \to \dfrac{1}{2}$; $\dfrac{s^7}{s^3} \to s^4$; $\dfrac{t}{t^2} \to \dfrac{1}{t}$

You do not need to write 1 of $\dfrac{1}{t}$ unless there is no other top term.

Therefore $\dfrac{6s^7t}{12s^3t^2} \to \dfrac{s^4}{2t}$

Simplify: (a) $\dfrac{4c^3}{8c^5}$ (b) $15a^8 \div 3a^5$ (c) $24d^8 \div 3d^4$.

8 Simplify: (a) $\dfrac{8a^2}{8a^4}$ (b) $\dfrac{12a^5b^4}{3a^3b^2}$ (c) $\dfrac{16a^4b^5}{2a^2}$.

9 Simplify: (a) $\dfrac{14a^7b^2}{21a^3b^3}$ (b) $\dfrac{12a^4b^5c^3}{80a^2b^4c^5}$ (c) $a^3b^2 \div 4a^4b^3$.

10 Simplify: (a) $\dfrac{8a^5b^4}{4a^3b^2}$ (b) $\dfrac{12a^6b^3}{2a^3b^4}$ (c) $\dfrac{a^8b^9}{a^8b^{10}}$.

11 Simplify: (a) $7a^5 \times 4b^2 \div 2a^3$ (b) $4a^6 \times 3a^4 \div 2a^3$ (c) $9b^7 \times 4b^3 \div 12b^5$.

---

12 **Example** $\dfrac{3a}{m} \div \dfrac{2a^2}{m^3} \rightarrow \dfrac{3a}{m} \times \dfrac{m^3}{2a^2} \rightarrow \dfrac{3am^3}{2a^2m} \rightarrow \dfrac{3m^2}{2a}$

Simplify:

(a) $\dfrac{c}{d} \div \dfrac{c^2}{d^2}$ (b) $\dfrac{b}{n^2} \div \dfrac{5}{n^2}$ (c) $\dfrac{a^2bd}{c^2} \div \dfrac{ab}{c}$ (d) $\dfrac{4a^2b}{9c^2d^2} \div \dfrac{16a^3b}{36c^2d}$.

13 Roots are the inverses of powers. $y^{1/x}$ is the xth root of y.

Examples $16^{1/2} = \sqrt{16} = 4$ $8^{1/3} = \sqrt[3]{8} = 2$ (because $2^3 = 8$)

A scientific calculator will have a power key, either $\boxed{y^x}$ or $\boxed{x^y}$, and a root key, $\boxed{y^{1/x}}$ or $\boxed{x^{1/y}}$ or $\boxed{\sqrt[x]{y}}$ or $\boxed{\sqrt[y]{x}}$ or $\boxed{\text{INV}}$ $\boxed{y^x}$

Examples 8^4 can be found by 8 $\boxed{y^x}$ 4 $\boxed{=}$, giving 4096.

$\sqrt[5]{32}$ or $32^{1/5}$ can be found by 32 $\boxed{y^{1/x}}$ 5 $\boxed{=}$, giving 2
(because $2^5 = 32$).

Find: (a) $1.6^{1/2}$ (b) $\sqrt[3]{125}$ (c) $\sqrt[3]{16}$ (d) $\sqrt[4]{100}$ (e) $\sqrt[5]{60}$.

14 Find the H.C.F. and L.C.M. (see exercise 2B, question 8, and exercise 2C, question 6) of:
(a) a^2 and a^5 (b) $2cd^2$ and $4d$ (c) $6a^2b^4$ and $27ab^3$.

15 For each part of question 14 state:
(i) how many times the H.C.F. divides into each expression
(ii) how many times each expression divides into the L.C.M.

16 $15b^2c^4$ is the answer to a simplification. Write four possible questions.

Project

Imperial units

Today we usually calculate using metric units, based on the tens or decimal system. The main exception to this is time. When carrying amounts from one column to another in a non-metric system you must remember that you do not carry tens as in normal arithmetic.

Examples

(a)
h	min	s	
16	46	51	
6	29	18	add
23	16	9	
1	1		

76 min

1 min 9s

1h 16min

(b)
yd	ft	in	
1	2	8	
3	2	9	add
5	2	5	
1	1		

5ft

1 ft 5in

1 yd 2ft

1 Add:

(a)
weeks	days
2	1
2	3
1	5

(b)
weeks	days
1	4
	5
3	6

(c)
min	s
5	42
3	27
21	4

(d)
days	h	min	s
2	7	31	19
1	17	21	42
1	9	14	22

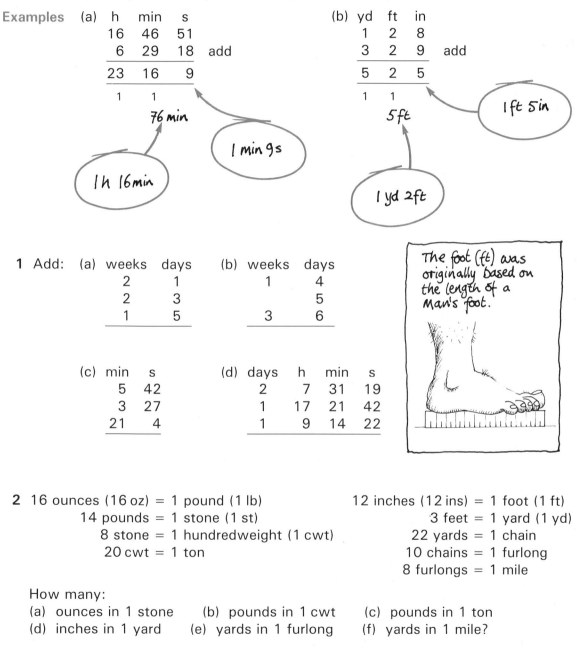

The foot (ft) was originally based on the length of a man's foot.

2

16 ounces (16 oz) = 1 pound (1 lb)
14 pounds = 1 stone (1 st)
8 stone = 1 hundredweight (1 cwt)
20 cwt = 1 ton

12 inches (12 ins) = 1 foot (1 ft)
3 feet = 1 yard (1 yd)
22 yards = 1 chain
10 chains = 1 furlong
8 furlongs = 1 mile

How many:
(a) ounces in 1 stone   (b) pounds in 1 cwt   (c) pounds in 1 ton
(d) inches in 1 yard   (e) yards in 1 furlong   (f) yards in 1 mile?

3 Add:

(a)	st	lb	oz
	1	8	14
	2	12	13
	1	6	8

(b)	tons	cwt	lb
	3	17	84
	3	14	72
	6	19	48

(c)	yds	ft	ins
	6	2	11
	4	1	9
	6	2	8

4 Investigate subtraction in non-metric units.

5 Investigate multiplication and division in non-metric units.

6 Investigate the present use of imperial units in Britain.

7 The graph can be used to convert between lbs and kg. It uses the fact that 10 lbs ≈ 4.5 kg. Check from the conversion graph that 4 lbs is about 1.8 kg, and that 2.8 kg is about 6 lbs 4 oz.

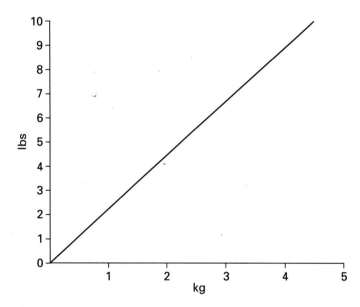

Now draw a conversion graph between metres and feet and inches, using the fact that 10 feet ≈ 305 cm.

A   Interior angle sum of polygons

For Discussion

One

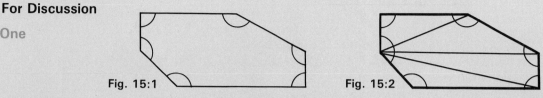

Fig. 15:1   Fig. 15:2

Figure 15:1 shows the interior angles of a six-sided polygon. By drawing diagonals from one vertex the polygon can be divided into triangles as in Figure 15:2. How does this show that the interior angles of a hexagon add up to 720°?

Two

Cathy says, 'If a polygon has n sides its interior angles add up to $(n - 2) \times 180°$.' What does she mean by this?

1 Find the interior angle sum of:
(a) a triangle   (b) a quadrilateral   (c) a pentagon   (d) an octagon
(e) a decagon.

*2 Find the interior angle sum of:
(a) a heptagon (7 sides)   (b) a nonagon (9 sides)   (c) a dodecagon (12 sides)
(d) an icosagon (20 sides).

*3 If a figure has all its sides and angles equal it is said to be 'regular'.
(a) What is a regular triangle called? How big is each angle?
(b) What is a regular quadrilateral called? How big is each angle?

*4 Copy the following table, completing the pentagon line, then continue it for a regular hexagon, a regular octagon and a regular decagon.

Number of sides	Name	Interior angle sum	Size of one interior angle
3	Equilateral triangle	$1 \times 180° = 180°$	$180° \div 3 = 60°$
4	Square	$2 \times 180° = 360°$	$360° \div 4 = 90°$
5	Regular pentagon	$3 \times 180° = \ldots$	$\ldots \div 5 = \ldots$
etc.			

5 All regular polygons fit exactly into a circle. For the pentagon shown in Figure 15:3, each angle at the centre is 360° ÷ 5 = 72°. Use this fact to draw a copy of Figure 15:3.

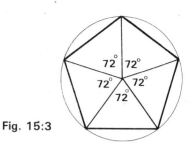

6 Calculate the angle between the spokes for each regular polygon from equilateral triangle to decagon (see Figure 15:3).

Fig. 15:3

7 Example The interior angle sum of a hexagon is 4 × 180° = 720°.

If the hexagon is regular each interior angle is 720° ÷ 6 = 120°.

Calculate the size of the interior angle of a regular polygon with:
(a) 5 sides   (b) 7 sides   (c) 15 sides.

8 A pentagon has one angle of 116°. What is the size of each other angle if they are equal to each other?

9 The angles of an octagon are in the ratio 1:2:3:4:5:6:7:8 (making 36 parts altogether). Calculate each angle.

10 How many sides has a polygon with an angle sum of:
(a) 1620°   (b) 2340°?

11 Does a polygon with an angle sum of 1000° exist? Give reasons for your answer.

12 The angles of a nonagon are $x°$, $x°$, $x°$, $2x°$, $2x°$, $(x + 3)°$, $(x + 4)°$, $(2x + 9)°$, and $(3x - 2)°$. Find each angle.

13 A heptagon has three smaller equal angles and four larger equal angles. Find the sizes of the smaller angles if the larger are 15 degrees more.

14 In Figure 15:4 quadrilateral ABCD has an angle sum of 360°. If E is taken as another corner, of size 180°, then the figure becomes a pentagon ABCDE and the angle sum becomes 360° + 180° = 540°.

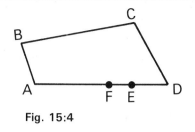

Fig. 15:4

Similarly, if F is taken as a sixth corner, then the angle sum of hexagon ABCDEF is 540° + 180° = 720°.

Use a continuation of this method for the angle sum of an octagon and a decagon.

15 Draw several *concave* polygons. Divide them into triangles and find out if their angle sum is the same as for convex polygons with the same number of sides.

16 Draw an interlacing polygon pattern like the one in Figure 15:5. We have used pentagons, but any regular polygon may be used.

Draw the outer circle first, then the two larger polygons. Draw the inside circle to just touch the sides of the larger polygons and draw the smaller polygons inside it.

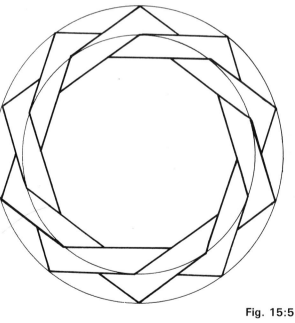

Fig. 15:5

17 Investigate tessellations of regular polygons.

B   Exterior angle sum of polygons

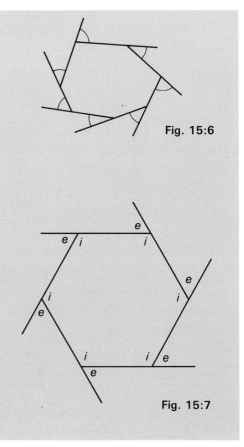

Figure 15:6 shows the seven exterior angles of a heptagon.

The exterior angles of all polygons total 360° (one complete turn).

Fig. 15:6

Example   Figure 15:7 shows the interior angles, marked i, and exterior angles, marked e, of a regular hexagon.

The six exterior angles total 360°, so $e = 60°$.

The interior and exterior angles form pairs of adjacent angles on a straight line, so that $e + i = 180°$, giving $i = 120°$ for the hexagon.

There are six interior angles, so the interior angle sum is $6 \times 120° = 720°$.

This is an alternative method to the $(n - 2) \times 180°$ formula.

Fig. 15:7

1   Calculate, as in the above example, the exterior angle, the interior angle, and the interior angle sum for:
   (a) an equilateral triangle   (b) a square   (c) a regular pentagon.

2   How many sides has a regular polygon if its exterior angles are:
   (a) 36°   (b) 10°   (c) 9°   (d) 20°   (e) 15°   (f) 18°   (g) 24°?

*3   Find the exterior angle, the interior angle, and the interior angle sum for:
   (a) a regular octagon   (b) a regular nonagon   (c) a regular decagon
   (d) a regular dodecagon (12 sides).

*4 Copy Figure 15:8 by drawing a regular hexagon inside a 3 cm radius circle, then producing its sides. Calculate the sizes of all thirty angles, writing your answers inside the angles.

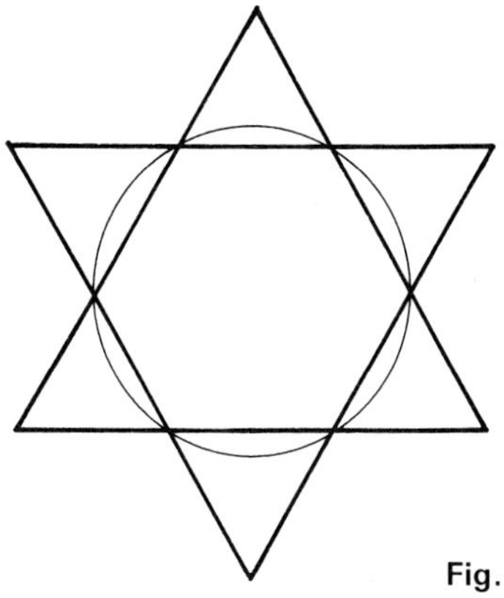

Fig. 15:8

*5 Repeat question 4 with a regular pentagon inside the circle. There will be 25 angles to find this time. See exercise 15A, question 5 if you have forgotten how to draw a pentagon inside a circle.

6 Which of the following angles cannot be the exterior angle of a regular polygon? Give reasons for your answers.
A, 20°; B, 25°; C, 30°; D, 90°; E, 180°

7 Which of the following could be interior angles of a regular polygon?
A, 160°; B, 105°; C, 36°; D, 135°; E, 180°

8 Each angle of a certain regular polygon is 170°.
(a) How many degrees is each exterior angle?
(b) How many sides has the polygon?

9 How many sides has a regular polygon with interior angles of:
(a) 156°   (b) $157\frac{1}{2}$°   (c) 165.6°?

10 How many sides has a regular polygon if its exterior and interior angles are in the ratio:
(a) 2:1   (b) 1:2?

11 ABCDE is a regular pentagon. Calculate:
(a) ∠AED   (b) ∠EAD   (c) ∠BAD.

12 Name the regular polygon with:
(a) the largest possible exterior angle
(b) the smallest possible interior angle
(c) the smallest possible number of sides
(d) the largest possible number of sides.

13 Construct each regular polygon up to a decagon inside circles of about 5 cm radius and draw very carefully all possible diagonals in each. These patterns are called Mystic Roses. Can you find a rule to work out how many diagonals are possible, given the number of sides?

14 Figures 15:9 and 15:10 show how to divide a line into any number of parts. Figure 15:11 shows how to use this to draw a polygon in a circle. AB is to be the diameter for a heptagon. It is divided into seven parts, then arcs are drawn from A and B to give point C. You always use point 2, but the number of parts that you divide the diameter into depends on the number of sides that the polygon has.

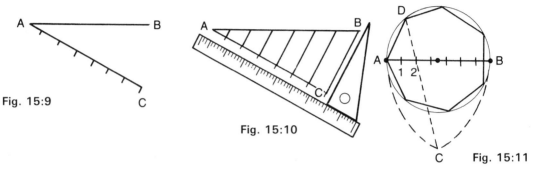

Fig. 15:9

Fig. 15:10

Fig. 15:11

15 All regular polygons fit exactly into a circle. Figure 15:12 shows how to find the centre and radius of this circle when you want the side (AB) to be a certain length. BC = AB and ∠B = 90°. Point 4 is where the perpendicular bisector of AB crosses AC. Point 6 is given by arc AC, centre B, and point 5 is midway between 4 and 6. Use compasses or dividers to mark points 7 to 12. Each numbered point is the centre of the circle for the polygon with that number of sides. The polygon is then drawn by stepping off its sides round the circle, as shown in Figure 15:13.

Note: This construction is only absolutely accurate for 4 and 6 sides, although the error is very small for up to 12 sides. Try to calculate the error in side length for various polygons.

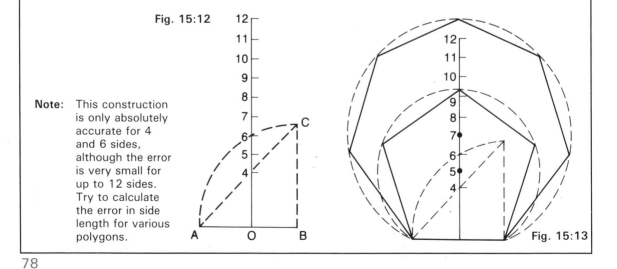

Fig. 15:12

Fig. 15:13

A Review of decimal places

For Discussion

One

This article appeared in *The Daily Telegraph* one day in January 1984. What approximations are used?

23 TONS OF PAPER USED IN YEAR BY SIZEWELL INQUIRY

By ROLAND GRIBBEN Business Correspondent

THE inquiry into plans to build a controversial nuclear power plant using American technology at Sizewell in Suffolk celebrates its first birthday on Wednesday and could have another before the marathon hearings are completed.

So far it has used five million sheets of paper weighing 23 tons. The inquiry is into the Central Electricity Generating Board's proposal to build a £1·2 billion pressurised water nuclear power station.

The paper, piled sheet on sheet, would reach a height of 1,542 feet, two-and-a-half times as high as the British Telecom tower in London.

More than seven million words have been spoken during the hearings at the Snape Maltings, Suffolk and Church House, Westminster. The most common is "day" — used over 80,000 times.

The Generating Board has already submitted almost a thousand documents and 3 cwt of paper. Its 38 witnesses spent nearly 40 days presenting evidence.

Over 50 opponents, including Mr Wedgwood Benn, former Labour Energy Secretary, have given evidence so far over a 44-day period. Opposition groups have submitted about 1,300 documents.

Two

Cindy's mum wants to plant eight bushes, equally spaced along a path with 10 metres between the first and the last. To find the gap between each bush she asks Cindy to find 10 ÷ 7 (Why seven?) using her calculator. What answer should Cindy give to her mum?

1 Examples   Rounded to the nearest whole number:

$6.1 \to 6$ $7.54 \to 8$ $21.9 \to 22$

Note that 30.5 can become either 30 *or* 31; both are equally correct, but most mathematicians 'round up', that is they say the answer is 31.

If the 'key figure' is 5 or more, increase the figure in front of it by 1.

Round to the nearest whole number:
(a) 6.3   (b) 8.4   (c) 9.7   (d) 4.6   (e) 24.8   (f) 18.5
(g) 19.5   (h) 8.39   (i) 7.64   (j) 14.4999

2 Examples $2.62 \to 2.6$ to 1 decimal place (1 d.p.)

$24.35 \to 24.4$ to 1 d.p.

$23.96 \to 24.0$ to 1 d.p.

Write correct to 1 decimal place:
(a) 2.43   (b) 8.52   (c) 6.49   (d) 17.955   (e) 8.47
(f) 24.364   (g) 14.503   (h) 26.51   (i) 48.999

3 Using a calculator find answers to the following, correct to 2 decimal places.
(a) $250 \div 13$ (b) $100 \div 7$ (c) $13.01 \div 3.1$ (d) $\sqrt{13}$ (e) $1 \div 16$
(f) $2.15 \div 2.7$ (g) $36.39 \div 2.6$ (h) $\sqrt{101}$

4 Give ten 4-figure numbers that become 3.1 correct to 1 d.p. and 3.10 to 2 d.p.

5 Find the sum of the numbers given in question 2 and the sum of your approximations.

What percentage error is made by summing all the approximations?

B   Significant figures

The first non-zero digit is the first significant figure.

Examples   28.4 has 3 significant figures.

0.0064 has 2 significant figures.

360 has either 2 *or* 3 significant figures: you cannot tell if the zero is a significant figure or not.

360.0 has 4 significant figures: the zero after the point would not be there unless it were significant.

1 State the number of significant figures in each of the following:
   (a) 246   (b) 460   (c) 308   (d) 0.0121   (e) 0.805   (f) 17.01
   (g) 24.0   (h) 0.004   (i) 3.5   (j) 50 000   (k) 0.1002   (l) 10.01
   (m) 0.020   (n) 0.002 001

2 Examples   When written correct to 3 significant figures (s.f.):
   4069 → 4070   4.896 → 4.90   0.041 23 → 0.0412

   Note that each approximated answer must be about the same size as the
   original number, so 4069 does not become 407 but 4070.

   Write correct to 3 significant figures:
   (a) 4083   (b) 3.046   (c) 19.97   (d) 20.408   (e) 1.295
   (f) 17046   (g) 0.024 64   (h) 2.004   (i) 10.0047   (j) 0.008 793
   (k) 3004   (l) 0.000 138 5   (m) 0.000 169 9

3 Write the numbers in question 2(a) to (m) correct to 2 significant figures.

*4 Write correct to 2 s.f.:
   (a) 17.843   (b) 1036.255   (c) 0.008 72   (d) 0.899   (e) 1006.426
   (f) 0.005 06   (g) 3450   (h) 1700   (i) 0.398   (j) 0.009 77

*5 Write the numbers in question 4 correct to 1 significant figure.

6 Calculations should always be checked by an estimated answer. One way of doing
   this is to approximate each number to one, or at most two, significant figures, so
   making the arithmetic very easy.

   Examples   (a) 3.85 × 165 ≈ 4 × 200, so 3.85 × 165 ≈ 800
              (b) 17.65 ÷ 0.82 ≈ 20 ÷ 0.8 → 200 ÷ 8, so 17.65 ÷ 0.82 ≈ 25

   Find approximate answers to:
   (a) 925 × 3.8   (b) 14.67 ÷ 1.25
   (c) 3.6 metres of curtain at £2.76 per metre
   (d) £321 shared equally between 12 people
   (e) the area of a kitchen floor 3.15 metres long and 1.86 metres wide
   (f) the average speed needed to travel 340 miles between 10:05 a.m. and 2:45 p.m.
   (g) the cost of 33 litres of petrol at 38 pence a litre
   (h) the cost of supplying 186 pupils with maths books at £5.85 each
   (i) the time taken to mark 146 exam papers if they take 25 minutes each on average
   (j) the price to charge 51 pupils each to hire a coach for £188.

7 Write the numbers in question 4, (a) to (f) only, correct to 2 decimal places.

8 A = {0.006 425, 0.000 781, 0.003 263, 0.008 97, 0.107}

B = {7.406, 5.3074, 0.016, 25, 0.0317}

C = {28 426, 170, 2745, 2.06, 2991.7}

(a) Sum the elements of each set, writing each answer correct to 2 s.f.

(b) Write each element correct to 2 s.f. then sum your approximations correct to 2 s.f.

(c) Use a calculator to find the percentage errors between the true sums and the approximated ones. Use the formula: % error = (error ÷ true) × 100.

9 If 1.63 is correct to 3 s.f. then the smallest value it could be is 1.625; anything less than this, say 1.6246, would be 1.62 correct to 3 s.f.

Similarly, 1.63 correct to 3 s.f. cannot be larger than 1.635. (Although we normally round 1.635 to 1.64, it is really exactly halfway between 1.63 and 1.64, so it could just as well become 1.63.)

The **range of error** is 1.635 − 1.625 = 0.01

What is the range of error if 197.6 is correct to 4 s.f.?

10 What is the range of error if 2000 is correct to:
(a) 4 s.f.   (b) 3 s.f.   (c) 2 s.f.   (d) 1 s.f.?

---

11 **Reminders** 7.61×10^2 is the standard form of 761

7.61×10^{-2} is the standard form of 0.0761

The indices (2 and − 2) tell you how many columns to move the figures 7, 6 and 1.

Numbers can be entered into a scientific calculator in standard form using the $\boxed{\text{EXP}}$ or $\boxed{\text{EE}}$ key.

Example $(7.61 \times 10^2) - (88.8 \times 10^{-3})$

7.61 $\boxed{\text{EXP}}$ 2 $\boxed{-}$ 88.8 $\boxed{\text{EXP}}$ 3 $\boxed{+/-}$ $\boxed{=}$

Answer: 7.61×10^2

The answer may be given in standard form or as an ordinary number (if it is not too big or too small). You may be able to switch it over; try the $\boxed{\text{INV}}$ or $\boxed{\text{2nd F}}$ key with the $\boxed{\text{EXP}}$ key or consult your handbook!

Give answers to the following as normal numbers correct to 3 significant figures.

(a) $(4.612 \times 10^2) \times (1.76 \times 10^{-1})$ (b) $(3.69 \times 10^{-3}) \div (2.5 \times 10^{-4})$

(c) $(8.105 \times 10^3) + (1.64 \times 10^2)$ (d) $(3.17 \times 10^8) \div (1.56 \times 10^7)$

(e) $\dfrac{(9.3 \times 10^{-5}) - (7.6 \times 10)}{(5.6 \times 10^4)}$ (f) $\dfrac{(8.1 \times 10^3) + (3.9 \times 10^{-2})}{(4.35 \times 10^{-1})}$

Be careful!

12 A rectangle has sides of 4.8 cm and 6.7 cm correct to 2 s.f.
   (a) What is the largest and the smallest possible area it could have?
   (b) What is the range of error in calculating its area?

13 A cuboid has sides of 7.6 cm, 5.7 cm and 6.4 cm correct to 2 s.f.
   (a) What is the largest and the smallest possible volume it could have?
   (b) What is the range of error in calculating its volume?

17 Constructions: triangles; perpendicular from a point

A Triangles from SAS; dropping perpendiculars

For Discussion

Dropping a perpendicular

(a) Draw any line XY and mark any point A above it.

(b) From A draw arcs 1 and 2 to give points B and C on XY.

(c) From B and C draw arcs 3 and 4 to give point D.

(d) Line up AD and draw AP.

Note: It is possible to save space by making the radius of the arcs in (c) smaller than those in (b).

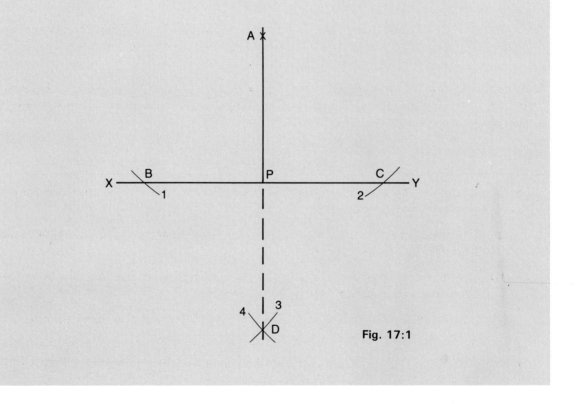

Fig. 17:1

1 Investigate ways of constructing the following angles using a ruler and a pair of compasses, but not a protractor. You can find help on page 232.
   (a) 60°   (b) 120°   (c) 30°   (d) 15°   (e) 90° (two methods)
   (f) 45°

2 Draw a small sketch of each of the following triangles, marking on each the given angle and lengths, then construct the triangles as accurately as possible.

Note: (i) Use a protractor for (a) and (b) but not for (c) to (g).
(ii) Each time take the first side given as the base of the triangle.

(a) △ABC; AB = 4 cm, ∠A = 75°, AC = 3 cm. Measure BC.
(b) △DEF; DE = 3 cm, ∠E = 110°, EF = 3 cm. Measure DF.
(c) △GHI; GH = 5 cm, ∠G = 30°, GI = 4 cm. Measure HI.
(d) △JKL; JK = 4 cm, ∠K = 120°, KL = 2 cm. Measure JL.
(e) △MNO; MN = 4.5 cm, ∠M = 90°, MO = 3.5 cm. Measure NO.
(f) △PQR; PQ = 6.5 cm, ∠Q = 45°, QR = 2.5 cm. Measure PR.
(g) △STU; ST = 4 cm, ∠S = 135°, SU = 5 cm. Measure TU.

3 On your triangles for question 2 drop the perpendicular from:
(a) A to BC   (b) E to DF   (c) I to GH   (d) K to JL   (e) M to NO
(f) R to PQ   (g) U to TS produced (made longer).

Use your perpendiculars to calculate the triangles' areas in cm², correct to 1 d.p.

4 Construct any isosceles triangle. Construct the perpendicular from the vertical angle (the unequal one) to the opposite side. Mark all equal angles and lines.

5 Construct parallelogram ABCD with AB = 6 cm, ∠B = 72°, and BC = 3.5 cm. By constructing the perpendicular from C to AB (it helps to produce AB first), calculate the area of the parallelogram.

6 Construct four copies of a triangle with sides 9 cm, 8 cm and 6 cm. Answer one of the following parts on each triangle.

(a) Construct the bisectors of each angle to give the incentre. Draw the incircle. Measure its radius.

(b) Construct the perpendicular bisector of each side to give the circumcentre. Draw the circumcircle. Measure its radius.

(c) Construct the medians, from the vertices to the midpoints of the opposite sides, to give the centroid (the centre of gravity).

(d) Construct the perpendiculars from each vertex to the opposite side to give the orthocentre.

Note: This project is continued in exercise 17B, questions 11 and 12.

B Triangles from AAS

For Discussion

Triangle ABC has one angle of 40°, one angle of 110°, and one side of length 4 cm.

(a) Which of the triangles in Figures 17:2 and 17:3 could be △ABC?

(b) Could △ABC be any other shape?

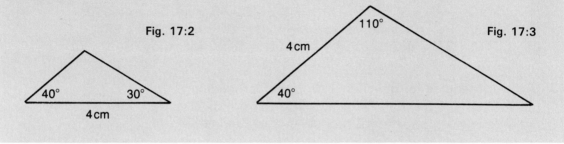

Fig. 17:2   Fig. 17:3

1 Draw a small sketch of the following triangles, then construct them accurately.

    (a) △ABC;   AB = 5 cm, ∠A = 35°, ∠B = 55°.
       Measure AC.

    (b) △DEF;   DE = 4 cm, ∠D = 100°, ∠F = 50°.
       Measure EF.

*2 Construct the following triangles:

    (a) △GHI;   GH = 6.5 cm, ∠G = 45°, ∠H = 45°.
       Measure GI.

    (b) △JKL;   JK = 7.2 cm, ∠J = 63°, ∠L = 72°.
       Measure JL.

    (c) △MNO;   NO = 8.4 cm, ∠N = 110°, ∠M = 45°.
       Measure NM.

    (d) △PQR;   QR = 6.8 cm, ∠P = 43°, ∠Q = 37°.
       Measure PQ.

*3 Construct isosceles triangle ABC, where AC = 4 cm and ∠A = ∠C = 70°.
Measure BC.

4 Construct isosceles triangle DEF, where DE = 4 cm and ∠F = 100°. Measure EF.

5 Construct three possible versions of isosceles triangle XYZ, with XY = 5 cm and
    ∠X = 25°. In each case measure XZ.

6 Construct two versions of △PQR, where PQ = 6 cm, ∠P = 40° and QR = 4.5 cm. In both cases measure PR.

7 Construct isosceles triangle GHI, with the perpendicular from I to GH of length 4 cm and the vertical angle I = 100°. Measure GH.

8 Construct quadrilateral ABCD, where AB = 5 cm, BC = 4 cm, AC = 7 cm, ∠BAD = 110° and ∠BCD = 90°. Measure BD.

---

9 A **locus** (plural: loci) is the path made by a moving point. Draw examples of the following loci:

(a) A moving point keeping the same distance from a fixed straight line.

(b) A moving point keeping the same distance from a fixed point.

(c) A moving point keeping the same distance from the circumference of a fixed circle.

(d) A moving point keeping the same distance from both arms of a fixed angle.

(e) A moving point keeping the same distance from two fixed points.

10 Draw the locus of the end of the valve of a cycle tyre as the cycle moves along the road.

11 On A4 paper construct a triangle with sides 15 cm, 12 cm and 13 cm. Carefully construct the circumcentre, centroid and orthocentre (see exercise 17A, question 6). What do you notice about the three centres?

12 A very large triangle drawn on A3 paper, with all its circles and centres in different colours, is a splendid sight!

---

18 Graphs: $y = x + c$; $y = mx$

A Review

For Discussion

Define the enclosed regions in Figure 18:1.

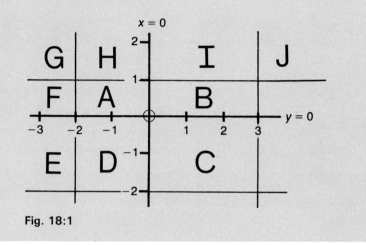

Fig. 18:1

1 (a) On squared paper draw x- and y-axes from -3 to 3 each. Label them 'x-axis' and 'y-axis', and also write on them their equations.
   (b) Draw a line joining A, $(-3, 3)$, to B, $(3, 3)$. Write its equation at the 'end' of it.
   (c) Draw a line joining C, $(-2, -3)$, to D, $(-2, 3)$. Write its equation below it.
   (d) Hatch /// the region of your graph where $x > 0$ and $y < 0$.
   (e) Hatch \\\\ the region where $-2 < x < 0$ and $0 < y < 3$.

2 Draw another grid as in question 1(a). Shade on your grid the region where $-1 < x < 3$ and $-3 < y < -1$.

---

3 Work out the value of $\dfrac{1}{x}$ correct to 2 decimal places for $x = 0.2, 0.4, 0.6, 0.8, 1,$ 2, 3, 4, 5, 6, 8, and 10. Write your answers as ordered pairs: (0.2, 5); (0.4, 2.5); etc. Plot the ordered pairs to give the graph of $y = \dfrac{1}{x}$. It is a smooth continuous curve and is called a 'reciprocal' graph. What is:
   (a) y when $x = 0$ (b) y when $x = \infty$ (infinity)   (c) x when $y = 0$
   (d) x when $y = \infty$?

Draw the other part of the curve, using $x = -0.2, -0.4,$ etc. down to -10.

B Equations of sloping lines

```
1Ø  FOR X = Ø TO 1ØØ
2Ø  LET Y = X
3Ø  PLOT X, Y
4Ø  NEXT X
```

For a BBC use this:
```
 5  MODE 4 ˙
1Ø  FOR X = Ø TO 1ØØØ
2Ø  LET Y = X
3Ø  PLOT 69, X, Y
4Ø  NEXT X
```

PLOT statements vary widely from computer to computer. The above program works on a ZX Spectrum. It works on an RML computer if you write PLOT X, Y, 1 or PLOT X, Y, 2. If necessary, adapt the program so that it will draw a line on your computer, then change line 2Ø to draw different lines, e.g. LET Y = 2*X; LET Y = X + 1.

1 Each of the following co-ordinates lies on one of the following lines. Pair them up, e.g. (2, 2) lies on $y = x$.
{co-ordinates} = {(4, −4), (1, 2), (−1, −1), (6, 3), (−5, 10), (2, 6) (6, −18)}
{lines} = {$y = 2x$, $y = 3x$, $y = \frac{1}{2}x$, $y = x$, $y = -x$, $y = -2x$, $y = -3x$}

2 Copy and complete the co-ordinates (3,), (0,), and (−3,) so that they will lie on:
(a) $y = x$ (b) $y = 2x$ (c) $y = 3x$ (d) $y = -x$ (e) $y = -2x$
(f) $y = -3x$.

3 Using your answers to question 2, draw the graphs of the six equations on one grid of squares. Use axes: x from −3 to 3; y from −10 to 10. Label each graph.

4 The points (4, 5), (0, 1), and (−3, −2) all lie on the line $y = x + 1$.

Copy and complete the following co-ordinates so that they also lie on $y = x + 1$:
(3,); (2,); (1,); (−1,); (−2, −1); (−4,).

5 Copy and complete the co-ordinates (3,), (0,), and (−3,) so that they will lie on:
(a) $y = x + 1$ (b) $y = x - 1$ (c) $y = x + 3$ (d) $y = x - 3$.

6 Taking axes: x from −4 to 4; y from −6 to 6, draw the lines whose equations are given in question 5. (Draw them all on the same set of axes.) Label each line.

7 (x, y) is a point on the y-axis. What is the value of x?

8 Without drawing any graphs, state the co-ordinates of the crossing point on the y-axis for:

(a) $y = x + 5$ (b) $y = x - 7$ (c) $y = x + 1.1$ (d) $y = x + a$.

9 The slope of a line is measured from a right-angled triangle drawn under it. The length of the vertical (upright) side of the triangle over the length of the horizontal (bottom) side of the triangle gives the slope as a fraction.

Figures 18:2 and 18:3 show two examples. Note that the bottom of the triangle is at the bottom of the fraction.

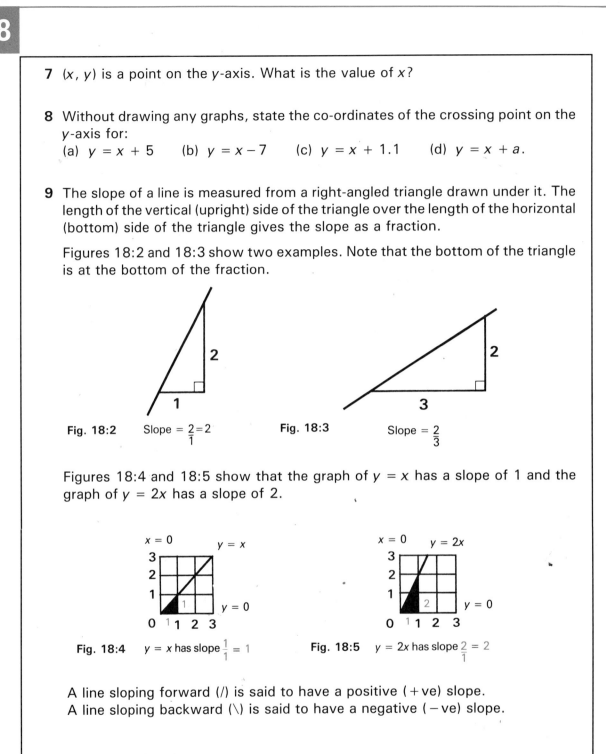

Fig. 18:2   Slope $= \dfrac{2}{1} = 2$

Fig. 18:3   Slope $= \dfrac{2}{3}$

Figures 18:4 and 18:5 show that the graph of $y = x$ has a slope of 1 and the graph of $y = 2x$ has a slope of 2.

Fig. 18:4 $y = x$ has slope $\dfrac{1}{1} = 1$

Fig. 18:5 $y = 2x$ has slope $\dfrac{2}{1} = 2$

A line sloping forward (/) is said to have a positive (+ve) slope.
A line sloping backward (\) is said to have a negative (−ve) slope.

State the slopes of the lines (a) to (g) in Figure 18:6.

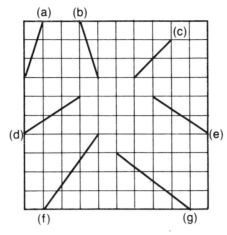

Fig. 18:6

10 Find the slope of : (a) $y = 4x$ (b) $y = \frac{1}{3}x$ (c) $y = -7x$.

11 Find, by drawing, the slope of the line joining:
(a) (3, 3) to (2, 0) (b) (2, 3) to (−1, 2) (c) (−1, 1) to (−3, −2)
(d) (−1, 0) to (0, −3) (e) (0, −1) to (3, −3) (f) (−1, −3) to (2, 3).

12 By considering your answers to question 11 find a way of calculating the slope of the line joining two points whose co-ordinates are given.

Make up ten pairs of points. Calculate the slopes of the lines passing through them, then check your answers by drawing.

19 Statistics: review; frequency tables

There are three statistical averages. All attempt to give an idea of the size of the data.

The mean is the result of sharing the total amount out equally.

Example   For £2, £7 and £9 the total amount is £18 and the mean is £18 ÷ 3 = £6.

The mode is the most frequent item. There can be more than one mode.

Example   For 2, 3, 2, 3, 2, 2, 4, 3, 5 and 3 the modes are 2 and 3.

The median is the middle item when the data is arranged in order. For an even number of items the median is taken as the mean of the two middle items.

Example   For 2, 2, 5, 6, 9, 9, 9 and 9 the two middle items are 6 and 9, so the median is $\frac{1}{2}(6 + 9) = 7\frac{1}{2}$.

For Discussion
Why do we need three kinds of average?

1 Find the mean, the mode and the median for:
   (a) 1, 2, 3, 4, 5, 5, 6, 7, 8 and 9   (b) 4, 4, 4, 4 and 12
   (c) 7, 3, 9, 11, 12, 14, 1, 6, 10 and 8   (d) 7, 1, 1, 7, 1, 4, 1, 7, 1, 1, 7 and 4.

2 When there are many items of data it is easier to use a frequency table.

   Example   Find the mean of this set of marks.

   Marks out of 10 for class 3C:
   4, 6, 6, 8, 7, 5, 10, 7, 9, 7, 6, 7, 5, 4, 6, 6, 7, 7, 5, 6, 7, 8, 7, 6, 8, 7, 6, 9, 8, 7.

Marks (x)	Tally	Frequency (f)	Total marks (f × x)
4	//	2	8
5	///	3	15
6	̶H̶T̶ ///	8	48
7	̶H̶T̶ ̶H̶T̶	10	70
8	////	4	32
9	//	2	18
10	/	1	10
Grand totals		30	201

30 pupils gained 201 marks; the mean is 201 ÷ 30 = 6.7 marks correct to 1 d.p.

Copy the following tables and complete them to find the means.

(a)

Marks (x)	Frequency (f)	Total marks (f × x)
4	5	
5	6	
6	6	
7	9	
8	2	
9	2	
Grand totals		

(b)

Weights (x)	Frequency (f)	Total weights (f × x)
180 g	2	
181 g	3	
182 g	9	
183 g	3	
184 g	2	
185 g	1	
Grand totals		

3 The mode, or modes, can be easily read from the frequency column. In the example for question 2 the mode is 7 marks, as this has the highest frequency. (Be careful that you do not say that the mode is 70; the mode must always be one of the original data items.)

Find the modes for question 2 (a) and (b).

4 Example Find the median for the marks in the example for question 2.

As there are 30 marks, the median mark will be the mean of the 15th and 16th marks. Add up the frequencies until you reach, or pass, 15:
2 + 3 + 8 = 13 (nearly there)
2 + 3 + 8 + 10 = 23 (past 15)
The 15th and 16th marks are both in the section for frequency 10, that is, the 7 marks section. The median is therefore 7 marks.

Find the medians for question 2 (a) and (b).

5 Copy and complete these tables to find the means and medians.

(a)

Score (x)	Tally	Frequency (f)	x × f
2	//	2	4
3	////		
4	ЦНТ ///	8	32
5	ЦНТ ////		
6	////		
7	///		
Grand totals		30	

(b)

Age in years (x)	Tally	Frequency (f)	x × f
11	⅃⼃Ⲧ /		
12	///		
13	⅃⼃Ⲧ ///		
14	⅃⼃Ⲧ //		
15	⅃⼃Ⲧ /		
Grand totals		30	

*6 Draw bar-charts for the data in question 5 (see Figure 19:1).

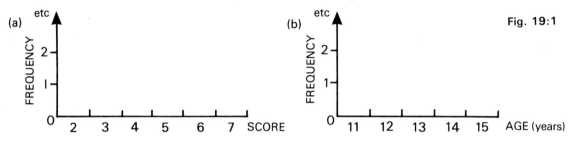

Fig. 19:1

7 One hundred pupils' marks in a test were:
4, 5, 2, 8, 5, 2, 6, 9, 5, 10, 2, 9, 5, 4, 3, 7, 4, 3, 7, 3, 5, 4, 1, 7, 4, 7, 5, 0, 5, 6,
7, 5, 4, 6, 1, 5, 10, 5, 6, 5, 6, 5, 4, 6, 5, 7, 3, 5, 8, 0, 4, 6, 9, 3, 5, 9, 3, 4, 6, 5,
6, 5, 5, 3, 6, 4, 7, 4, 7, 5, 5, 6, 1, 8, 5, 6, 2, 6, 2, 4, 3, 5, 6, 5, 1, 7, 5, 8, 3, 8,
5, 3, 8, 6, 4, 4, 6, 4, 5, 2.

Construct a frequency table like the one in question 2, but for marks from 0 to 10.
Find the three averages, then draw a bar-chart using a vertical axis from 0 pupils to
26 pupils and a horizontal axis from 0 marks to 10 marks.

8 Write Pascal's triangle (page 237) up to   1   8   28   56   70   56   28   8   1.

Plot row 8 (the one above the last one) as a bar-chart, using a vertical scale of 1 cm
to 10 units. Each bar on the horizontal axis is to be 1 cm wide, with no gaps between
the bars. Draw a smooth curve through the mid-points of the tops of each bar.

The bell-shaped curve you have drawn is the one normally found when random
samples are taken. Figures 19:2 and 19:3 show two examples of such a 'normal'
curve.

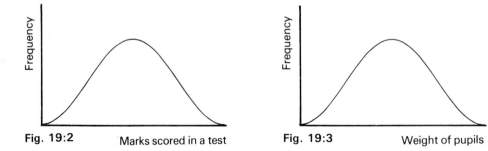

Fig. 19:2   Marks scored in a test   Fig. 19:3   Weight of pupils

9 When dealing with a widely ranging set of data we obtain a far better idea of the distribution if we group the data. The following chart shows the results for 120 pupils in a third-year exam at Huish Episcopi School in June 1988.

Class	Tally	Frequency (f)	Middle (m)	f × m
30–39	//	2	34.5	69
40–49	LHT ///	8	44.5	356
50–59	LHT LHT LHT LHT LHT	25	54.5	1362.5
60–69	LHT LHT LHT LHT LHT	25	64.5	1612.5
70–79	LHT LHT LHT LHT LHT LHT /	31	74.5	2309.5
80–89	LHT LHT LHT LHT //	22	84.5	1859
90–100	LHT //	7	95	665
	Totals	120		8233.5

We assume all members of each class (like 30–39) scored the middle mark (34.5). This usually gives an acceptably accurate mean, as the 'too high' marks should cancel out the 'too low' marks if the distribution is 'normal' (see Figure 19:2). In our example, we assume 25 pupils scored 54.5 marks each, giving them a total mark of $25 \times 54.5 = 1362.5$ marks. In fact, their true marks totalled 1391, not too far out!

We can then calculate an approximate mean by dividing the total mark (8233.5) by the number of pupils (120). This gives a mean of 68.6. (The true mean was 68.1, so you can see how accurate this method can be.)

We cannot give the mode or the median from a grouped frequency table, but we can say that the modal class is 70–79. The median class can be found by adding up the frequencies until we reach the class in which the middle pupil would lie. There are 120 pupils, so the middle pupils are 60th and 61st. Add up:

$2 + 8 = 10$ $10 + 25 = 35$ $35 + 25 = 60$

The 60th pupil comes in the 60–69 class, the 61st in the 70–79 class. Either class could be called the median class. That is what comes of using real data!

130 pupils are set a mathematics test at 11 +. Their percentage scores are given on page 96. Draw up a grouped frequency table, then calculate an approximate mean, and state the modal class and the median class. Illustrate your table with a frequency polygon, plotting at the middle value for each class.

```
82  35  72  60  49  94  24  56  50  66  44  82  54  62  42  78  46
96  24  98  38  88  62  58  30  78  34  30  94  54  62  76  44  97
75  88  40  70  90  44  76  67  68  79  36  91  14  59  75  70  28
13  76  80  71  42  91  44  77  67  36  84  79  75  76  50  59  49
78  83  76  41  39  29  81  46  97  79  97  68  47  23  62  88  51
21  73  91  51  84  53  51  78  49  31  84  77  91  23  11  79  64
65  64  47  66  37  69  47  65  31  80  67  81  80  92  60  80  65
37  44  96  84  62  51  37  57  88  76  86
```

10 The following data gives the ages of 100 people in two countries. The people were selected at random by central government computers in the two countries.

Country A
```
0   34  16  28  0   32  13  46  0   30  22  47  6   31  22  48  7   12
24  49  8   12  24  41  8   16  18  51  8   17  26  55  54  25  1   13
26  1   24  58  32  1   28  59  31  21  4   29  60  61  40  4   35  35
4   40  61  35  5   45  64  4   5   44  68  35  17  13  75  71  14  18
37  38  18  14  9   19  16  3   1   21  4   2   23  19  2   23  28  27  2
10  11  3   21  11  2   4   16  19
```

Country B
```
0   46  54  63  5   17  29  3   61  26  36  0   70  34  35  40  4   2   16
19  21  70  30  79  0   42  56  64  5   11  16  29  36  72  2   4   55
66  12  14  20  4   76  35  4   57  67  13  15  23  37  79  79  35  19
20  22  32  62  77  71  61  35  25  21  15  3   65  58  3   1   1   3
59  64  24  16  15  69  51  39  38  45  52  63  15  13  25  31  75
33  47  60  16  25  35  74  44  48  44
```

Draw up frequency tables for the two sets of data, using classes 0–9 years, 10–19 years, etc. Calculate estimates for the means, and state the modal classes and the classes in which the medians lie.

One country was in Europe. One was in Africa. Say with reasons which you think is the African data.

11 Range and interquartile range

The range of a set of data is the amount by which the largest item exceeds the smallest.

The interquartile range is the spread of the middle 50% of the data, that is with the top 25% and the bottom 25% excluded. This is a useful measure because it cuts out any 'freak' data that may occur at either extreme.

Example   Use the data 1, 1, 2, 3, 5, 7, 8, 9, 10, 10, 11, 14, 15, 16, 16, 17, 19, 20, 24, 25, 28, 29, 31, 32, 35, 39.

The range is $39 - 1 = 38$.

There are 26 items, so 25% is $6\frac{1}{2}$ items. The middle 50% then go from about 8 to about 25, an interquartile range of 17.

Find the ranges and interquartile ranges for the data given in questions 9 and 10.

Worksheets 19A and 19B may be used here.

12 Construct a frequency table and then a bell-shaped curve for the following three sets of test results.

A 1, 7, 2, 3, 4, 1, 6, 2, 0, 1, 3, 2, 1, 2, 3, 4, 1, 4, 0, 4, 2, 5, 3, 6, 2, 5, 3, 2, 5, 2.

B 6, 7, 3, 8, 6, 9, 8, 10, 5, 6, 7, 4, 8, 7, 8, 6, 7, 5, 9, 8, 8, 4, 10, 9, 8, 7, 9, 9, 8, 5.

C 2, 5, 6, 3, 4, 6, 5, 7, 3, 5, 4, 5, 3, 6, 7, 4, 5, 6, 5, 4, 6, 5, 5, 6, 7, 5, 4, 8, 4, 5.

Two of your curves should be 'skewed'. A skew is often caused when a set of results is not 'normal'. Test A was too hard (most pupils had poor results) and test B was too easy.

13 After using a new plant food a scientist counted the number of flowers on each stem of a plant and obtained the results shown in the table.

No. of flowers on stem	1	2	3	4	5	6	7
Frequency	1	3	9	12	25	12	2

Plot a bell-shaped curve for his results and on the same set of axes plot the normal curve as shown by line 7 of Pascal's triangle. If the plant had previously produced a 'normal' number of flowers why should the scientist be pleased?

Using your calculator

Japan's Seikan tunnel

The Seikan railway tunnel, linking the two northern main islands of Japan, is 37 km long. It was started in 1964 and took sixteen years to build. It replaces with a rapid train ride at 240 km/h the hazardous ferry crossing which took $4\frac{1}{2}$ hours to cover the 112 km sea route; in 1954 a ferry sank, drowning 1155 people.

The tunnel cost over £350 million to build. Three thousand, six hundred workers worked 8-hour shifts for 24 hours a day to excavate 1.85 million cubic metres of rock for the three interconnected tunnels: a drainage tunnel, the rail tunnel, and a service

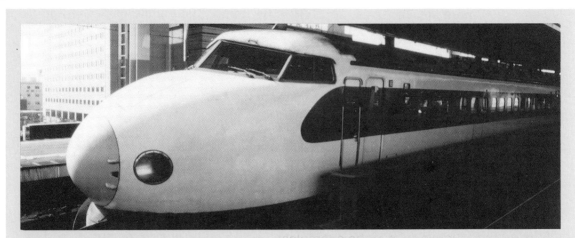

tunnel. At its deepest it is 100 metres below the sea bed and it is sealed with an average 25 cm thick layer of cement; 7.5 tonnes for every 2.8 m³ of rock removed.

There were two major floodings during the construction, causing 10 months of delay, and pumps have been installed capable of moving 700 000 gallons per minute. These should prevent any disaster if there is a serious breach in the future.

Use your calculator to help you answer the following questions.

1 How many minutes does the train take to pass through the tunnel?

2 What was the average cost of building each kilometre of the tunnel?

3 What was the average speed of the ferry?

4 How many times as fast as the ferry is the train?

5 How many cubic metres of earth were removed per worker, on average?

6 How many million man-hours were spent on the tunnel?

7 How many million tonnes of cement were used in sealing the tunnel?

8 In one flood, 40 tonnes of water poured in per minute. Could the pumps they have installed cope with a breach of this seriousness? (1 gallon of water weighs 4.54 kg.)

20 Expansion: brackets

Examples $-3 \times -6 = 18$ $-3 \times 6 = -18$

1 Simplify:
(a) -2×3 (b) -2×-3 (c) 3×-2 (d) $3 \times a$ (e) $a \times 3$
(f) $a + a$ (g) $a \times a$ (h) $4 \times c$ (i) $3 \times ab$ (j) $-2 \times f$ (k) $-3 \times g$
(l) $-3 \times 2a$.

2 **Examples** $2(4 + a) \rightarrow 8 + 2a$ $3(2a - b) \rightarrow 6a - 3b$

Expand the following, as in the examples:
(a) $2(a + 1)$ (b) $6(a - 2)$ (c) $4(3a + 4)$ (d) $8(10 - 2a)$
(e) $4(a - b + c)$ (f) $6(-p + q - r)$.

*3 Simplify:
(a) $2a \times 3$ (b) $-3 \times 4a$ (c) -4×-4 (d) 3×-8 (e) 7×7
(f) $7a \times 7$ (g) $d \times d$ (h) $2d \times d$ (i) $-2d \times 5$ (j) -4×-5
(k) $2 \times 3a$ (l) $2a \times a$ (m) $2a + a$ (n) $3b \times b$ (o) $3b + b$
(p) $4a \times 4a$ (q) -3×-5 (r) $-2a \times -2$ (s) $5 \times -2a$
(t) $-5 \times 2a$.

*4 Expand:
(a) $3(a - 2)$ (b) $3(t + 1)$ (c) $2(1 - k)$ (d) $4(4 + b)$ (e) $2(-e + 2)$
(f) $3(-e + 2)$ (g) $3(a + b)$ (h) $4(a - b)$ (i) $2(x + y + z)$
(j) $4(2x + 1)$ (k) $3(4x + 1)$ (l) $2(a - x + k)$ (m) $3(-x + 7)$
(n) $2(1 - b - c)$ (o) $2(2 + m - n)$ (p) $3(-a - f + 5)$.

5 **Examples** $-2(4 + a) \rightarrow -8 - 2a$
                          $-2(4 - a) \rightarrow -8 + 2a$

Expand:
(a) $-6(x - 3)$ (b) $-4(x - 3)$ (c) $-(a + c)$ (d) $-(x - y)$
(e) $-2(3 - x)$ (f) $-(a + 3b)$ (g) $-(3g - 2h)$ (h) $3a(-2 + h)$.

6 **Examples** $a + 2(b - c) \rightarrow a + 2b - 2c$

                          $a - 2(b - c) \rightarrow a - 2b + 2c$

                          $a - (b - c) \rightarrow a - b + c$

Expand:
(a) $a + 2(b + c)$ (b) $b - 2(a + c)$ (c) $a - (b + c - d)$
(d) $5a + (3b - 4c)$ (e) $6b - (2c + 4d)$ (f) $4 - 3(2m + 3q - s)$.

7 Examples $5a - (a - 3b) \rightarrow 5a - a + 3b \rightarrow 4a + 3b$
$5a - 2(3b - a) \rightarrow 5a - 6b + 2a \rightarrow 7a - 6b$
Note: The brackets are multiplied by -1 and by -2, but not by the $5a$.

Expand and simplify, as in the examples:
(a) $5a - (3a + 2b)$ (b) $7b - (4b - 2a)$ (c) $6a - (5a - 4b)$
(d) $7m - (3m + 4n)$.

8 Expand and simplify:
(a) $4m + (3m - 4c)$ (b) $6m + (8d - 2m)$ (c) $8a + (5b - 11a)$.

9 Expand and simplify:
(a) $3 + 2(a - 2)$ (b) $6a - 3(a + 2b)$ (c) $4b - 2(a + b)$ (d) $4 - 2(a - 3)$.

10 Expand and simplify:
(a) $5d - 2(b - 3c + d)$ (b) $6 - 6(m + 2)$ (c) $6 - 3(a - 2)$ (d) $a - 4(a - 3c)$.

If your teacher permits it, you may omit some or all of questions 11 to 14, which provide
extra practice on the ideas of this chapter.

11 Expand and simplify:
(a) $2a - (a + 3b)$ (b) $5b + (2b - 3c)$ (c) $2c - (3b - 4c)$
(d) $3a + (b - 2a)$.

12 Expand and simplify:
(a) $a + (p - q)$ (b) $a - (p - q)$ (c) $a - (a + 3b)$ (d) $b + (2b - 3c)$.

13 Expand and simplify:
(a) $5a + 4(a + 3b)$ (b) $4 + 2(a - 3)$ (c) $a + (p + q)$ (d) $a - (p + q)$.

14 Expand and simplify:
(a) $2c - (3b - c)$ (b) $2a + (b - 2a)$ (c) $4 + 2(k - 1 - t)$
(d) $6 - 3(4 - 1)$.

15 Example $4a^3 \times 3a^2 \rightarrow 12a^5$ and $4a^3 \times 2b \rightarrow 8a^3b$
so $4a^3(3a^2 + 2b) \rightarrow 12a^5 + 8a^3b$

Expand the brackets, then collect like terms for:
(a) $3a(a + b)$ (b) $4b(b - 3c)$ (c) $6a(a^2 + 3b^2)$ (d) $4a(c^2 + 4d)$
(e) $2ad + 4a(c^2 + 4d)$ (f) $a^5 + 5a^2(3a^3 - d^2)$ (g) $2a^4 - 4a^2(a^2 + b^2)$
(h) $a^3(2a^4 - 3b)$ (i) $2a + 3d - (4a - 2d)$ (j) $(2a + 3d) - (4a - 2d)$
(k) $-(2a + 3d) - (4a - 2d)$ (l) $3c + 3d - (3d + 4e)$.

21 Area: surface area

A prism is a solid with a constant cross-section (the same shape all through it).

For Discussion

Calculate the surface area of each prism. All dimensions are in centimetres.

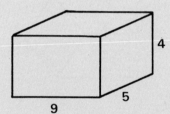

Fig. 21:1

A rectangular prism
or a cuboid.

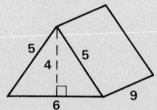

Fig. 21:2

A triangular prism.

Fig. 21:3

A trapezoidal prism.

1 Example   Find the surface area of the cuboid in Figure 21:4.

Front: 3×8 $= 24\,\text{cm}^2$
Back: 3×8 $= 24\,\text{cm}^2$
Top: 5×8 $= 40\,\text{cm}^2$
Bottom: 5×8 $= 40\,\text{cm}^2$
L. Side: 3×5 $= 15\,\text{cm}^2$
R. Side: 3×5 $= 15\,\text{cm}^2$

Total surface area $= 158\,\text{cm}^2$

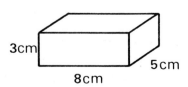

Fig. 21:4

Calculate the surface for each cuboid in Figure 21:5.

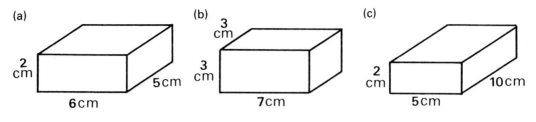

(a) 2 cm, 6 cm, 5 cm

(b) 3 cm, 3 cm, 7 cm

(c) 2 cm, 5 cm, 10 cm

Fig. 21:5

2 Calculate the surface area of:
   (a) a cuboid of length 12 cm, breadth 5 cm, and height 5 cm
   (b) a cuboid of length 9 cm, breadth 8 cm, and height 6 cm
   (c) a cube of side 4 cm.

3 Either by drawing each face separately, or by just imagining them, calculate the total surface area of each prism in Figure 21:6. All dimensions are in centimetres.

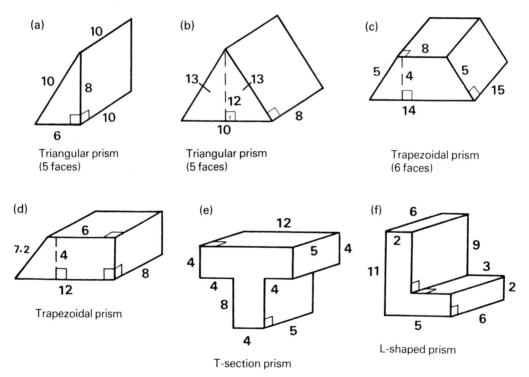

(a) 10, 10, 8, 10, 6
Triangular prism
(5 faces)

(b) 13, 12, 13, 10, 8
Triangular prism
(5 faces)

(c) 8, 5, 4, 5, 14, 15
Trapezoidal prism
(6 faces)

(d) 6, 7.2, 4, 8, 12
Trapezoidal prism

(e) 12, 4, 5, 4, 4, 4, 8, 5, 4
T-section prism

(f) 6, 2, 9, 11, 3, 2, 5, 6
L-shaped prism

Fig. 21:6

4 The total surface area of a cube is 294 cm².

   (a) Calculate the area of one face.   (b) Find the length of one edge.

---

5 Stuart makes an open box (i.e. no top) with outside dimensions: length 705 mm, breadth 560 mm, height 485 mm.

   (a) Calculate in cm² correct to 3 s.f. the outside surface area of the box.

   (b) The box is veneered on the outside with veneer costing £9.85 per square metre. Calculate the cost of the veneer used.

   (c) The wood used in making the box is 12 mm thick. Calculate the inside measurements of the box and the cost of lining it with satin at £4.75 per m².

6 Figure 21:7 shows the net for a triangular prism. Draw similar nets, to a scale of 1:2, for the solids in Figure 21:6. Remember to put tabs on every other edge. Make up the solids.

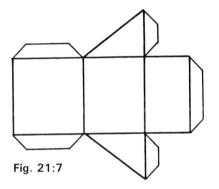

Fig. 21:7

7 The 2-D representations of 3-D objects in this chapter are drawn in Oblique Projection, where one face is seen as its true shape. In Isometric Projection no face is seen as its true shape, but the effect is more realistic. Figure 21:8 shows an isometric drawing of the trapezoidal prism (c) in Figure 21:6. Copy it onto isometric grid paper (make sure you use it the correct way round, with one set of lines vertical), then draw isometric views of the other solids in this chapter.

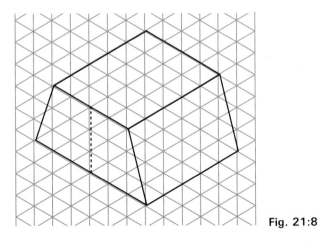

Fig. 21:8

22 Equations: inequalities and harder equations

A Inequalities

$2 < x < 8$ can be read as 'x is more than 2 but less than 8'.
$2 \leqslant x \leqslant 8$ can be read as 'x is at least 2 but not more than 8'.

1 Use inequality signs to write:
(a) x is more than 5
(b) x is less than 3
(c) x is more than 5 but less than 9
(d) x is at least 3 but not more than 6
(e) x is more than 4 but not more than 7
(f) x is at least 1 but less than 3.

2 List all possible integral values of x (include 0 where appropriate) if:
(a) $3 < x < 7$ (b) $6 \leqslant x < 9$ (c) $-3 < x < -1$ (d) $-3 \leqslant x \leqslant -1$
(e) $-3 < x \leqslant -1$ (f) $1 > x > -1$ (g) $-3 \leqslant x < -1$ (h) $1 \geqslant x > -1$
(i) $1 \geqslant x \geqslant -1$ (j) $-2 < x \leqslant 0$.

3 **Example** If $x + 4 > 9$ then $x > 5$.

State the range of values for x if:
(a) $x + 3 > 8$ (b) $x + 2 > 5$ (c) $x - 3 > 0$ (d) $x - 5 < 3$ (e) $2x \geqslant 6$.

*4 List all possible integral values of x (include 0 where appropriate) if:
(a) $2 < x < 5$ (b) $7 > x > 3$ (c) $1 \leqslant x < 3$ (d) $3 \leqslant x \leqslant 4$
(e) $4 \geqslant x > 2$ (f) $-4 < x < -2$ (g) $-4 \leqslant x < -2$ (h) $-4 \leqslant x \leqslant -2$
(i) $-3 < x < 1$ (j) $2 < x < 3$.

*5 State the range of values for x if:
(a) $x + 8 > 9$ (b) $x - 1 > 2$ (c) $x + 4 < 8$ (d) $2x > 16$ (e) $2x \leqslant 6$.

In questions 6 to 8 state the range of values of x which satisfies each inequality.

6 (a) $7x \leqslant 63$ (b) $2x \leqslant 1$ (c) $x - 9 > -3$ (d) $3x - 4 < 5$
(e) $4x + 2 > 4$

7 (a) $x + 6 > 4$ (b) $x + 1 < -7$ (c) $3x + 1 > 3$ (d) $4x + 10 > 6$
(e) $6x + 27 < 0$

8 (a) $\dfrac{x}{2} < 5$ (b) $\dfrac{3x}{4} < 6$ (c) $\dfrac{2x}{3} > 10$ (d) $\dfrac{3x}{7} \geqslant 9$

9 In Figure 22:1 the region hatched is *below* $y = x$, so $y \leqslant x$. The hatched region is *above* $y = 0$ so $y \geqslant 0$. It is to the *left* of $x = 2$, so $x < 2$: note that the dotted line shows $x = 2$ is not included. In set notation the hatched region is $\{(x, y); x \geqslant y \geqslant 0; x < 2\}$, meaning the set of all points on a graph where y is equal to or less than x and y is 0 or more, and where x is less than 2.

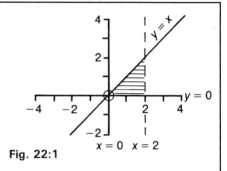

Fig. 22:1

Using axes from -4 to 4 each, hatch the following regions. Remember to label each line with its equation.

(a) $\{(x, y); \ -3 \leqslant x \leqslant 1; \ -2 < y < 3\}$ (Hint: Draw $x = -3, x = 1, y = -2,$ and $y = 3$.)

(b) $\{(x, y); x \geqslant y > -1; \ x < 1\}$ (Hint: Draw $y = x, y = -1$ and $x = 1$.)

(c) $\{(x, y); \ 2x \leqslant y < 3; \ x \geqslant -1\}$

(d) $\{(x, y); \ 2x \geqslant y \geqslant 0; \ x < 2\}$

(e) $\{(x, y); \ x + 1 \geqslant y > 1; \ x < 3\}$

(f) $\{(x, y); \ x - 1 \leqslant y \leqslant 3; \ x \geqslant 0\}$

B Harder equations

Equations such as those in questions 1 to 3 below are probably easiest to solve by inspection, that is by thinking what number should replace the letter to make the equation true. However, if there is more than one letter-term this method cannot be used. Instead you need the 'balance' or 'change sides' method.

Example Solve $2x - 6 = 5x + 9$.

$$2x - 6 = 5x + 9$$
$$\rightarrow \quad -6 = 5x - 2x + 9$$
$$\rightarrow \quad -6 = 3x + 9$$

Now the inspection approach may be used, giving $x = -5$.

Solve the equations in questions 1 to 8 to find the values of the letters.

1 (a) $q - 7 = -7$ (b) $3 - r = 4$ (c) $4h = 3$ (d) $\dfrac{t}{5} = 10$

*2 (a) $x - 5 = -3$ (b) $2 - y = 5$ (c) $g + 5 = -1$ (d) $2w + 1 = 5$

*3 (a) $2t + 3 = 6$ (b) $3b - 1 = 8$ (c) $2 - 2e = 4$ (d) $3r - 1 = -1$

4 (a) $4q + 5 = 3q + 7$ (b) $5u - 6 = 2u - 3$ (c) $6m + 7 = 3m + 16$

5 (a) $4x - 21 = 7 - 3x$ (b) $6a - 9 = 7 - 2a$ (c) $5t - 11 = 2t - 2$

6 (a) $4k - 10 = 2k - 10$ (b) $9 - 3s = 15 - 4s$ (c) $12 + 2n = -2n + 16$

7 (a) $3f - 10 = 8f + 30$ (b) $6u + 1 = 4u - 9$ (c) $5x - 12 = 8x + 6$

8 (a) $3 - 3c = 2c + 13$ (b) $3 + 2h = 6h + 11$ (c) $2i - 5 = 7 + 3i$

---

9 **Example** $3(a + 2) = 2(a - 1) \rightarrow 3a + 6 = 2a - 2 \rightarrow a + 6 = -2 \rightarrow a = -8$

Solve:
(a) $4(q - 3) = 2(q + 6)$ (b) $6(w + 2) = 3(w + 5)$
(c) $3(3e - 4) = 4(e + 2)$ (d) $2(3r - 5) = 4(5 - r)$
(e) $2(2t - 6) = 4(2t + 8)$ (f) $6(2 - 3y) = 2(3y - 6)$
(g) $6 + u(u + 5) = u(u + 3)$ (h) $4 + 3x(x - 2) = 7 - 3(x - x^2)$.

10 Write at least two equations with u on both sides where the solution is $u = 4$.

11 Write a set of consecutive numbers. Find how many different runs of numbers from your list give the same total.

For example: 1   2   3   4   5   6   7   8   9   10   11

           21   21   21

Try to establish rules. Use algebra to explain what is happening.

Investigate the numbers formed by two consecutive numbers; by three consecutive numbers; four; more!

23 Graphs: $y = mx + c$

For Discussion

	x-axis	y-axis	equations
(a)	0 to 3	0 to 7	$y = 2x + 1$
(b)	−3 to 2	−6 to 2	$y = 2x − 2$
(c)	0 to 3	−3 to 3	$y = −2x + 3$
(d)	−2 to 2	−4 to 2	$y = −2x − 3$
(e)	−2 to 3	−2 to 2	$y = \frac{1}{2}x − 1$
(f)	−6 to 0	0 to 3	$y = −\frac{1}{3}x + 1$

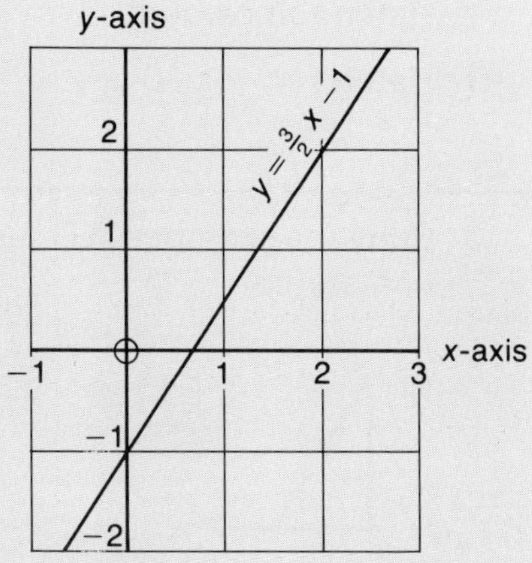

Fig. 23:1

1 Draw the following linear graphs:

	x-axis	y-axis	equation			x-axis	y-axis	equation
(a)	0 to 4	0 to 5	$y = x + 1$		(d)	−6 to 0	−3 to 0	$y = \frac{1}{3}x$
(b)	0 to 4	−1 to 6	$y = 2x − 1$		(e)	−2 to 4	0 to 6	$y = \frac{1}{2}x + 3$
(c)	0 to 3	−5 to 1	$y = −2x + 1$		(f)	−3 to 3	−5 to 1	$y = −x − 2$

2 Answer the following on the graphs (a) to (f) that you drew for question 1. (Do part (a) on question 1(a), etc.)

(a) Draw the lines $x = 3$ and $y = 1$.
Hatch /// the triangular region enclosed by your three lines.
This region is written as $\{(x, y); \ y \leqslant x + 1; \ y \geqslant 1; \ x \leqslant 3\}$.
We read this as 'The set of points on a graph such that y is $x + 1$ or less, y is 1 or more, and x is 3 or less.'
This tells us that the region is *under* $y = x + 1$, *above* $y = 1$, and to the *left* of $x = 3$.

(b) Draw the lines $x = 1$ and $x = 3$.
Hatch the trapezium-shaped region enclosed by the two upright lines, the sloping line and the x-axis.
This is the region $\{(x, y): \ y \leqslant 2x − 1; \ y \geqslant 0; \ x \geqslant 1; \ x \leqslant 3\}$.
The region is *below* $y = 2x − 1$; *above* $y = 0$; to the *right* of $x = 1$; to the *left* of $x = 3$.

(c) Draw the line $x = 2$.
Hatch the triangular region $\{(x, y); \ y \geqslant − 2x + 1; \ y \leqslant 0; \ x \leqslant 2\}$.

23

(d) Draw the lines $x = -4$ and $x = -1$.
Hatch (be careful!) $\{(x, y): y \geqslant \frac{1}{3}x; x \geqslant -4; x \leqslant -1\}$.

(e) Draw the lines $x = -1$ and $x = 2$.
Hatch (be careful!) $\{(x, y): y \geqslant \frac{1}{2}x + 3; x \geqslant -1; x \leqslant 2\}$.

(f) Hatch $\{(x, y): 0 \geqslant y \geqslant -x - 2; 2 \geqslant x \geqslant 1\}$.

---

3 Copy the sketches in Figure 23:2, numbering the axes to give each line the equation stated.

(a) 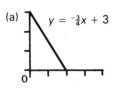 $y = -\frac{3}{4}x + 3$

(b) 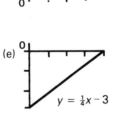 $y = -2x + 6$

(c) 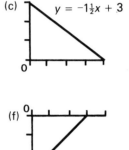 $y = -1\frac{1}{2}x + 3$

(d) 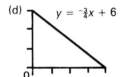 $y = -\frac{3}{4}x + 6$

(e) 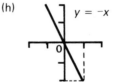 $y = \frac{1}{4}x - 3$

(f) $y = 2x - 3$

(g) $y = \frac{1}{2}x + 4$

(h) $y = -x$

(i) $y = -x + 2$

Fig. 23:2

4 To represent three-dimensional objects we need a third axis, the z-axis. Figure 23:3 shows a cuboid on three axes. The x- and y-axes are in the horizontal plane. The z-axis is upright.

For the cuboid drawn, corner C is at (4, 3, 2). State the co-ordinates of the other corners.

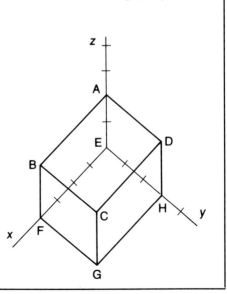

Fig. 23:3

Project

Where it's at

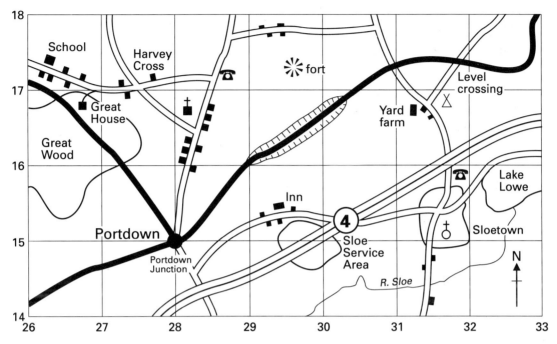

1 In the map there is a public telephone in the square with grid reference 2817. Its six-figure reference is 287172.

Each square is of side 1 km. The fort is 2.85 km from Sloetown cross-roads on a three-figure bearing of 315° (cardinal bearing NE).

Using this map plan a walk starting at 263174. Choose at least ten special features that you pass, or might see, on your walk. For each feature write its grid reference and its bearing and direct distance from the school.

Ask a classmate to check and comment on your guide while you do the same for theirs. Try to suggest improvements.

2 When astrologers prepare your birth-chart for character analysis they need to know the latitude and longitude of your birthplace. Use an atlas to find yours. Find out about latitude and longitude and write a report of your findings. Design card models to illustrate your report.

3 Moslems should always face Mecca when they pray. How do they manage this?

24   Volume: prism and cylinder

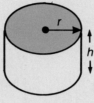

Fig. 24:1

A cylinder is a prism with a circle as its cross-section.

The volume of a prism is its cross-section area multiplied by its height (or length).

Hence: The volume of a cylinder is $\pi r^2 h$.

Example Find the volume of the cylinder in Figure 24:2.

$r = 8$ cm; $h = 14$ cm.
Talking π as $\frac{22}{7}$, the volume is
$\frac{22}{7} \times 8 \times 8 \times 14 = 2816$ cm^3.

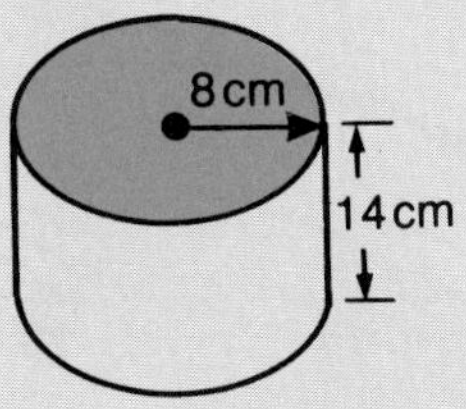

Fig. 24:2

1 Find the cross-section area (coloured green) and the volume of each prism in Figure 24:3. Measurements are in centimetres.

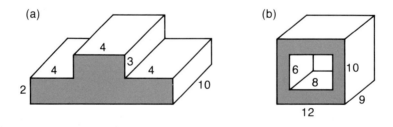

Fig. 24:3

2 Taking $\pi = \frac{22}{7}$, find the volume of a cylinder with:
   (a) radius 1 cm, height 21 cm   (b) radius 21 cm, height 9 cm.

*3 Find the volumes of the solids in Figure 24:4. Take $\pi = \frac{22}{7}$.

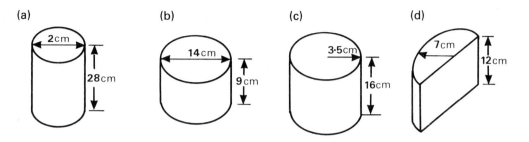

(a) 2cm 28cm (b) 14cm 9cm (c) 3·5cm 16cm (d) 7cm 12cm

For questions 4 to 6 use the ⬚π key or take $\pi = 3.142$. Give answers correct to 3 significant figures.

4 A cylindrical tank has a radius of 17 cm and a height of 84 cm. How many litres will it hold?

5 Find the height of a cylinder of volume 2376 cm³ and radius 6 cm.

6 Find the radius of a cylinder of volume 1408 cm³ and height 28 cm.

---

7 A brass rod, 12 cm radius and 16 cm long, is to be melted down and re-cast into 4 cm-long rods of 3 cm radius. How many rods can be made?

8 Water flows through a 7 cm-radius pipe at the rate of 3 metres per second. How many litres will the pipe discharge in 1 minute? (Take π as $\frac{22}{7}$.)

Using your calculator

Sand

C

Next time you relax on a sandy beach consider how useful those tiny particles of rock are!

In Britain alone, 50 million tonnes are used each year. One firm employs 12 men who produce 1250 tonnes a day from a 90-acre site, selling it at about £4.30 a tonne for use in the making of concrete.

Most sand is mainly quartz, the most common form of silica. When heated to 1480°C it melts and is used to make glass. At a Rockware Glass factory, 2000 million glass jars and bottles are made a year, consuming 450 000 tonnes of silica sand. (The average bottle is three-quarters sand.)

Sand also plays a vital role in metal-casting, and the chips that are the 'brains' of calculators and computers are made from a pure form of silicon, which is manufactured from silica. How should we manage without it!

Use your calculator to help you answer the following questions.

1 How many tonnes of sand are used in Britain each day on average?

2 How many pounds' worth of sand does each of the 12 men produce per year on average?

3 An acre is about 4050 m². How many kilograms of sand are produced each day from each m² of the site?

4 What percentage of the sand used in Britain is produced by the firm described above? Use the formula:

One amount as a percentage of another amount $= \dfrac{\text{1st amount}}{\text{2nd amount}} \times 100.$

5 The density of dry sand is about 1.5 g/cm³.

A hopper is 1 metre square and 50 cm deep. What weight of dry sand will it hold?

6 To convert °C to °F use the formula:
Double the Celsius figure, subtract a tenth of the answer, then add 32 (Burrell's rule).

At what Fahrenheit temperature does sand melt?

7 How many grams of sand are used to make an average bottle?

8 What is the weight of an average bottle made by Rockware Glass?

25 Probability: exclusive and independent events

For Discussion

1 I throw a six with a fair die. What effect does this have on the probability of a six next throw?

2 I pick an ace from a pack of 52 playing cards. What effect does this have on the probability of picking a second ace?

Outcomes of events can be exclusive, independent, or non-independent.

Outcomes are **exclusive** when only one of them can happen in any one trial.

Example   Scoring 3, 4 or 5 in one throw of a die.

Outcomes are **independent** when all the outcomes can happen in any one trial, but no outcome alters the probability of any other.

Example   Throwing a double six with two dice.

Outcomes are **non-independent** (or **dependent**) when all the outcomes can happen in any one trial but one successful outcome alters the probability of others.

Example   Picking two aces from a pack of cards, without replacing the first ace.

Exclusive outcomes

Often these can be found by considering all possibilities.

Example   Find the probability of throwing an odd number with a die.

There are three successful outcomes, 1, 3, and 5. There are six possible outcomes.

So P(odd number) is $\frac{3}{6}$ or $\frac{1}{2}$.

If you cannot list all the successful outcomes you can find the answer by adding their probabilities. We could answer the above example in this way:

P(scoring 1) $= \frac{1}{6}$
P(scoring 3) $= \frac{1}{6}$
P(scoring 5) $= \frac{1}{6}$

So P(1, 3 or 5) $= \frac{1}{6} + \frac{1}{6} + \frac{1}{6} = \frac{3}{6}$ or $\frac{1}{2}$.

Here is an example which cannot be done by listing possibilities:

A conjuror has a biased pack of cards. The probability of picking an ace is $\frac{1}{8}$. The probability of picking a king is $\frac{1}{16}$.

What does biased mean here?

The probability of picking either an ace or a king is

$\frac{1}{8} + \frac{1}{16} \rightarrow \frac{2}{16} + \frac{1}{16} = \frac{3}{16}$.

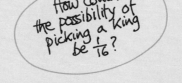
How could the possibility of picking a king be $\frac{1}{16}$?

What is the probability of picking an ace or a king with a fair pack of 52 playing cards?

Independent outcomes

As with exclusive outcomes, these can sometimes be found by listing all possibilities, but the method can be very long.

Example Find the probability of throwing two sixes in a row with a fair die.
If the first die comes up 1, the second die could come up 1, 2, 3, 4, 5, or 6, making six possibilities. Similarly for the first die coming up 2, 3, 4, 5 or 6. So there are $6 \times 6 = 36$ different possibilities.

You could write them all out if you wish to check this.

Only 1 of the 36 ways is a successful outcome (6 on the 1st, 6 on the 2nd), so P(two sixes) is $\frac{1}{36}$.

We can also find the answer to the above example by multiplying the probabilities of the successful outcomes: $P(6)$ is $\frac{1}{6}$. So $P(6 \text{ and } 6) = \frac{1}{6} \times \frac{1}{6} = \frac{1}{36}$

This can be extended to find quickly the probability of a many-outcomed event.

Example Suppose the probability of a boy baby is $\frac{1}{2}$.
P(a family of 6 boys) $= \frac{1}{2} \times \frac{1}{2} \times \frac{1}{2} \times \frac{1}{2} \times \frac{1}{2} \times \frac{1}{2} = \frac{1}{64}$

Summary Exclusive outcomes: $P(A \text{ or } B) = P(A) + P(B)$

Independent outcomes: $P(A \text{ and/then } B) = P(A) \times P(B)$

Probability fractions

Probabilities may be given as common fractions, as decimals, or as percentages, for example $\frac{1}{2}$ chance $= 0.5$ chance $= 50\%$ chance.

Common fractions are best (discuss why) but you need to know how to add and multiply fractions (or own a fraction calculator!).

1 What is the probability that a stranger was born
   (a) in August   (b) in Spring (March to May)?

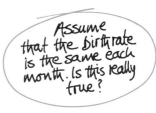

Assume that the birthrate is the same each month. Is this really true?

2 To apply for a free gift, I've taken the labels off all my tins of cat food. I know that the varieties were 6 lamb, 4 fish and 3 beef. I pick a tin for my cat's tea. What is the probability that she gets:
   (a) fish   (b) beef   (c) lamb
   (d) beef or lamb   (e) not fish
   (f) beef or lamb or fish?

3 In class 3Q there are 25 pupils. They vote for their favourite subject. 11 vote for PE, 4 for CDT, 5 for Maths, 2 for English, and 3 for History.

   A pupil is selected at random. What is the probability that this pupil:

   (a) voted for PE   (b) did not vote for History
   (c) voted for either Maths or CDT   (d) voted for either History or English?

4 Calculate the probability when tossing a fair coin of:
   (a) four heads in a row   (b) five heads in a row.

5 In a fête lucky dip there are 45 Polos, 40 bubble gums, and 4 fifty-pence pieces. At the start of the fête what is:

   (a) P(picking a Polo)   (b) P(picking a bubble-gum)   (c) P(picking a 50p)
   (d) P(picking a Polo or a bubble-gum)   (e) P(not picking a 50p)?

6 Forty people at the fête in question 5 have a lucky dip. They pick 23 Polos and 17 bubble-gums. What is now the probability of the outcomes (a) to (e)?

7 What is the probability of selecting a black ace or a red king from a packet of 52 playing cards?

*8 Munchmores are chocolate-covered sweets. They all look the same. A box of Munchmores contains 20 nut centres, 15 fruit centres, and 12 toffee centres. A Munchmore is picked at random. What is the probability that its centre is:

   (a) nut   (b) fruit   (c) toffee   (d) not fruit   (e) toffee or nut
   (f) toffee or fruit?

*9 Ten minutes after opening the the box of Munchmores in question 8, I have eaten 10 nut centres, 9 fruit centres, and 5 toffee centres. What are now the probabilities (a) to (f)?

10 I record the departure times of the 8 o'clock train. The result is:

Leaves at 8 o'clock: 9 times
Leaves up to 5 minutes late: 21 times
Leaves over 5 minutes late: 7 times

Based on this data, what is the probability that tomorrow's 8 o'clock train will depart:
(a) at 8 o'clock   (b) 5 minutes late   (c) over 5 minutes late   (d) late?

11 The probability of a species of bird laying 3 eggs is given as $\frac{1}{2}$. The probability of the bird laying 4 eggs is $\frac{1}{4}$. The probability of the bird laying 5 eggs is $\frac{1}{8}$.

What is the probability of the bird laying:
(a) 3 or 4 eggs   (b) 4 or 5 eggs   (c) 3 or 4 or 5 eggs
(d) not 3, 4 or 5 eggs?

12 What is the probability of at least two heads when a coin is tossed three times?

13 A loaded die has a probability of $\frac{1}{5}$ that it scores a 3. What is the probability of:

(a) not scoring a 3   (b) scoring two 3s in a row
(c) scoring three 3s in a row   (d) not scoring three 3s in a row?

14 A bookmaker rates the probability of the favourites winning in two races as 2 to 1 against (probability $\frac{1}{3}$) and 3 to 1 against (probability $\frac{1}{4}$). What is, according to the bookmaker's reckoning, the probability of:

(a) the first horse losing   (b) the second horse losing   (c) both horses winning
(d) the first winning, the second losing   (e) the first losing, the second winning
(f) at least one horse winning?

15 A bag contains 3 black, 2 white and 1 green counters. If each picked counter is replaced in the bag state the probability of picking:

(a) a black   (b) a white   (c) a black then a white
(d) a black then another black   (e) a white then a black   (f) at least one black
(g) two greens in a row   (h) a green then a white   (i) a white then a green
(j) one white and one green.

16 The Venn diagram shows the result of a survey of all the pupils at a school. G ⇒ 'Girls' and C ⇒ 'Like computer games'.

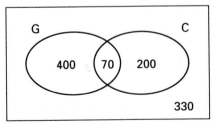

Fig. 25:1

Explain why, for a pupil selected at random:

(a) P (being a boy) = 0.53

(b) P (liking computer games) = 0.27

(c) P (being a boy and liking computer games) cannot be found by adding 0.53 and 0.27 from parts (a) and (b) to give 0.8

(d) P (being a boy and liking computer games) = 0.6.

---

17 My old alarm clock has a probability of $\frac{2}{3}$ that it will go off. If it doesn't there is still a probability of $\frac{2}{3}$ that I'll wake up anyway in time to catch the 8 o'clock bus. Even if it does go off there is a probability of $\frac{1}{6}$ that I'll sleep through it and not get to the bus stop in time. The bus itself is not very reliable either. There is a probability of $\frac{1}{8}$ that it will not come.

These facts are illustrated on the tree diagram in Figure 25:1.

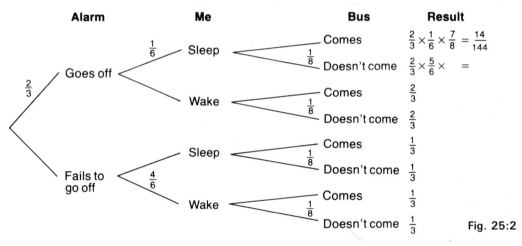

Fig. 25:2

Copy the tree diagram, then write in the seven missing fractions and complete the results column. It is better not to simplify the answer fractions.

Add all your result fractions. They should total 1. Why?

Use your tree diagram to find the probability that:
(a) I get to work   (b) I get to the bus stop in time but the bus does not come
(c) I do not get to the bus stop in time.

18 Investigate the probability of a drawing pin shaken from a box landing point down.

19 Investigate how you could set up an insurance scheme which would pay out when pupils accidentally forget their lunch money.

Project

Quincunx and tree diagrams

For Discussion

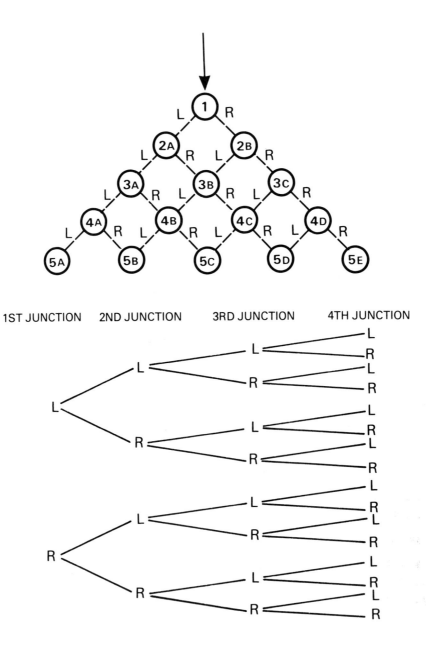

26 Simultaneous equations by graph and by substitution

A Solution by inspection and by graph

For Discussion

One

If $y = x + 1$

When x is:	3	2	1	0	-1	-2
then y is:	4	3	2	1	0	-1

If $y = 2x - 1$

when x is:	3	2	1	0	-1	-2
then y is:	5	3	1	-1	-3	-5

These values may be plotted to give the graphs of the lines, showing that their common point is $x = 2$ and $y = 3$.

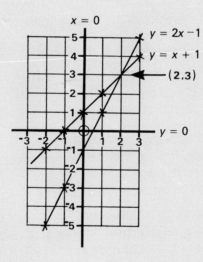

Fig. 26:1

Two

Find two equations in each set that are true for the given values of x and y.
(a) $x = 3$; $y = 2$ $\{y = x + 3, y = 2x - 4, y = 3x - 4, y = x - 1\}$
(b) $x = 1$; $y = 3$ $\{y - x = 2, y = 2x - 4, y - 2x = 1, y = 3x + 1\}$
(c) $x = 2$; $y = -1$ $\{y = x + 1, x - y = 3, y = 2x - 1, y + 2x = 3\}$

Three
Find the solutions of the following pairs of equations by drawing graphs.

(a) $y = x - 1$ and $y = 2x - 4$. Take x from 0 to 4 and y from -4 to 4.
(b) $y = x + 1$ and $y - 2x = 2$. Take x from 0 to 2 and y from 0 to 4.
(c) $y + 3x = 4$ and $x - y = 0$. Take x from 0 to 2 and y from 0 to 4.
(d) $y = x + 1$ and $y - 3x = 2$. Take x from -2 to 1 and y from 0 to 5.

B   Solution by substitution

Example   Find where the line $x = 2$ crosses the line $2x + 2y = 11$.

Substitute the value $x = 2$ into $2x + 2y = 11$, giving
$4 + 2y = 11 \rightarrow 2y = 7 \rightarrow y = 3\frac{1}{2}$.

Answer: The lines cross at $x = 2$, $y = 3\frac{1}{2}$, i.e. $(2, 3\frac{1}{2})$.

Example   Find where the line $y = x - 6$ crosses the line $x + y = 4$.

Substitute the value $y = x - 6$ into $x + y = 4$, giving
$x + (x - 6) = 4 \rightarrow x + x - 6 = 4 \rightarrow 2x - 6 = 4 \rightarrow 2x = 10 \rightarrow x = 5$.
Substituting $x = 5$ into $y = x - 6$ gives $y = -1$.

Answer: The lines cross at $x = 5$, $y = -1$, i.e. $(5, -1)$.

Check: If $x = 5$ and $y = -1$, is it true both that $y = x - 6$ and that $x + y = 4$?

1 Find where the following lines cross:
(a) $x = 3$; $x + y = 4$ (b) $x = 1$; $2x + y = 7$ (c) $x = 3$; $x + 2y = 9$
(d) $y = 3$; $x + 2y = 9$ (e) $x = 3$; $2x - y = 9$ (f) $y = 5$; $x - 2y = 17$.

2 Find where the following lines cross:
(a) $y = x + 4$; $x + y = 12$ (b) $y = x - 1$; $2x + y = 11$
(c) $y = x + 2$; $3x + y = 18$.

*3 Use the substitution method to find the solutions of the following equations; that is, find the values of x and y that make both equations true.

Check each time that your answers *do* make both equations true.
(a) $y = x - 3$; $3x + y = 9$ (b) $y = x - 1$; $2x + y = 5$
(c) $y = x - 2$; $2x + y = 10$

*4 Example Solve simultaneously by substitution: $x = 2y - 1$ and $y + 2x = 2$.

Substitute for x, giving $y + 2(2y - 1) = 2$
$\rightarrow y + 4y - 2 = 2 \rightarrow 5y - 2 = 2 \rightarrow 5y = 4$
$\rightarrow y = \frac{4}{5}$.
Now substitute $y = \frac{4}{5}$ into $x = 2y - 1$, to give $x = \frac{8}{5} - 1 = \frac{3}{5}$.

Answer: The solution is $(\frac{3}{5}, \frac{4}{5})$.

Solve:
(a) $y = x + 1$; $x + 2y = 5$ (b) $y = x - 3$; $2x + 2y = 10$
(c) $x = 2 - y$; $y + 2x = 1$.

5 Solve the following equations simultaneously, remembering to check your answers by substituting them into both equations. Be very careful with minus signs.

Example $3x - 2(x + 1) \rightarrow 3x - 2x - 2$

$3x - 2(x - 1) \rightarrow 3x - 2x + 2$

(a) $y = 2x - 5$; $3x - 2y = 8$ (b) $x = y - 5$; $2x + 3y = 10$
(c) $x = 3y - 4$; $2x - 2y = 8$ (d) $y = 4 + 2x$; $3x - y = -4$
(e) $x = 14 - 4y$; $4y - x = 10$ (f) $y = -2x - 2$; $2x - 3y = 6$

6 By considering their graphs, or otherwise, explain why the following pairs of equations have no simultaneous solutions:
(a) $y = x + 1$; $y - x = 2$ (b) $y = x + 1$; $2y - 2x = 2$

7 (a) Copy and complete the following tables.

$y = x^2$

x	-4	-3	-2	-1	0	1	2	3	4
y	16								

$y = x + 6$

x	-4	-3	-2	-1	0	1	2	3	4
y	2								

(b) What pairs of values for x and y appear in both tables?

(c) By drawing graphs of $y = x^2$ and $y = x + 6$ on the same grid, illustrate the simultaneous solutions to these two equations.

8 Solve simultaneously: $y = x^2$ and $y - 4x = 3$.

The two pentagons are similar. They both have the same size angles. Each side of the smaller pentagon is in the ratio 2 : 3 with the corresponding side on the larger.

2 cm → 3 cm
1 cm → 1.5 cm

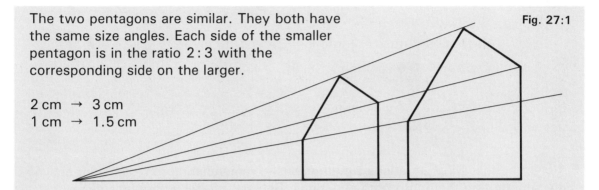

Fig. 27:1

For Discussion

One
You will need 14 strips of thin card, as shown in Figure 27:2, and 14 drawing pins.

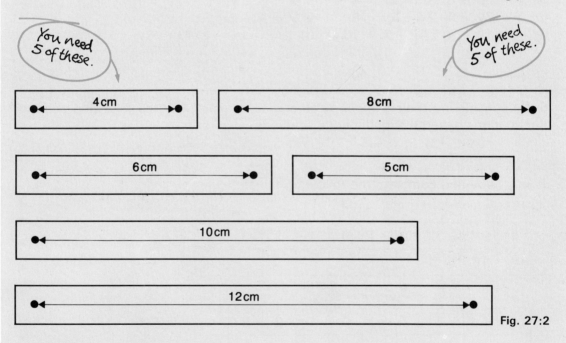

You need 5 of these.

You need 5 of these.

4 cm

8 cm

6 cm

5 cm

10 cm

12 cm

Fig. 27:2

Use the drawing pins, point upwards, to make:

(a) a triangle with sides 4 cm, 5 cm and 6 cm
(b) a triangle with sides twice as long as those in (a)
(c) a quadrilateral with all sides 4 cm long
(d) a quadrilateral with sides twice as long as those in (c).

Are your two triangles similar? Are your two quadrilaterals similar?

What are the missing words?

Triangles are similar if their corresponding angles are _____
or if their corresponding sides are in the same _____ .

Polygons with four or more sides are only similar when their corresponding
angles are _____ and their _____ _____ are in the
_____ _____ .

Two

Which pairs of shapes in Figure 27:3:
(i) must be similar   (ii) could be similar   (iii) cannot be similar?

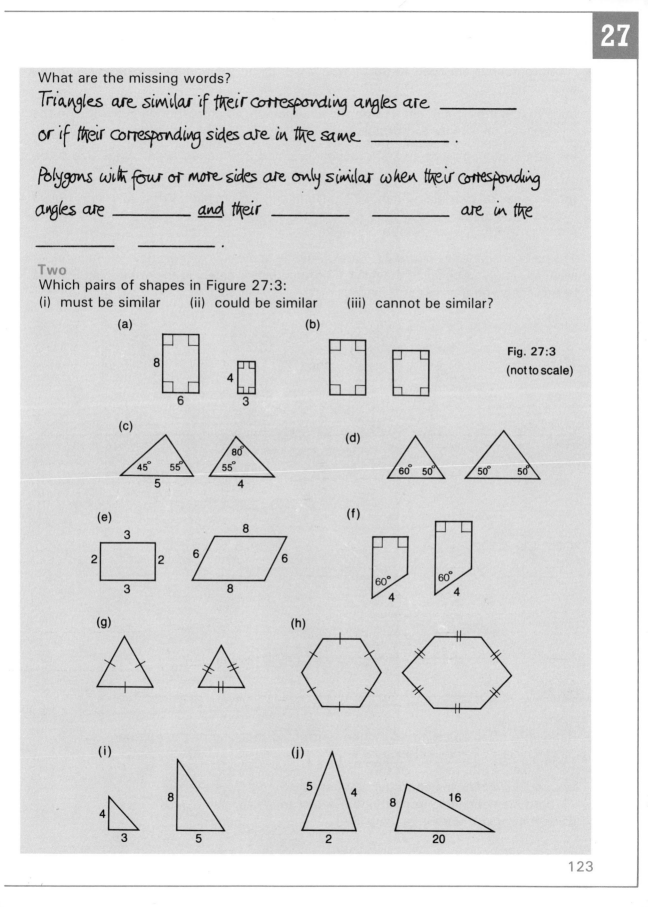

Fig. 27:3
(not to scale)

1 A photograph is enlarged so that a tree 2 cm tall on the original is 6 cm high on the enlargement.

(a) What is the ratio of lengths on the enlargement to corresponding lengths on the original, as simply as possible?

(b) The original photograph is 5 inches long and 3.5 inches wide. What size is the enlargement?

(c) A house on the enlargement is 3 cm long and 1.5 cm high. What size is the house on the original?

2 The pairs of shapes in Figure 27:4 are all similar and drawn accurately. By measuring, state as simply as possible the ratio of corresponding sides, in the order shape on the left to shape on the right.

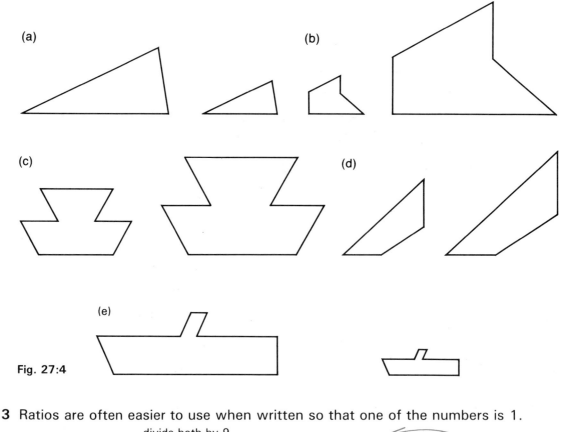

(a)

(b)

(c)

(d)

(e)

Fig. 27:4

3 Ratios are often easier to use when written so that one of the numbers is 1.

Example $9:12$ $\xrightarrow{\text{divide both by 9}}$ $1:\frac{12}{9}$

We could simplify the improper fraction $\frac{12}{9}$ to $1\frac{1}{3}$ but when changing in a ratio it is easier to leave improper fractions unsimplified.

This is the scale factor of the enlargement.

Write the following in the form $1:n$, leaving n as an unsimplified improper fraction where it is not an integer.

(a) $6:12$ (b) $5:20$ (c) $5:12$ (d) $8:10$ (e) $15:20$

4 Write ratios (a) to (e) in question 3 in the form $n:1$, leaving n as an unsimplified improper fraction.

Example $9:12 \xrightarrow{\text{divide both by 12}} \frac{9}{12}:1$

5 Example   A model of a building is made using a scale of $3:100$. A door on the model is 7 cm high. How high is the real door?

Scale $3:100 \xrightarrow{\text{divide both by 3}} 1:\frac{100}{3}$

The scale factor is $\frac{100}{3}$.

The real measurements are $\frac{100}{3} \times$ the model ones.

The real door is $\frac{100}{3} \times 7\,\text{cm} \approx 233\,\text{cm}$ high.

Example   The west tower is 8 metres high. How high should it be on the model?

Scale $3:100 \xrightarrow{\text{divide both by 100}} \frac{3}{100}:1$

The model measurements are $\frac{3}{100} \times$ the real ones.

The model tower is $\frac{3}{100} \times 8\,\text{m} = 0.24\,\text{m}$ high.

For the same model as in the example calculate:

(a) the true length of the building, if the model is 0.5 m long

(b) the true height of the library roof, if on the model it is 18 cm high

(c) the true width of an archway, if it is 8 cm wide on the model

(d) the model length of the long gallery, which is 15 metres long

(e) the model width of the balcony, which is 4 metres long

(f) the model width of the front door, which is 150 cm wide.

6 A statue of a statesman is made larger than the man in the ratio $8:5$.

(a) The man is 6 ft tall. How tall is the statue?

(b) The statue has a waist measurement of 64 inches. What is the waist measurement of the man?

7 For the pairs of similar shapes in Figure 27:5 find first the ratio of the lengths, then calculate the lengths of the sides marked with letters. The drawings are not to scale.

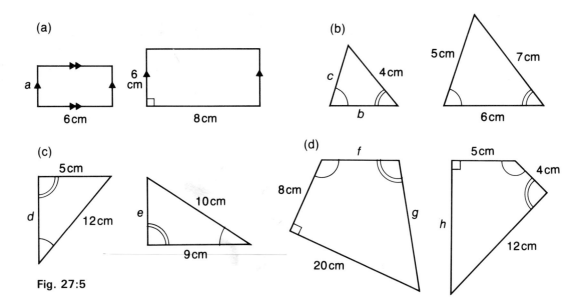

Fig. 27:5

8 Say which of the following shapes are always similar:
(a) squares (b) rectangles (c) circles (d) triangles
(e) equilateral triangles (f) right-angled triangles (g) isosceles triangles
(h) regular hexagons (i) pentagons (j) parallelograms

9 By considering the pairs of similar shapes in Figure 27:6, write a connection between the ratio of corresponding lengths and the ratio of areas for any two similar shapes.

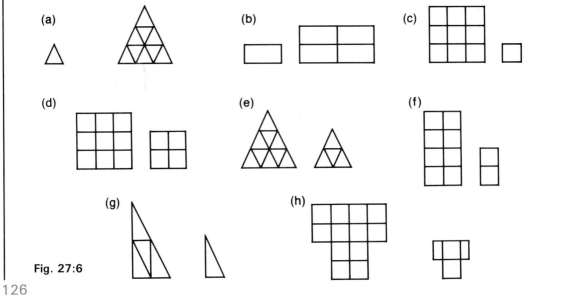

Fig. 27:6

Practise this construction. (Your teacher will tell you if you need to learn it.)

To draw two tangents to a given circle such that they make a given angle θ.
Given a circle (Figure 28:7) and a certain angle (Figure 28:8):
Draw any diameter AOB. Construct the tangent at A (Figure 28:1).
Copy angle θ such that $\angle BOC = \theta$ (Figure 28:6). Construct the tangent at C (Figure 28:1). Then $\angle APC$ will equal θ, as required (Figure 28:9).

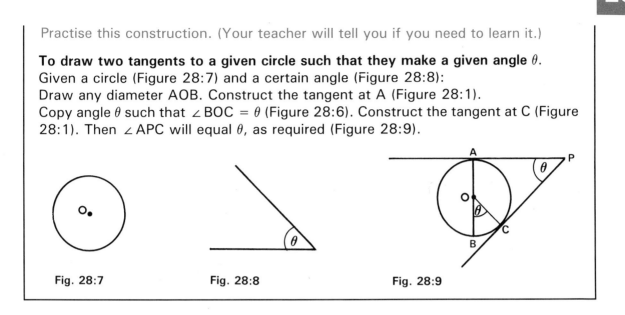

| Fig. 28:7 | Fig. 28:8 | Fig. 28:9 |

B Symmetry and angle properties involving tangents

For Discussion

For Figure 28:10

(a) name the line of symmetry

(b) name two right angles

(c) name an angle equal to $\angle$ ATO

(d) name an angle equal to $\angle$ AOT

(e) name a length equal to TA

(f) name two lengths equal to OA

(g) if $\angle$ ATO = 24° find the sizes of all the other angles (excluding reflex ones).

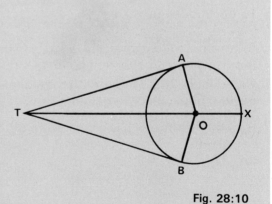

Fig. 28:10

1 Copy Figure 28:10. If $\angle$ AOB reflex = 256° calculate $\angle$ OTB.

*2 Copy Figure 28:10. If $\angle$ AOT = 77° mark the sizes of the other seven acute and obtuse angles.

3 Construct Figure 28:11 accurately. XY is the tangent at P, OP = 3 cm, XP = 4 cm and PY = 4 cm.

Measure:
(a) ∠XOP   (b) ∠YOP   (c) ∠OXP
(d) ∠OYP   (e) OX   (f) OY.

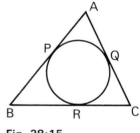

Fig. 28:11

4 Copy Figures 28:12 to 28:14. Make the larger radius 2 cm and the smaller radius 1 cm. In Figure 28:12 leave 1 cm between the two circles.

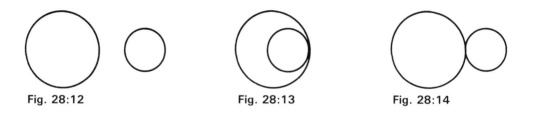

Fig. 28:12   **Fig. 28:13**   **Fig. 28:14**

(a) On Figure 28:12 draw four lines, each of which is a tangent to both circles.

(b) On Figure 28:13 draw one line which is a tangent to both circles.

(c) On Figure 28:14 draw three lines, each of which is a tangent to both circles.

The tangents you have drawn are called **common tangents**.

5 AOP is the diameter of a circle, centre O, and TP is a tangent. If △APT is isosceles, calculate ∠PAT.

6 Copy Figure 28:15 (start with the incircle). Mark clearly three pairs of equal lines.

If AB = 6 cm, AC = 5 cm and BP = 4 cm, calculate:
(a) AP   (b) AQ   (c) BC.

Fig. 28:15

7 Mark a point P on your book. Place a ruler to touch P and draw a line along the *other* edge of your ruler. Repeat for many different positions of the ruler, keeping one edge touching P.

C Calculations involving tangents

For Discussion

Figure 28:16 is a sketch of the running track that Jim Shuse is designing for the new school field, which is a rectangle 80 metres by 20 metres. The track is to be 100 metres around the inside edge and is to have four 1 metre-wide lanes. The curves are to be as gentle as possible.

Draw a scale diagram of the best design for the track.

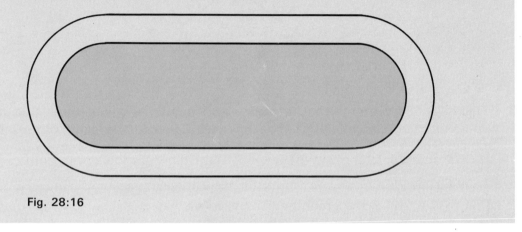

Fig. 28:16

You may use a calculator for this exercise, giving answers correct to 3 s.f. Use the π key or take π = 3.142.

In questions 1 to 3 calculate the circumference and area of each circle.

1 Radius 5 cm.

*2 (a) Radius 2 cm   (b) Diameter 14 cm   (c) Radius 24 cm
    (d) Diameter 2.2 cm

3 (a) Radius 0.7 cm   (b) Diameter 21 cm

4 Figure 28:17 represents a belt around two equal wheels.

   (a) Calculate the length of the belt if AB = 25 cm and the radii of the wheels are 10 cm.

   (b) Calculate the area enclosed by the belt.

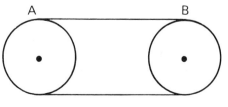

Fig. 28:17

5 In Figure 28:18, AD and BC are common tangents. ∠AOB = 120°.

Copy Figure 28:18, then calculate:
(a) ∠OAX   (b) ∠OBX   (c) ∠AXB   (d) ∠CXD
(e) ∠XCQ   (f) ∠XDQ   (g) ∠CQD.

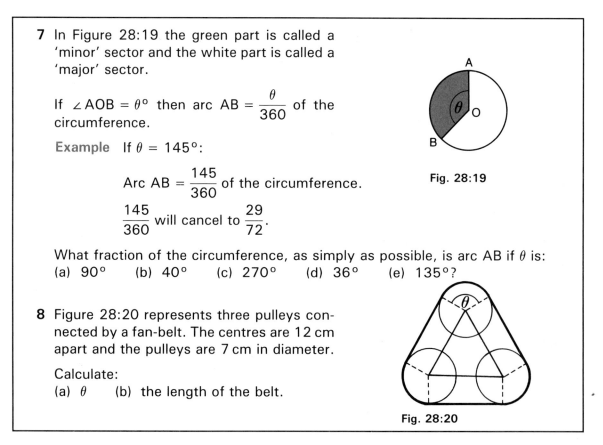

Fig. 28:18

6 If Figure 28:18 represents a belt around two unequal wheels then the belt would touch two-thirds of the circumference of each wheel. Calculate the length of the belt if the radii are 6 cm and 3 cm and the straight parts of the belt are 12 cm long.

7 In Figure 28:19 the green part is called a 'minor' sector and the white part is called a 'major' sector.

If ∠AOB = θ° then arc AB = $\dfrac{\theta}{360}$ of the circumference.

Example If θ = 145°:

Arc AB = $\dfrac{145}{360}$ of the circumference.

$\dfrac{145}{360}$ will cancel to $\dfrac{29}{72}$.

Fig. 28:19

What fraction of the circumference, as simply as possible, is arc AB if θ is:
(a) 90°   (b) 40°   (c) 270°   (d) 36°   (e) 135°?

8 Figure 28:20 represents three pulleys connected by a fan-belt. The centres are 12 cm apart and the pulleys are 7 cm in diameter.

Calculate:
(a) θ   (b) the length of the belt.

Fig. 28:20

29 Simultaneous equations by elimination

A Adding and subtracting algebraic terms

For Discussion

(i) $+3x$
   $-2x$ Add
   $+\ x$

(ii) $-2b$
   $-4b$ Add
   $-6b$

(iii) $6d$
   $-6d$ Add
   0

(iv) $+3x$
   $-2x$ Subtract
   $+5x$

(v) $-3e$
   $-5e$ Subtract
   $+2e$

(vi) $-4h$
   $-4h$ Subtract
   0

Notes: In (iv), $+3x - -2x \rightarrow +3x + 2x \rightarrow +5x$

In (v), $-3e - -5e \rightarrow -3e + 5e \rightarrow +2e$

1 Add the following. (There is no need to copy the questions.)

(a) $+4x$
   $+5x$

(b) $+3y$
   $-2y$

(c) $+2e$
   $-4e$

(d) $-5y$
   $-3y$

(e) $+3k$
   $-\ k$

(f) $+9x$
   $-9x$

(g) $-4m$
   $-3m$

(h) $-2x$
   $4x$

(i) $-\ h$
   $+9h$

(j) $-6y$
   $-6y$

(k) $+3a$
   $-5a$

(l) $5x$
   $-5x$

(m) $-2y$
   $-4y$

(n) $+4x$
   $-4x$

(o) $+6p$
   $-8p$

(p) $-7d$
   $-5d$

(q) $5b$
   $5b$

(r) $-6z$
   $+8z$

2 Subtract the terms in question 1.

Questions 3 and 4 may be omitted if you had questions 1 and 2 correct.

*3 Add:

(a) $+7x$
   $+4x$

(b) $+3y$
   $-5y$

(c) $-2x$
   $7x$

(d) $-6k$
   $-4k$

(e) $3a$
   $3a$

(f) $+9n$
   $-2n$

*4 Subtract the terms in question 3.

5 Example Find the values of x and y that make both $x + 3y = 9$ and $x - 2y = -1$.

$$x + 3y = 9$$
$$\underline{x - 2y = -1 \text{ Subtract}}$$
$$5y = 10 \rightarrow y = 2$$

Substitute $y = 2$ into $x + 3y = 9$, giving $x + 6 = 9 \rightarrow x = 3$.

Answer: $x = 3$ and $y = 2$ make both equations true.

Check: If $x = 3$ and $y = 2$ then $x + 3y \rightarrow 3 + 6 \rightarrow 9$ (correct), and $x - 2y \rightarrow 3 - 4 \rightarrow -1$ (correct).

Find the values of x and y that make both pairs of the following true:

(a) $x + 2y = 4$
     $x + y = 3$ (subtract)

(b) $x + 2y = 12$
     $x - 3y = 2$ (subtract)

(c) $3x + 2y = 16$
     $2x - 2y = 4$ (add)

6 (a) $4a - 2f = 16$
         $a - 2f = 1$ (subtract)

(b) $2x + 3y = 14$
     $2x - y = 6$ (subtract)

(c) $2g + k = 7$
     $-2g + 3k = 5$ (add)

7 (a) $x + 3y = 5$
         $x + y = 3$ (subtract)

(b) $3c - h = 0$
     $2c + h = 5$ (add)

(c) $3x + y = 5$
     $2x - y = -5$ (add)

8 (a) $2x + 2y = 8$
         $2x - 5y = 8$ (subtract)

(b) $2r - 3t = -3$
     $3r + 3t = 18$ (add)

(c) $a + n = 0$
     $a - n = 2$ (subtract)

9 Figure 29:1 shows a curve of pursuit. A car passes point A at 0800. Simultaneously a dog at B gives chase at a half of the car's speed. The lines show the dog's heading at intervals of a $\frac{1}{2}$ second.

Copy and continue the diagram, twice the size shown, then investigate the effect if the dog runs faster or slower, or starts nearer or further away.

Figure 29:2 and 29:3 suggest two other possibilities. Try them, then investigate some of your own.

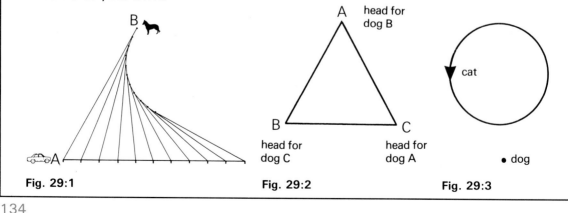

Fig. 29:1   Fig. 29:2   Fig. 29:3

B Elimination method

1 Example $3x + 4y \xrightarrow{\ \times 2\ } 6x + 8y$
$\qquad\qquad\ 2x - 3y \ (x) \xrightarrow{\ \times 3\ } 6x - 9y$

Multiply the following expressions to make the letter in brackets have the same coefficient (number in front) in both lines.

(a) $2p + 3y$ (b) $4x + \ y$ (c) $2x + 3e$ (d) $4x + 3k$
$\quad\ p + \ y \ (p)$ $\qquad 2x - 2y \ (x)$ $\qquad 5x + 2e \ (e)$ $\qquad 3x - \ k \ (k)$

2 If the terms to be eliminated have the same signs, subtract the equations.

Same Sign Subtract

Example $6x + 8f$
$\qquad\qquad \underline{6x - 9f} \text{ (subtract)}$
$\qquad\qquad \quad 17f$

Notes: The $6x$ terms will be eliminated by subtraction as both have an (unwritten) $+$ sign in front of them.

Example $2n + 7y$
$\qquad\qquad \underline{3n - 7y} \text{ (add)}$
$\qquad\qquad \ 5n$

Notes: The $7y$ terms will be eliminated by addition as they have different signs in front of them.

Eliminate either the x or the y terms from:

(a) $4x - 7y$ (b) $3x + 2y$ (c) $3x - 7y$ (d) $2x + 3y$ (e) $\quad 3x - 2y$
$\quad \underline{4x + 2y}$ $\qquad \underline{3x - 3y}$ $\qquad \underline{2x - 7y}$ $\qquad \underline{5x - 3y}$ $\qquad \underline{-3x + 5y}$

(f) $x - 6y$ (g) $2x - y$ (h) $\quad 4x + 2y$ (i) $3x + 8y$ (j) $2x - 7y$
$\quad \underline{x - 5y}$ $\qquad \underline{3x + y}$ $\qquad \underline{-5x + 2y}$ $\qquad \underline{8x - 8y}$ $\qquad \underline{3x - 7y}$

*3 Example

$$5b + 2e \xrightarrow{\times 3} 15b + 6e$$
$$- 2b + 3e \quad (e) \xrightarrow{\times 2} - 4b + 6e \text{ (subtract)}$$
$$\overline{19b}$$

Multiply one or both of the following pairs of equations to make the letter-term indicated in brackets the same. Then eliminate that term by addition or subtraction.

(a) $2x + q$
    $3x + 2q$ (q)

(b) $2x + 3y$
    $3x + 5y$ (x)

(c) $3n + 4f$
    $2n - 2f$ (f)

(d) $a + 2y$
    $3a - 4y$ (y)

(e) $2c + 2p$
    $3c - 7p$ (c)

(f) $4x - y$
    $3x + 2y$ (y)

(g) $3x + 2k$
    $4x - 4k$ (k)

(h) $4e + 5f$
    $3e + 2f$ (e)

4 Example

$$3a + 5n = 21 \xrightarrow{\times 2} 6a + 10n = 42$$
$$2a + 3n = 13 \xrightarrow{\times 3} 6a + 9n = 39 \text{ (subtract)}$$
$$\overline{n = 3}$$

Substitute $n = 3$ into $3a + 5n = 21$
$$3a + 15 = 21 \rightarrow 3a = 6 \rightarrow a = 2$$

Answer: Both equations are satisfied by $a = 2$ and $n = 3$.

Check: If $a = 2$ and $n = 3$ then $3a + 5n \rightarrow 6 + 15 \rightarrow 21$ (correct), and
$$2a + 3n \rightarrow 4 + 9 \rightarrow 13 \text{ (correct)}.$$

Solve simultaneously, eliminating the term indicated in the brackets:

(a) $x + 2y = 8$
    $3x - 4y = 4$ (x)

(b) $2d + 3y = 11$
    $3d - 2y = 10$ (y)

(c) $2c + 3p = 2$
    $3c - 2p = 16$ (c)

Solve simultaneously the equations in questions 5 to 8, deciding for yourself which term is easier to eliminate.

5 (a) $2x + 3y = 12$
      $3x + 5y = 19$

   (b) $2h + j = 6$
      $3h + 2j = 11$

   (c) $2a - 2y = 2$
      $3a + 4y = 24$

6 (a) $4x - y = 13$
      $3x + 2y = 29$

   (b) $2e + 2k = 6$
      $4e - k = 12$

   (c) $2x + 2y = -17$
      $3x - 2y = 2$

7 (a) $2c + 3y = 12$
      $2c - 3y = 24$

   (b) $3a - 2h = 1$
      $5a - 3h = 3$

   (c) $8x + 4y = 8$
      $6x - 8y = 39$

8 (a) $e = 2c - 1$
      $e = 3c - 5$

   (b) $f = 2b$
      $3f + b = 14$

   (c) $y = 2x - 8$
      $x - y = 5$

   (d) $5(x + y) = 2x - y$
      $2(2x + 3y) = 3y - 2$

   (e) $g - 2d + 6 = 3g - 5d + 7 = 4$

30 Arithmetic: fractions; calculators

Test yourself, then practise where necessary with questions 9 to 17.

1 Add: 4.29   23   200   1.7   0.085   5

5 Subtract $3\frac{5}{8} - 1\frac{1}{6}$

2 Subtract 12.9807 from 106.05

6 Subtract $2\frac{3}{4} - \frac{9}{11}$

3 Multiply 18.7 by 0.908

7 Multiply $1\frac{3}{4} \times \frac{8}{21}$

4 Divide 1.421 by 0.35

8 (a) $2\frac{3}{5} \div 1\frac{4}{15}$ (b) $6\frac{2}{3} \div 4$

---

*9 Add:
(a) $3.4 + 0.56 + 7 + 2.8$ (b) $6.9 + 1.03 + 5 + 0.12$
(c) $120 + 0.36 + 15 + 7.3$ (d) $46 + 0.81 + 100 + 1.123$

*10 Subtract:
(a) 1.89 from 8   (b) 7.65 from 9   (c) 4.6 from 7.85
(d) 3.92 from 7.051   (e) 7.903 from 8.01   (f) 6.079 from 10.01

*11 Multiply:
(a) 16.7×0.89 (b) 1.69×0.83 (c) 1.06×1.06

*12 Divide:
(a) 0.875 by 0.7   (b) 2.6 by 0.8   (c) 0.356 by 0.04   (d) 40.8 by 0.17
(e) 13.064 by 0.23   (f) 1.691 by 1.9

*13 Divide:
(a) 5.1 by 0.05   (b) 26 by 1.3   (c) 0.0378 by 0.35

*14 Subtract:
(a) $3\frac{3}{5} - 2\frac{1}{4}$ (b) $1\frac{1}{4} - \frac{1}{8}$ (c) $5\frac{3}{5} - 1\frac{1}{3}$ (d) $3\frac{1}{9} - 1\frac{1}{12}$

*15 Subtract:
(a) $2\frac{1}{9} - \frac{1}{4}$ (b) $17\frac{1}{5} - 16\frac{1}{3}$ (c) $14\frac{2}{9} - \frac{11}{12}$ (d) $4\frac{3}{5} - 3\frac{9}{10}$

*16 Multiply:
(a) $1\frac{7}{9} \times \frac{3}{10}$ (b) $3\frac{3}{7} \times \frac{7}{8}$ (c) $4\frac{7}{8} \times 1\frac{7}{13}$

*17 Divide:
(a) $1\frac{5}{7} \div 4$ (b) $1\frac{4}{9} \div \frac{5}{6}$ (c) $\frac{4}{15} \div 2\frac{2}{5}$ (d) $\frac{9}{16} \div 3\frac{3}{8}$ (e) $\frac{4}{11} \div \frac{1}{6}$
(f) $6\frac{1}{2} \div 8\frac{1}{8}$

18 Example Find a rough answer to $\dfrac{3.15 \times 2.7}{4.5}$

$$\dfrac{3.15 \times 2.7}{4.5} \;\rightarrow\; \dfrac{3 \times 3}{5} \;\rightarrow\; \text{about } 2$$

The exact answer may be found by arithmetic (cancelling first) or by using a calculator.

Work out a rough answer to:

(a) $\dfrac{28 \times 3.6}{4.9 \times 2.16}$ (b) $\dfrac{2.2 \times 3.5}{1.4}$ (c) $\dfrac{1.62 \times 1.5}{3.6}$ (d) $\dfrac{3.7 \times 52}{0.08}$

(e) $\dfrac{12.6 \times 0.85}{0.56 \times 15}$ (f) $\dfrac{3.78 \times 6.3}{0.14 \times 81}$ (g) $\dfrac{25.6 \times 0.09}{36 \times 1.3}$

19 Calculator memories

Calculators can have two kinds of memory, which we will refer to as 'accumulating' and 'store'.

The **accumulating** memory key is usually marked $\boxed{\text{M}+}$ (add to memory) or $\boxed{\text{SUM}}$ (to sum is to add). This key adds what is on display to whatever is already in the memory.

The **store** memory key is usually marked $\boxed{\text{STO}}$ (store) or $\boxed{\text{M in}}$ (put in memory) or $\boxed{x \rightarrow \text{M}}$ (put x (the display) into memory). This key replaces what is in the memory with what is on display.

Subtracting from the memory

Sometimes there is a $\boxed{\text{M}-}$ key, otherwise change the display to negative by the $\boxed{+\backslash-}$ key then use $\boxed{\text{M}+}$.

Recalling the memory

This is usually done by pressing a $\boxed{\text{MR}}$ (memory recall) key.

Emptying the memory

Your calculator may use $\boxed{\text{MC}}$ (memory cancel), or $\boxed{\text{MRC}}$ (first press recalls memory, second press clears memory), or you may need to clear the memory by 0 $\boxed{\text{STO}}$ (store zero).

Special functions

A few calculators automatically accumulate the display.
Some calculators always store the display, even when you have switched them off.
Some treat the $\boxed{\text{M}+}$ key as $\boxed{=}$ then $\boxed{\text{M}+}$, so if you are in the middle of a calculation you add the answer, not what is on display, when you press the $\boxed{\text{M}+}$ key.
Some have an $\boxed{\text{EXC}}$ or $\boxed{x \leftrightarrow \text{M}}$ key. This swaps over what is in the memory with what is on display, so you can carry out two separate calculations without losing

one of them, or swap over when you have e in the memory and f on display, but wish to find $e \div f$. (Note that the $\boxed{1/x}$ reciprocal key can also be used to do this as the reciprocal of $\dfrac{f}{e}$ is $\dfrac{e}{f}$.)

Use memory keys to help you do the following questions. Work out an approximate answer each time to check your method.

(a) Find the cost of 16 books at £5.95 each and 23 books at £8.99 each.

(b) $17p \times 6 + 85p \times 7 + 14p - 56p \times 2 + 99p \times 3 + 92p - 16p \times 8$

(c) $\dfrac{14.36 + 17.1}{16.7 - 4.2}$

(d) Display the first ten terms of the sequence 1, 2, 4, 8, 16, . . . using the $\boxed{1}$ key once, then only memory keys.

(e) Display the first ten terms of the sequence 1, 1, 2, 3, 5, 8, . . . using the $\boxed{1}$ key once, then only the $\boxed{M+}$, $\boxed{+}$, $\boxed{RM}$ and $\boxed{=}$ keys.

20 Write about the memory keys that are on your calculator. What are they, and what do they do? Give examples.

21 Find answers to the expressions in question 18, correct to three significant figures where appropriate. Compare your answers with the approximate answers obtained in question 18.

Hints: $\dfrac{a \times b}{c \times d}$ $a \boxed{\times} b \boxed{\div} c \boxed{\div} d \boxed{=}$

Note the second $\boxed{\div}$ where you might have expected a $\boxed{\times}$. If you do press $\boxed{\times}$ there you will work out $\dfrac{a \times b \times d}{c}$.

Some calculators may need $\boxed{=}$ before the first $\boxed{\div}$.

Experiment to make sure your calculator works out $\dfrac{3 \times 8}{2 \times 3} = 4$.

22 You should be able to answer most of these questions without a calculator.

Find:

(a) $(2\tfrac{1}{3})^2$ (b) $(4\tfrac{1}{2})^2$ (c) $(1\tfrac{1}{2})^3$ (d) $\sqrt{9} - \sqrt{4}$ (e) $\sqrt{(9-4)}$

(f) $\sqrt{9} \times \sqrt{4}$ (g) $\sqrt{(9 \times 4)}$ (h) $\sqrt{9} + \sqrt{4}$ (i) $\sqrt{(9+4)}$ (j) $\sqrt{9} \div \sqrt{4}$

(k) $\sqrt{(9 \div 4)}$ (l) $\sqrt{16} \times 49$ (m) $\sqrt{(16+49)}$.

23 Using your answers to question 22 as a guide, say for which of the following a is equal to b.

(a) $a = \sqrt{x} + \sqrt{y}; \quad b = \sqrt{x + y}$ (b) $a = \sqrt{x} - \sqrt{y}; \quad b = \sqrt{x - y}$

(c) $a = \sqrt{x} \times \sqrt{y}; \quad b = \sqrt{x \times y}$ (b) $a = \sqrt{x} \div \sqrt{y}; \quad b = \sqrt{\dfrac{x}{y}}$

24 State what each of the following formulae is used for (you have met them all before), then use a calculator to answer each part correct to 3 s.f.

Use the π key or take $\pi = 3.142$. Answers are given at the end.

(a) $C = \pi d$. Find d if $C = 7.298$
(b) $A = \frac{1}{2}bh$. Find b if $A = 15.6$ and $h = 7.7$
(c) $V = s^3$. Find V if $s = 17.6$
(d) $A = \pi r^2$. Find r if $A = 10$
(e) $A = 4\pi r^2$. Find r if $A = 27.6$
(f) $A = \frac{1}{2}(a + b)h$. Find A if $a = 7, b = 6.2$ and $h = 1.35$
(g) $S = (n - 2) \times 180°$. Find n if $S = 4320°$.

(h) $T = \dfrac{d}{v}$. Find T in minutes if $d = 1$ km and $v = 28$ km/h.

(i) $h^2 = a^2 + b^2$. Find h if $a = 16$ and $b = 15.8$

Answers: (a) 2.32   (b) 4.05   (c) 5450   (d) 1.78   (e) 1.48
(f) 8.91   (g) 26   (h) 2.14   (i) 22.5

25 You must observe the rule BODMAS when using a calculator; i.e. the order of working is Brackets, Of, Divide, Multiply, Add, Subtract, ('Of' replaces 'multiply' in such statements as 'Six lots of five make thirty'.)

Example $4 + 4 \div 4 = 4 + 1 = 5$ BUT $(4 + 4) \div 4 = 8 \div 4 = 2$

Notes: Some calculators 'know' BODMAS, and will give the correct answer (5) to the first example as long as you only press ⊟ once. Other calculators will give the wrong answer (2) to the first example. This is because they work out $4 + 4$ as soon as you press the next function key (the $\div$).

Some calculators have a bracket key. This will be very useful in the following questions. Otherwise you must use the memory store or write down a part answer. Experiment with different ways of showing that $(7 + 6) - (8 - 1) = 6$.

The answers to the following questions are given at the end.

Find:

(a) $(4 + 6) - (9 \div 3)$ (b) $7.7 \times (1.6 + 3.5)$ (c) $\dfrac{4.8 + 2.6}{3.1 \times 7.7}$ (d) $\dfrac{300}{1.9 + 8.2}$

(e) $\dfrac{4.6}{14.2 - 0.97}$ (f) $\dfrac{3.9 \times 560}{4.9 + 7.12 \times 3.3}$ (g) $147 - (92 \times 16) \div 11$

(h) $2.46 \times 1.8 - 9.7 \times 6.3$ (i) $\sqrt{16.7}$ (j) $\dfrac{(32)^2 + (16)^2}{(43)^2}$

(k) $\dfrac{4(36 - 9.76)}{4.35 \times 2.8}$ (l) $\dfrac{1}{15} + \dfrac{1}{37}$ (m) $(3.9)^3 \div (46)^2$.

Answers: (a) 7   (b) 39.3   (c) 0.310   (d) 29.7   (e) 0.348
(f) 76.9   (g) 13.2   (h) -56.7 (i) 4.09   (j) 0.692
(k) 8.62   (l) 0.0937   (m) 0.0280

26 Example   Find x if $3x^2 - x = 5$.

First guess a likely answer, say 2.
Using a calculator we find that $3x^2 - x$ when $x = 2$ is 10, which is too big (we want 5).
Try $x = 1$, which gives 2, too small.
So try $x = 1.5$, and so on until you find as accurate an answer as you require.

Note   Use the calculator memory to store the value of x you are trying.

One problem with this method of solving equations is that there are usually two answers to x^2 equations, often three answers to x^3 equations and so on, so when you have found one answer you have to try again to find others! Not easy! Try to solve the following. All solutions are between -2 and 3.

(a) $x^3 = 16$ (one solution)   (b) $4x^2 + x = 5$ (two solutions)

(c) $3x^3 - 2x = 4$ (one solution)

(d) $\dfrac{x}{x^2 - 4} = 0$ (one solution)   (e) $\dfrac{x^2}{3 + x} = 1$ (two solutions)

(f) $x^3 - 2x^2 - x + 1 = 0$ (three solutions).

27 In question 24, a, b, d, h, and r are lengths. Explain how you can tell which formulae find lengths, which find areas, and which find volumes.

28 Refer back to exercise 3A, question 11. Use the same idea, but now include zero, so that you have to use ten digits. We have found five multiples of 3, three multiples of 4, one multiple of 6, four multiples of 7, and nine more for multiples of numbers between 27 and 78. Can you find them all? If you find any that we have missed please write to tell us.

31 Transposition: change of subject

A Simple equations

For Discussion

One

Examples

(i)   If $u = s - t$
then $s = u + t$

(ii) If $-v = s - n$
then $s = -v + n$, or (better) $s = n - v$

(iii) If $p = sr$
then $s = \dfrac{p}{r}$.

Two

Often a flow method is useful when changing the subject. It can always be used, provided the subject letter only appears once in the expression.

Example   Make s the subject of $c = 4s - 8t$.

Write a flow-diagram, beginning with the new subject and describing what happens to it.

$$s \xrightarrow{\times 4} 4s \xrightarrow{-8t} 4s - 8t.$$
$$\downarrow$$
$$c$$

Now reverse the flow using inverse operations
$(+ \leftrightarrow - ; \quad \times \leftrightarrow \div ; \quad \sqrt{} \leftrightarrow (\ )^2):$

$$\xleftarrow{\div 4} \qquad \xleftarrow{+ 8t}$$

$$\dfrac{c + 8t}{4} \xleftarrow{\div 4} c + 8t \xleftarrow{+ 8t} c$$

We have now made s the subject:

$$s = \dfrac{c + 8t}{4}.$$

In questions 1 to 5 make r the subject.

1 (a) $m = r - 4$ (b) $m = r - g$ (c) $m = r + 5$ (d) $m = r + p$
(e) $c = 3r$ (f) $c = mr$

*2 (a) $p = r + 6$ (b) $p = r + m$ (c) $y = 4 - r$ (d) $m = b + r$ (e) $t = r - 4$

*3 (a) $c = 4r$ (b) $t = pr$ (c) $m = vr$ (d) $p = m + r$ (e) $a = 4r$

4 (a) $c = 4r - 5$ (b) $c = 4r - b$ (c) $c = 3r + 1$ (d) $c = ar + b$ (e) $D = 2ar$

5 (a) $M = 2abr$ (b) $p = 4r - 6$ (c) $p = Vr - g$ (d) $v = 4rst$ (e) $C = 2\pi r$

6   Example   Make s the subject of $p - s = g$.

     Method One $p - s = g \rightarrow p = g + s \rightarrow p - g = s$
         Answer: $s = p - g$

     Method Two $s \xrightarrow{\text{taken away from } p} p - s$
       $p - g \xleftarrow{\text{taken away from } p} g$
       Answer: $s = p - g$

       Note: 'taken away from' is a self-inverse; it does not
             change when you reverse the flow.

   Make s the subject of:
   (a) $q - s = a$ (b) $b - s = c$ (c) $p = m - s$ (d) $-k = m - s$.

---

7   Rewrite the formulae in exercise 30, question 24, so that a different letter is the
   subject.

B   Harder equations

Example   Make p the subject of $m = 6p^2$.

     Method One $m = 6p^2 \rightarrow p^2 = \dfrac{m}{6} \rightarrow p = \sqrt{\dfrac{m}{6}}$

     Method Two $p \xrightarrow{(\ )^2} p^2 \xrightarrow{\times 6} 6p^2$
       $\sqrt{\dfrac{m}{6}} \xleftarrow{\sqrt{}} \dfrac{m}{6} \xleftarrow{\div 6} m$

         Answer: $p = \sqrt{\dfrac{m}{6}}$

Example   Make f the subject of $c = \dfrac{3f}{4} + b$

     Method One $c = \dfrac{3f}{4} + b \rightarrow \dfrac{3f}{4} = c - b \rightarrow f = \dfrac{4(c - b)}{3}$

Method Two

$$f \xrightarrow{\times 3} 3f \xrightarrow{\div 4} \frac{3f}{4} \xrightarrow{+b} \frac{3f}{4} + b$$

$$\frac{4(c - b)}{3} \xleftarrow{\div 3} 4(c - b) \xleftarrow{\times 4} c - b \xleftarrow{-b} c$$

Answer: $f = \dfrac{4(c - b)}{3}$

Note the brackets around $(c - b)$; this is so that the *whole* of it is multiplied by 4.

1 Make h the subject of:

(a) $c = 3h^2$ (b) $d = 7h^2$ (c) $e = 5h^2$ (d) $f = 3h^2$ (e) $g = \dfrac{2h^2}{7}$

(f) $a = \dfrac{3h^2}{2}$.

2 Make f the subject of:

(a) $q = \dfrac{f}{3} + p$ (b) $m = \dfrac{2f}{3} - p$ (c) $c = \dfrac{f}{2} + p$ (d) $d = \dfrac{2f}{3} - bc$.

3 The average speed of a car which travels d kilometres in t hours is given by the formula $s = \dfrac{d}{t}$.

Rewrite this formula to state:
(a) the distance travelled, given the speed and the time
(b) the time taken to cover d km at s km/h.

4 Use the formulae you wrote in question 3 to find:
(a) the speed of a car which covers 280 km in 5 hours
(b) the distance a car travelling at 95 km/h can cover in 2 hours
(c) the time it will take a car travelling at 50 km/h to cover 20 km.

5 The area of a circle is given by the formula $A = \pi r^2$.

Rewrite the formula to give the radius of a circle in terms of its area.

6 The formula $C = \frac{5}{9}(F - 32)$ converts Fahrenheit temperature to Celsius. Find the formula to change Celsius temperature to Fahrenheit.

Use your formula to change 15°C to °F.

7 (a) Find a when $C = 3a + b$.

   (b) Find b when $r = 4(a + b)$.

8 (a) Find R when $V = ab(R - r)$.

   (b) Find n when $A = 360 (n - 2)$.

9 To change a speed of k km/h to metres per seco...
Write a formula to change metres per second t...

10 From the top of a cliff of height m metres the horizo...
Write a formula for m in terms of k.

11 A simple pendulum is a small heavy mass on the end of a thin cord. A simple pendulum of length l metres takes t seconds for one complete swing, where

$$t = 2\pi \sqrt{\left(\frac{l}{g}\right)},$$ g being the acceleration due to gravity.

Rewrite the formula to give g when t and l are measured.

Carry out experiments to find the value of g.

12 Find some formulae used in science. Rewrite each one to make each variable in turn the subject.

e square on the
n of the squares

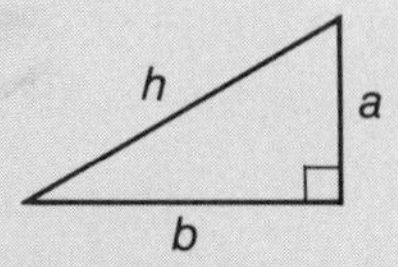

Fig. 32:1

$= 5.6^2 + 8.2^2$
$+ 67.24$
$h = \sqrt{98.60}$

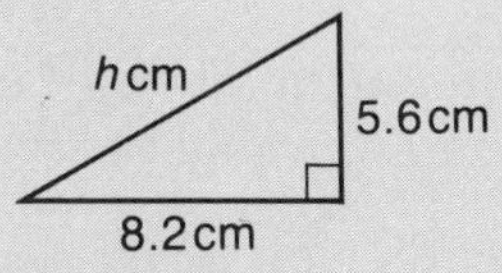

Fig. 32:2

32:3, $9.5^2 = a^2 + 5.7^2$
$^2 - 5.7^2 = a^2$
$0.25 - 32.49 = a^2$
$\rightarrow a^2 = 57.76 \rightarrow a = \sqrt{57.76}$
$\rightarrow a = 7.6$ to 2 s.f.

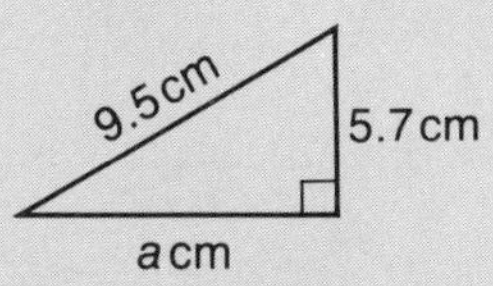

Fig. 32:3

```
EM "PYTHAG"
.Ø  PRINT "RIGHT-ANGLED TRIANGLES"
 2Ø  PRINT "Calculate hypotenuse or side?"
 3Ø  PRINT "Type H or S"
 4Ø  INPUT A$
 5Ø  IF A$ <> "S" AND A$ <> "H" THEN GOTO 3Ø
 6Ø  CLS      (Clear screen)
 7Ø  IF A$ = "H" THEN GOTO 1ØØ
 8Ø  PRINT "Length of hypotenuse?"
 9Ø  INPUT H
1ØØ  PRINT "Length of side A?"
11Ø  INPUT A
12Ø  IF A$ = "H" THEN GOTO 18Ø
13Ø  IF H > A THEN GOTO 16Ø
14Ø  PRINT "Side must be SHORTER than hypotenuse!"
15Ø  GOTO 1Ø
16Ø  PRINT "Third side is ∧"; SQR (H*H − A*A)
17Ø  GOTO 2Ø
18Ø  PRINT "Length of side B?"
19Ø  INPUT B
2ØØ  PRINT "Hypotenuse is ∧"; SQR (A*A + B*B)
21Ø  GOTO 2Ø
```

1 Sketch right-angled triangles and show clear working, as in the examples, for:

(a) $a = 7$ cm, $b = 8$ cm; find h (b) $a = 5.1$ cm, $b = 4.6$ cm; find h

(c) $h = 3.1$ cm, $b = 2.9$ cm; find a (d) $h = 24$ cm, $b = 15$ cm; find a.

*2 Calculate the side marked x in each triangle in Figure 32:4.

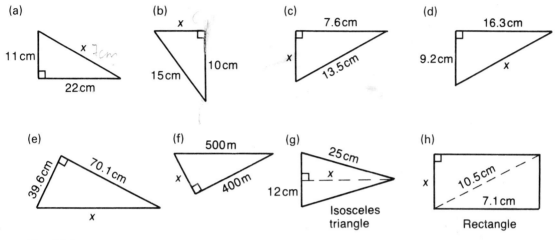

Fig. 32:4

*3 (a) Sketch a ladder leaning against a wall, seen from the side to make a right-angled triangle. Calculate the length of the ladder if it reaches 10 metres up the wall when its base is 1.5 metres from it.

    (b) Check your answer by a scale drawing.

*4 A plane flies 15 km due north then 18 km due east.

    (a) Sketch the journey. Calculate how far the plane is from its starting point when it reaches the end of its journey.

    (b) Check your answer by a scale drawing.

5 Calculate the altitude (height) to the 10 cm side, and hence the area, of an isosceles triangle whose sides are 13 cm, 13 cm and 10 cm.

6 The end of a house is an isosceles triangle, sides 9 m, 6 m and 6 m, on top of a rectangle 9 m wide by 10 m high.

    (a) Calculate the height of the ridge (top) of the roof above the top of the walls, correct to the nearest metre.

    (b) Use your answer to part (a) to help you find the total area of the end of the house, correct to the nearest m².

7 Figure 32:5 shows a right-angled triangle, an acute-angled triangle and an obtuse-angled triangle.

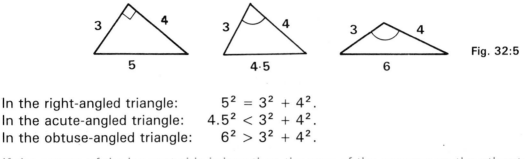

Fig. 32:5

In the right-angled triangle: $\quad 5^2 = 3^2 + 4^2$.
In the acute-angled triangle: $\quad 4.5^2 < 3^2 + 4^2$.
In the obtuse-angled triangle: $\quad 6^2 > 3^2 + 4^2$.

If the square of the longest side is less than the sum of the squares on the other two sides then the triangle is acute-angled; if it is more then the triangle is obtuse-angled.

Are the following triangles right-angled, acute-angled or obtuse-angled?
(a) 25 cm, 24 cm, 7 cm   (b) 4 cm, 3 cm, 2 cm   (c) 16 cm, 12 cm, 8 cm
(d) 3 cm, 3 cm, 4 cm   (e) 8 cm, 12 cm, 13 cm   (f) 1 km, 2.4 km, 2.6 km

8 The diagonals of a rhombus are 8 cm and 6 cm long. Calculate the length of its side correct to the nearest mm and check your answer with an accurate diagram.

9 For Figure 32:6 calculate:
   (a) AD correct to 1 d.p. (you will need to draw an extra line parallel to AD)
   (b) the area of the trapezium to the nearest 1 cm^2
   (c) the lengths of the diagonals in cm correct to 1 d.p.

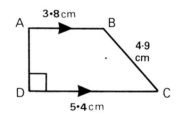

Fig. 32:6

10 For Figure 32:7
   (a) calculate BC^2 (but not BC)
   (b) calculate BD in cm correct to 1 d.p., using your answer to part (a)
   (c) check your answer to part (b) by drawing.

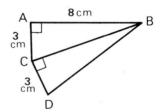

Fig. 32:7

11 Calculate x in Figure 32:8. Only find *one* square root.

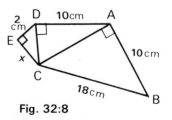

Fig. 32:8

12 For Figure 32:9 find, as square roots, the lengths *a*, *b*, *c*, *d*, and *e*.

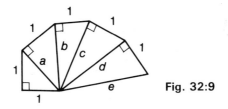

Fig. 32:9

13 One side of a right-angled isosceles triangle is 8 cm. Calculate two sets of answers for the lengths of the other two sides.

14 Calculate the distance between the points whose co-ordinates are $(-4, -2)$ and $(-6, 3)$. Leave your answer as a square root.

Now write a formula to find the distance between any two points with co-ordinates (x, y) and (X, Y).

15 (a) For Figure 32:10 show that θ is 90° if the large quadrilateral is a square.
(b) Explain how Figures 32:10 and 32:11 show that $c^2 = a^2 + b^2$.
(c) Make a moving model of this proof.

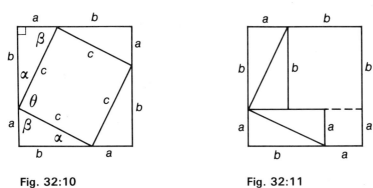

Fig. 32:10   Fig. 32:11

16 The following computer program, 'Intri', finds which right-angled triangles have integral sides, up to a shortest side of 100 units.

```
 5 REM "INTRI"                    60 FOR H = B + 1 TO A + B - 1
10 PRINT "Integral-sided right-angled    70 IF H*H > = Y THEN GOTO 90
   triangles"                     80 NEXT H
20 FOR A = 3 TO 40               90 IF H*H = Y THEN PRINT
30 LET X = A*A                       A;" ";B;" ";H
40 FOR B = A + 1 TO 100         100 NEXT B
50 LET Y = B*B + X              110 NEXT A
```

33 Algebra: problems; sequences

A Finding the number

> **Example** When you double a number and add 6 the answer is 24. Find the number.
>
> Let x be the number. Then:
>
> $$x \xrightarrow{\text{doubled}} 2x \xrightarrow{\text{6 added}} 2x + 6 \xrightarrow{\text{makes 24}} 2x + 6 = 24.$$
>
> If $2x + 6 = 24$, then $2x = 18$, giving the answer $x = 9$.

For Discussion

Find the number if:
(a) when you treble it the answer is 12
(b) when you halve it the answer is 4
(c) when you double it and add 6 the answer is 14
(d) when you halve it and add 6 the answer is 14
(e) when you double it and subtract 9 the answer is 21.

1 Write the algebraic equation and solve it to find the number if:
(a) when you double it the answer is 12
(b) when you halve it the answer is 17
(c) when you double it and add 4 the answer is 16
(d)· when you halve it and subtract 5 the answer is 19.

*2 Write an algebraic equation and solve it to find the number if:
(a) when 7 is added the answer is 12
(b) when 6 is subtracted the answer is 7
(c) when you double it and subtract 11 the answer is 1.

*3 Write an algebraic equation and solve it to find the number in each of the following.
(a) If you double a number and then take away 3 the answer is 9.
(b) If you treble a number and then add 1 the answer is 10.
(c) If you treble a number and then add 7 the answer is 28.
(d) When a number is trebled and then 6 is taken away the answer is 21.
(e) When a number is trebled and then 11 is taken away the answer is 49.
(f) If you quarter a number and then add 7 the answer is 35.
(g) If you quarter a number and then take away 9 the answer is 0.

4 Write an algebraic equation and solve it to find the number in each of the following.
  (a) When a number is doubled and the answer is taken away from 16 the final answer is 6.
  (b) When a number is trebled and the answer is taken away from 48 the final answer is 21.
  (c) When a number is halved and the answer is taken away from 12 the final answer is 9.
  (d) When a number is quartered and the answer is taken away from 21 the final answer is 16.

5 Example   The sum of two consecutive numbers is 55. Find each number.

If x is the smaller number, then the next number is $x + 1$.
So: $x + (x + 1) = 55 \rightarrow 2x + 1 = 55 \rightarrow x = 27$.

Answer: The numbers are 27 and 28.

Write an equation and solve it to find:
  (a) two consecutive numbers whose sum is 143
  (b) three consecutive numbers whose sum is 75
  (c) two consecutive *odd* numbers whose sum is 64
  (d) three consecutive *even* numbers whose sum is 132.

6 Example   Alan has £8 more than Bill, who has £2 more than Colin. Together they have £42. How much have they each?

Colin has the smallest amount; let this be £x. Then Bill has £$(x + 2)$ and Alan has £$(x + 10)$.
So: $x + (x + 2) + (x + 10) = 42 \rightarrow 3x + 12 = 42 \rightarrow x = 10$.

Answer: Colin has £10; Bill has £12; Alan has £20.

Note: By letting the *smallest* amount be x we avoided having to use minus signs, which tend to trip up unwary pupils!

  (a) David has £7 more than Enid, who has £3 more than Frank. Together they have £64. How much have they each?

  (b) Share £27 so that Dora has £2 more than Ellen, who has £2 more than Francis.

  (c) Share £70 so that A has twice as much as B, who has twice as much as C.

  (d) Mary and Joan receive the same pocket money, which is 50p less than Michael receives. If all three receive a total of £3.20 how much does each receive?

  (e) A rectangle is twice as long as it is wide. It has a perimeter of 60 metres. Find its length and breadth.

  (f) Jane is twice as old as Mike, who is two years younger than Barry. If the sum of their ages is 26 years how old are they?

7 Example Find the value of b in Figure 33:1 if the total area is 63 cm².

Area A = $3b \times b = 3b^2$; Area B = $b \times b = b^2$; Area C = $3b \times b = 3b^2$.
Total area = $3b^2 + b^2 + 3b^2 = 7b^2$.
Therefore $7b^2 = 63 \rightarrow b^2 = 9 \rightarrow b = 3$.

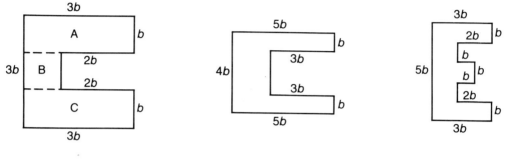

Fig. 33:1   Fig. 33:2   Fig. 33:3

Find b in:
(a) Figure 33:2 if the area is 224 cm²   (b) Figure 33:3 if the area is 810 cm².

8 The sum of two numbers (x and y) is 23. Their difference is 5. Form two equations in x and y and solve them simultaneously to find the numbers.

9 Two apple trees and one pear tree cost £13. Three apple trees and two pear trees cost £22. Use simultaneous equations to find the cost of each kind of tree.

10 Solve the equations in questions 8 and 9 graphically.

11 Some computers will give the answer 5 to the following:

```
1Ø  LET A$ = "A + 3"
2Ø  LET A = 2
3Ø  PRINT VAL(A$)      (Use EVAL on BBC)
```

If yours does give answer 5 then you can use the following program to solve an equation like $2x + 3 = 5$.

```
1Ø  PRINT "Type part of equation on left of ="
2Ø  INPUT L$
3Ø  PRINT "Type part of equation on right of ="
4Ø  INPUT R$
5Ø  FOR X = −25 to 25
6Ø  IF VAL(L$) = VAL(R$) THEN PRINT "Solution of ‸";L$;"‸ = ‸";R$;
    "‸ is ‸";X
7Ø  NEXT X
```

The program only works for an 'X' equation, and only finds the solution if X is an integer from -25 to 25. Remember that the computer will misunderstand '2X'; you must type '2*X'. The process is called 'iteration' (repeating) because the computer repeatedly tries to see if L$ = R$ for different values of X.

If your computer does not work out VAL(A$) to be 5 then you have to write the equation into the program lines:

```
1Ø  FOR X = - 25 to 25
2Ø  IF 2*X + 3 = 5 THEN PRINT "Solution is ‸";X
3Ø  NEXT X
```

B Making expressions

For Discussion

One

Example   A mother has s sons and d daughters. How many children has she?

Answer: She has $s + d$ children.

(i)   How many members in a youth club with b boys and g girls?
(ii) How much will p people collect altogether if they each collect £g?
(iii) A group of c children share p pounds equally between them. How much will one child receive? How much will be received altogether by: (a) 3 children (b) 5 children   (c) g children?

Two
Continue the sequence $1, \frac{1}{3}, \frac{1}{9}, \ldots$

1 (a) In a school there are b boys and g girls. How many pupils are there altogether?

   (b) Going from home to school a girl cycles c miles and then goes by bus for d miles. How many miles does she travel from home to school?

   (c) How far does the girl in part (b) travel altogether each day (that is, from home to school and back again)?

   (d) If I take t apples from a box of c apples how many are left?

   (e) If b boys each have s sweets, how many have they altogether?

   (f) If g girls share t sweets equally, how many will each receive?

   (g) What is the total cost of b books at p pounds each?

2 Example   Write an expression for the area
and perimeter of the rectangle in
Figure 33:4, which has a length
of *a* units and a width of *b* units.

Fig. 33:4

Answer: Area = $a \times b = ab$ square units.

Perimeter = $a + b + a + b = 2a + 2b$ units.

Copy each of the shapes in Figure 33:5, including its name, then write an expression
for its area and an expression for its perimeter.

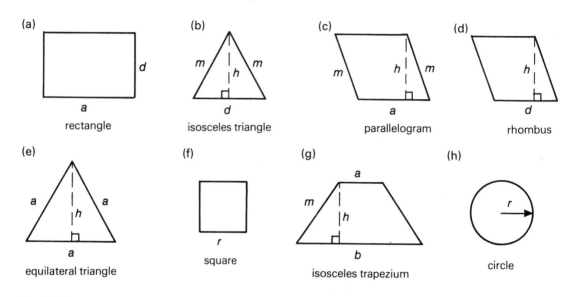

(a) rectangle   (b) isosceles triangle   (c) parallelogram   (d) rhombus

(e) equilateral triangle   (f) square   (g) isosceles trapezium   (h) circle

Fig. 33:5

*3   Using the expressions you have found in question 2, find the area and perimeter of
each figure if $a = 6.928$, $b = 21.872$, $d = 12$, $h = 8$, $m = 10$ and $r = 21$. All
measurements are in centimetres. Use the π key or take $\pi = \frac{22}{7}$.

4   How long will it take to travel *M* miles at *V* m.p.h.?

5   From a length of cloth, *c* metres long, *p* pieces are cut, each *d* centimetres long. How
much cloth is left, in centimetres?

6   Share £*t* between A and B in the ratio $x : y$.

7   A train travelling at a constant speed covers *m* km in *f* hours. How far would it travel
in *x* hours?

8 Write the three-digit number whose hundreds digit is x, tens digit is y, and units digit is z. (The answer is not xyz.)

9 A three-digit number has a units digit x, a tens digit twice that, and a hundreds digit twice the tens digit. Write an expression for the number. Also write all the numbers that it could be.

10 The cost of G gallons of milk is P pounds. If the price of G gallons is increased by x pounds how many gallons will P pounds now buy?

11 I travel for p hours at x km/h, then for q hours at y km/h. Write expressions for:
(a) my total time   (b) my total distance   (c) my average speed.

12 At what price must I sell an article if I paid x pence for y articles and wish to make $z\%$ profit?

13 Example   Write the first five terms of the sequence whose nth term is $\dfrac{n+1}{2}$.

For the 1st term, $n = 1$, giving $\dfrac{1+1}{2} = 1$

For the 2nd term, $n = 2$, giving $\dfrac{2+1}{2} = 1\frac{1}{2}$

Similarly the 3rd term is $\dfrac{3+1}{2} = 2$

the 4th term is $\dfrac{4+1}{2} = 2\frac{1}{2}$

the 5th term is $\dfrac{5+1}{2} = 3$

Find the first five terms of the sequence whose nth term is:

(a) $\dfrac{n+2}{2}$ (b) $2n-1$ (c) $n(n+1)$

(d) $n^2 - n$ (e) $\dfrac{n(n-1)}{2}$ (f) $\dfrac{n-1}{n}$

14 Find the nth term of the following sequences.
(a) 2, 4, 6, 8, 10, . . .   (b) 0, 1, 2, 3, 4, 5, . . .
(c) 1, 8, 27, 64, 125, . . .   (d) 3, 8, 15, 24, 35, . . .
(e) $\frac{1}{2}, \frac{2}{3}, \frac{3}{4}, \frac{4}{5}, \frac{5}{6},$ . . .   (f) 1, 6, 15, 28, 45, . . .

15 It costs £c to dig a tunnel n metres long, where $c = an + bn^2$. If a 3-metre tunnel costs £15 000 and a 4-metre tunnel costs £24 000, use simultaneous equations to find a and b, then find the cost of a 5-metre tunnel.

16 Prove by algebra that if the digits of a number are x, y and z, and $x + y + z$ is divisible by 9, then the number divides exactly by 9.

17 Use algebra to explain what is happening in this flow-chart.

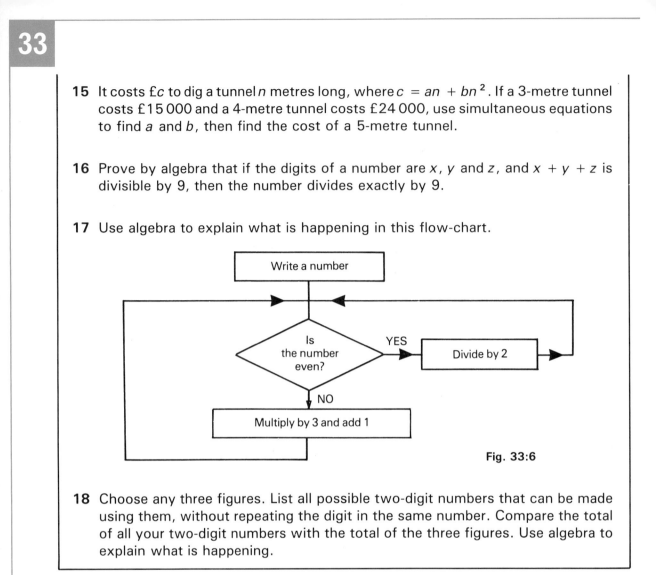

Fig. 33:6

18 Choose any three figures. List all possible two-digit numbers that can be made using them, without repeating the digit in the same number. Compare the total of all your two-digit numbers with the total of the three figures. Use algebra to explain what is happening.

Using your calculator

Volcanoes

There are about 500 active volcanoes on Earth. When they erupt they may send out rocks, poisonous gases or molten lava at 1200°C. The tallest is Lascar, in Chile, 6 km above sea level. Aniakchak in Alaska has the largest crater, 10 km in diameter.

Some volcanoes erupt rarely, but with great violence. In 1883 Krakatoa, near Java, caused a tidal wave that drowned 36 000 people and sent debris 5400 km from one side of the Indian Ocean to the other. In 1902 Mount Pelée, in the West Indies, exploded with a fireball of poisonous gas that killed 30 000 people in the first minute and 40 000 people altogether.

Other volcanoes, like Kilauea and Mauna Loa in Hawaii, erupt frequently but comparatively gently. About 100 000 earthquakes are recorded on Kilauea each year and in the past 100 years it has erupted over fifty times. Between 1969 and 1971 one continuous eruption buried 40 km² of forest.

During its life, Mauna Loa has spewed out 41 000 km³ of lava, enough to put a 30 cm layer on every country in the world, including, in 1975, enough lava to build a 5000 km motorway.

1 Mount Snowdon, in Wales, is 3560 feet high. How many times higher is Lascar? (Take 30 cm as 1 foot.)

2 How many kilometres is it round the crater of Aniakchak? $(C = \pi d)$

3 The world has a diameter of 12 740 km. What fraction of its circumference did the debris from Krakatoa travel in 1883?

4 How many times the number of pupils in your school were killed by the combined eruptions of Krakatoa in 1883 and Mount Pelée in 1902?

5 How many years would Kilauea take to notch up a million earthquakes?

6 On average Kilauea erupts every x days. What is the value of x?

7 A football pitch is 119 metres by 91 metres. How many pitches have the same area as the forest buried by Kilauea between 1969 and 1971? (1 km² = 1 000 000 m²)

8 Find the world's approximate land area in millions of km². (30 cm = 0.0003 km)

9 How long would a 5000 km journey take at an average speed of 110 km/h?

For Discussion

Figure 34:1 has **point symmetry**. The dot is the centre of symmetry. For every point on the rectangle there is a corresponding point diametrically opposite it through the centre of symmetry.

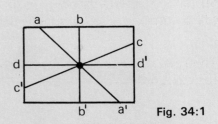

Fig. 34:1

A rectangle also has two **lines of symmetry** and **rotational symmetry** of order 2.

Figure 34:2 shows an isosceles triangle. It has one line of symmetry and rotational symmetry of order 1, but *no* point symmetry.

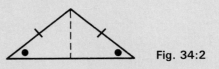

Fig. 34:2

The simplest way to recognise point symmetry is that the figure looks the same after a rotation of 180°.

1   Copy and complete this table for the Persian Carpet symbols in Figure 34:3.

Shape	(a)	(b)	(c)	(d)	(e)	(f)	(g)	(h)	(i)	(j)
Line symmetry: no. of axes										
Rotational symmetry: order										
Point symmetry: yes/no										

(a)   (b)   (c)   (d)   (e)

(f)   (g)   (h)   (i)   (j)

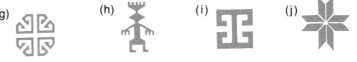

Fig. 34:3

2 State all the symmetry of:
(a) an equilateral triangle   (b) a parallelogram   (c) a rhombus
(d) a square   (e) a regular pentagon   (f) a regular hexagon.

3 The shapes in Figure 34:4 are all the possible nets for a cube. State all the symmetries for each net.

(a)   (b)   (c)   (d)   (e)   (f)   (g)   (h)   (i)   (j)   (k)

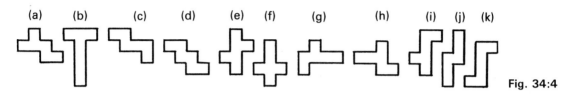

Fig. 34:4

4 Try to draw a shape with:
(a) rotational symmetry more than order 1, but no line symmetry
(b) line symmetry and rotational symmetry of order 1
(c) two lines of symmetry and order 4 rotational symmetry
(d) four lines of symmetry and order 2 rotational symmetry.

5 Figure 34:5 shows the net to be used when making the cube drawn in Figure 34:6. Copy the net and complete it so that when folded up it will look like Figure 34:6. Repeat for the other possible cube nets.

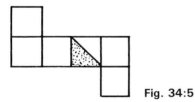

Fig. 34:5

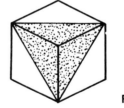

Fig. 34:6

6 A tetrahedron is a solid with four equilateral triangular faces. Draw different nets for it, checking each one by making the solid.

7 What shapes are metal nuts? Why? Investigate other possibilities. Investigate the spanners used. Write about your findings, with suitable illustrations, diagrams and tables.

8 Find five ways to cut along the lines of Figure 34:7 so that the square is divided into two identical pieces. Each way must be completely different, not just a reflection or a rotation of another way.

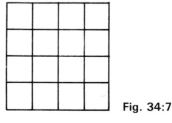

Fig. 34:7

9 Frame a square of 49 squares and cut out 25 card rectangles, each the size of two squares. Two players take it in turns to lay a piece on the board to cover two squares. The winner is the last who can lay a piece.

If you find this too easy you could try it with a 169-squares board!

10 One for the summer holiday! Develop question 9 into a computer game. Not too difficult if two people play, but how about getting the computer to play against you?

Project

Using tables

Introduction

Before the days of calculators, mathematicians used books of tables to make arithmetic easier. Books of four-figure tables were the most often used; they gave only the first four figures of an answer, and even then the last figure was not reliable; you can see that your calculator is much more accurate as well as much easier to use. This project will give you a chance to find out how the tables were read.

Part One Reading four-figure tables

	0	1		7	8	9	Mean differences			
							1	2	3	4
1.5	2.250	2.280		2.465	2.496	2.528	3	6	9	12

This is part of a table of squares.

$(1.58)^2$ is given as 2.496.

To find $(1.583)^2$ you look along the row to the mean difference column headed 3, then add the figure 9 given on this row to the 2.496 for $(1.58)^2$, giving $(1.583)^2 = 2.505$. Similarly $(1.504)^2$ is given as 2.262, by adding 12 to the end of 2.250.

Numbers bigger than 9.999 can be found by ignoring the decimal points in the table and adjusting the size of the answer to agree with your estimation of it.

For instance, to find 151.1^2, read the figures for 1.511^2 from the table, giving 2283.

151.1^2 lies between 100^2 and 200^2, that is between 10 000 and 40 000, so the table gives us an answer of 22 830.

Write down some numbers; find their squares as given by a table of squares and compare them with the answers given by your calculator.

Part Two Using square-root tables

You will find two sets of square-root tables in a table book. Two are needed because the same figures can give two different answers depending on their place value.

For instance, $\sqrt{4.2}$ is 2.049 but $\sqrt{42}$ is 6.481.

Numbers bigger than 99 are found, as with squares, by using the figures given in the table, but adjusting their place value according to your estimation. (It is often easier to estimate from the answers rather than the question.)

For example, to find $\sqrt{4238}$, the figures will either be 2.059 (from 4.238) or 6.510 (from 42.38).

2.059 gives about 2, or 20, or 200 etc. None of these square to give anything like 4238.

6.510 gives about 6 or 60 or 600 etc., and 60^2 gives 3600, which is near to 4238. Hence the table gives $\sqrt{4238}$ as 65.10.

Write down some numbers, find their square roots as given by the table book, then compare your answers with those given by the calculator.

Part Three Square roots from a graph

Using a large piece of graph paper, preferably one with 1 mm squares, draw a graph of $y = x^2$ for values of x from 0 to 10, taking x at 0.25 intervals. (You should use a calculator.) Take y from 0 to 100, using the largest possible scale. Work out how to read $\sqrt{16}$ on your graph, then use it for other numbers.

Part Four Square roots the old way!

Find $\sqrt{686.44}$

Step 1 Divide the number in pairs each side of the point.

Step 2 Write above the first block the nearest square root of the number in that block (its square being less than the number). In our example it will be a 2.

Subtract the square of this number from the number in the block.

Bring down the next block.

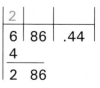

Step 3 Double the top number and write the answer in front. Find the biggest figure which can be put after the number you have just written which multiplies the number so formed to give less than the result of Step 2.

In our example we end up with 4_6, for $4_6 \times 6 = 276$, while 47×7 gives 329, which is bigger than 286.

```
        2 |      |
      6 | 86 | .44 |
      4
  46  | 2  86
```

Step 4 Write the figure used in Step 3 above the block.

Subtract the product (here $46 \times 6 = 276$).

Bring down the next block.

```
        2 |  6   |
      6 | 86 | .44 |
      4
  46  | 2  86
      | 2  76 —
      |   10   .44
```

Step 5 Repeat Step 3.

In our example, $26 \times 2 = 52$.

Try 521×1; 522×2; 523×3, which is too big.

```
        2 |  6   |
      6 | 86 | .44 |
      4
  46  | 2  86
      | 2  76
 52₂  |   10   .44
```

Step 6 Repeat Step 4, then Step 3, etc. until the remainder is 0 (or until bored!).

As with long division, extra 0s may be written after the point for as long as necessary.

In our example the answer comes to exactly 26.2

Here is another one to follow, then try some of your own.

Find $\sqrt{8916}$ correct to 2 decimal places.

```
        2 |  6  | .2
      6 | 86 | .44 |
      4
  46  | 2  86
      | 2  76
 522  |   10   44
      |   10   44 —
      |         0
```

```
         9 | 4 . 4 | 2
       89 | 16 | .00 | 00
       81 —
   18₄ | 8  16
       | 7  36 —
  188₄ |    80  00
       |    75  36 —
 1888₂ |     4  64  00
       |     3  77  64 —
                etc.
```

162

A Review; multiplication by a constant

Example $X = \begin{pmatrix} 2 & 1 & -1 \\ 3 & -4 & 0 \end{pmatrix}$ $Y = \begin{pmatrix} 4 & 1 & -5 \\ -6 & 3 & -4 \end{pmatrix}$ $Z = \begin{pmatrix} -1 \\ -2 \end{pmatrix}$

$X + Y = \begin{pmatrix} 6 & 2 & -6 \\ -3 & -1 & -4 \end{pmatrix}$ $X - Y = \begin{pmatrix} -2 & 0 & 4 \\ 9 & -7 & 4 \end{pmatrix}$

Z cannot be combined with X or Y by addition or subtraction because of its different order; X and Y are 2 by 3 matrices; Z is a 2 by 1 matrix.

All matrices may be multiplied by a constant.

$2X = \begin{pmatrix} 4 & 2 & -2 \\ 6 & -8 & 0 \end{pmatrix}$ $\frac{1}{2}Z = \begin{pmatrix} -\frac{1}{2} \\ -1 \end{pmatrix}$

1 $A = \begin{pmatrix} 2 & 3 & 1 \\ -2 & 1 & 4 \end{pmatrix}$ $B = \begin{pmatrix} 1 & -2 \\ 0 & 2 \\ 3 & 0 \end{pmatrix}$ $C = (1 \ 4 \ 3)$ $D = \begin{pmatrix} 4 & 1 & -3 \\ 0 & 2 & 0 \end{pmatrix}$ $E = \begin{pmatrix} -3 \\ 1 \\ 2 \end{pmatrix}$

$F = \begin{pmatrix} 2 & -2 \\ 0 & 1 \end{pmatrix}$ $G = \begin{pmatrix} 2 & -3 \\ 4 & 3 \end{pmatrix}$ $H = \begin{pmatrix} 2 \\ 0 \\ -1 \end{pmatrix}$ $I = (-2 \ 3 \ 4)$ $J = \begin{pmatrix} 2 & 1 & 3 \\ -2 & 0 & 2 \end{pmatrix}$

Find, if possible:
(a) A + B   (b) A + D   (c) A + I   (d) A + J   (e) B + D   (f) F + G
(g) F + J   (h) A − B   (i) A − D   (j) D − A   (k) C − I   (l) J − A
(m) E − H   (n) C − E.

*2 Find:

(a) $4\begin{pmatrix} \frac{1}{4} & \frac{1}{2} & 1 \\ 2 & 0 & \frac{3}{4} \end{pmatrix}$ (b) $5\begin{pmatrix} 0 & \frac{1}{5} & -1 \\ \frac{2}{5} & 2 & 1 \end{pmatrix}$ (c) $4\begin{pmatrix} -\frac{1}{2} & 1 & -2 \\ 0 & -\frac{1}{4} & -1 \end{pmatrix}$ (d) $8\begin{pmatrix} -\frac{1}{2} & -4 & \frac{1}{4} \\ 2 & -\frac{3}{4} & 0 \end{pmatrix}$

(e) $2\begin{pmatrix} -1.2 & 3.4 & -1.4 \\ 0.5 & 6.1 & -3.2 \end{pmatrix}$ (f) $10\begin{pmatrix} 0.04 & 0.3 & 0.5 \\ 3.04 & 4.6 & 0.4 \end{pmatrix}$.

3 Find:

(a) $\frac{1}{2}\begin{pmatrix} -6 & 7 & 5 \\ -9 & 3 & 2 \end{pmatrix}$ (b) $0.25\begin{pmatrix} 4 & 3 & -8 \\ 6 & 7 & 0 \end{pmatrix}$ (c) $0.75\begin{pmatrix} 8 & 6 & -4 \\ 2 & 0 & 1 \end{pmatrix}$

(d) $-6\begin{pmatrix} -4 & -3 & 0 \\ 2 & 1 & -2 \end{pmatrix}$ (e) $-\frac{1}{2}\begin{pmatrix} -4 & 8 & -6 \\ 0 & -1 & 1 \end{pmatrix}$ (f) $-\frac{1}{4}\begin{pmatrix} 8 & -6 & 5 \\ -7 & 2 & 3 \end{pmatrix}$.

4 $A = \begin{pmatrix} 2 & 3 \\ -1 & 2 \end{pmatrix}$ $\qquad B = \begin{pmatrix} 4 & -3 \\ -2 & 0 \end{pmatrix}$ $\qquad C = \begin{pmatrix} 2 & -1 \\ -3 & 2 \end{pmatrix}$

Find:
(a) $2B + C$ (b) $3(A + B)$ (c) $3A + 3B$ (d) $4(A - B)$
(e) $2(A + B - C)$.

B   Multiplication of a column matrix

For Discussion

	Winners	Runners-up
Team A	4	7
Team B	6	4

Points
$$\begin{array}{l} \text{Winners} \\ \text{Runners-up} \end{array} \begin{pmatrix} 3 \\ 1 \end{pmatrix}$$

Total points:
$$\begin{array}{l} \text{Team A} \\ \text{Team B} \end{array} \begin{pmatrix} 4 & 7 \\ 6 & 4 \end{pmatrix} \begin{pmatrix} 3 \\ 1 \end{pmatrix} \rightarrow \begin{pmatrix} 4 \times 3 + 7 \times 1 \\ 6 \times 3 + 4 \times 1 \end{pmatrix} = \begin{pmatrix} 19 \\ 22 \end{pmatrix}$$

1 Using the same points score as in the For Discussion, find the total points for each of the following teams:

(a) $\begin{array}{l} \text{Team E} \\ \text{Team F} \end{array} \begin{pmatrix} 7 & 5 \\ 4 & 8 \end{pmatrix}$ (b) $\begin{array}{l} \text{Team G} \\ \text{Team H} \end{array} \begin{pmatrix} 8 & 3 \\ 7 & 4 \end{pmatrix}$ (c) $\begin{array}{l} \text{Team J} \\ \text{Team K} \end{array} \begin{pmatrix} 7 & 6 \\ 5 & 8 \end{pmatrix}$

2 Multiply:

(a) $\begin{pmatrix} 4 & 5 \\ 6 & 2 \end{pmatrix} \begin{pmatrix} 4 \\ 2 \end{pmatrix}$ (b) $\begin{pmatrix} 5 & 0 \\ 8 & 6 \end{pmatrix} \begin{pmatrix} 4 \\ 1 \end{pmatrix}$ (c) $\begin{pmatrix} 6 & 3 \\ 4 & 5 \end{pmatrix} \begin{pmatrix} 2 \\ 1 \end{pmatrix}$ (d) $\begin{pmatrix} 4 & 5 \\ 3 & 0 \end{pmatrix} \begin{pmatrix} 0 \\ 4 \end{pmatrix}$

*3 Multiply:

(a) $\begin{pmatrix} 3 & 1 \\ 4 & 2 \end{pmatrix} \begin{pmatrix} 2 \\ 0 \end{pmatrix}$ (b) $\begin{pmatrix} 1 & 2 \\ 0 & 6 \end{pmatrix} \begin{pmatrix} 1 \\ 0 \end{pmatrix}$ (c) $\begin{pmatrix} 3 & 1 \\ 2 & 2 \end{pmatrix} \begin{pmatrix} 3 \\ 2 \end{pmatrix}$ (d) $\begin{pmatrix} 4 & 5 \\ 5 & 4 \end{pmatrix} \begin{pmatrix} 0 \\ 1 \end{pmatrix}$

(e) $\begin{pmatrix} 5 & 8 \\ 3 & 7 \end{pmatrix} \begin{pmatrix} 7 \\ 8 \end{pmatrix}$ (f) $\begin{pmatrix} 8 & 6 \\ 6 & 7 \end{pmatrix} \begin{pmatrix} 5 \\ 7 \end{pmatrix}$ (g) $\begin{pmatrix} 5 & 8 \\ 8 & 8 \end{pmatrix} \begin{pmatrix} 7 \\ 6 \end{pmatrix}$ (h) $\begin{pmatrix} 6 & 6 \\ 7 & 8 \end{pmatrix} \begin{pmatrix} 9 \\ 8 \end{pmatrix}$

4 Multiply:

(a) $\begin{pmatrix} -4 & 3 \\ 2 & 6 \end{pmatrix} \begin{pmatrix} -4 \\ 2 \end{pmatrix}$ (b) $\begin{pmatrix} -1 & -3 \\ 2 & -4 \end{pmatrix} \begin{pmatrix} 4 \\ 1 \end{pmatrix}$ (c) $\begin{pmatrix} -5 & 3 \\ 0 & 3 \end{pmatrix} \begin{pmatrix} -4 \\ 2 \end{pmatrix}$ (d) $\begin{pmatrix} -6 & -1 \\ 3 & 4 \end{pmatrix} \begin{pmatrix} -4 \\ -2 \end{pmatrix}$

5 Multiply:

(a) $\begin{pmatrix} 5 & -1 & 3 \\ 6 & 2 & -4 \end{pmatrix} \begin{pmatrix} 5 \\ -4 \\ 3 \end{pmatrix}$ (b) $\begin{pmatrix} 1 & -4 & 7 \\ -2 & 1 & -5 \\ 6 & 1 & -4 \end{pmatrix} \begin{pmatrix} 2 \\ 1 \\ 0 \end{pmatrix}$ (c) $\begin{pmatrix} -8 & 6 & -7 \\ 1 & -2 & 1 \\ 4 & -5 & 0 \end{pmatrix} \begin{pmatrix} -2 \\ 1 \\ -4 \end{pmatrix}$

6 Find the values of the letters if:

(a) $3\begin{pmatrix} a & b \\ c & d \end{pmatrix} = \begin{pmatrix} 6 & 12 \\ -9 & 0 \end{pmatrix}$ (b) $k\begin{pmatrix} 4 & 2 \\ 0 & -2 \end{pmatrix} = \begin{pmatrix} 12 & 6 \\ 0 & -6 \end{pmatrix}$

(c) $k\begin{pmatrix} 6 & 8 \\ 0 & 4 \end{pmatrix} = \begin{pmatrix} 9 & 12 \\ 0 & 6 \end{pmatrix}$ (d) $4\begin{pmatrix} a & b \\ c & d \end{pmatrix} = \begin{pmatrix} 7 & 9 \\ -6 & 2 \end{pmatrix}$

(e) $a\begin{pmatrix} a & 2a \\ 2b & -3a \end{pmatrix} = \begin{pmatrix} 16 & c \\ 64 & 2d \end{pmatrix}$ (f) $-\frac{1}{2}\begin{pmatrix} a & b \\ c & d \end{pmatrix} = \begin{pmatrix} \frac{1}{8} & -\frac{1}{4} \\ \frac{1}{3} & -\frac{1}{5} \end{pmatrix}$

(g) $\begin{pmatrix} a & 3 \\ 2 & b \end{pmatrix}\begin{pmatrix} 1 \\ 2 \end{pmatrix} = \begin{pmatrix} 8 \\ 8 \end{pmatrix}$ (h) $\begin{pmatrix} s & t \\ s & 2 \end{pmatrix}\begin{pmatrix} 1 \\ 2 \end{pmatrix} = \begin{pmatrix} 11 \\ 6 \end{pmatrix}$ (i) $\begin{pmatrix} u & u \\ v & 1 \end{pmatrix}\begin{pmatrix} 3 \\ 1 \end{pmatrix} = \begin{pmatrix} 20 \\ 0 \end{pmatrix}$

C Multiplication by a row matrix

For Discussion

Cost		Number bought		Total cost	
Bites	Chews	John	Raj	John	Raj
(9p	10p)			(66p	58p)

$$\begin{pmatrix} 4 & 2 \\ 3 & 4 \end{pmatrix} =$$

Example $(2 \ -4)\begin{pmatrix} 3 & 2 \\ 1 & -1 \end{pmatrix} = (2 \times 3 + -4 \times 1 \qquad 2 \times 2 + -4 \times -1)$

$$= (6 + -4 \qquad 4 + 4) = (2 \ 8)$$

1 Multiply:

(a) $(1 \ 2)\begin{pmatrix} 3 & 1 \\ 2 & 1 \end{pmatrix}$ (b) $(2 \ 3)\begin{pmatrix} 0 & 1 \\ 2 & 2 \end{pmatrix}$ (c) $(1 \ 2)\begin{pmatrix} 2 & 3 \\ 0 & 1 \end{pmatrix}$

*2 Multiply:

(a) $(2 \ 4)\begin{pmatrix} 4 & 3 \\ 2 & 3 \end{pmatrix}$ (b) $(3 \ 3)\begin{pmatrix} 5 & 1 \\ 0 & 0 \end{pmatrix}$ (c) $(5 \ 6)\begin{pmatrix} 4 & 1 \\ 2 & 2 \end{pmatrix}$ (d) $(3 \ 6)\begin{pmatrix} 7 & 8 \\ 2 & 0 \end{pmatrix}$

3 Multiply:

(a) $(3 \ -3)\begin{pmatrix} 4 & -2 \\ 3 & 4 \end{pmatrix}$ (b) $(-6 \ 4)\begin{pmatrix} -5 & 4 \\ 3 & -2 \end{pmatrix}$ (c) $(2 \ 6)\begin{pmatrix} 3.5 & 2.7 \\ -0.6 & 0.4 \end{pmatrix}$

4 Multiply:

(a) $(2 \ -1)\begin{pmatrix} 1.5 & -1.2 \\ -2.1 & 4.1 \end{pmatrix}$ (b) $(2.5 \ 1.1)\begin{pmatrix} 4 & 8 \\ 6 & 3 \end{pmatrix}$ (c) $(2 \ 2)\begin{pmatrix} \frac{1}{2} & -\frac{1}{4} \\ 2 & 8 \end{pmatrix}$

5 Multiply:

(a) $(4 \quad 6)\begin{pmatrix} \frac{1}{2} & \frac{3}{4} \\ \frac{1}{3} & -\frac{2}{3} \end{pmatrix}$

(b) $(\frac{1}{2} \quad -\frac{1}{4})\begin{pmatrix} 6 & 10 \\ 8 & 16 \end{pmatrix}$

(c) $(3 \quad 4)\begin{pmatrix} \frac{1}{2} & 2 \\ -\frac{1}{4} & -\frac{3}{8} \end{pmatrix}$

6 State the value of the letters if:

(a) $(-2 \quad 3)\begin{pmatrix} m & 3 \\ -2 & n \end{pmatrix} = (-14 \quad 9)$

(b) $(m \quad 2)\begin{pmatrix} -4 & n \\ -6 & 5 \end{pmatrix} = (0 \quad 1)$

(c) $(2 \quad p \quad 3)\begin{pmatrix} -1 & q & -4 \\ 2 & -5 & r \\ -4 & 6 & 2 \end{pmatrix} = (-22 \quad 44 \quad -14)$

(d) $(p \quad 3 \quad -2)\begin{pmatrix} 1 & 5 & r \\ -8 & q & r \\ -4 & -2 & r \end{pmatrix} = (-16 \quad 1 \quad 16)$

(e) $(a \quad b \quad c)\begin{pmatrix} a & b & b \\ c & a & c \\ b & b & b \end{pmatrix} = (2bc \quad b \quad 4c)$

A   The universal set

The symbol ξ is used for the universal set. The universal set contains all the elements to be used in a particular question.

ξ is shown on a Venn diagram as a rectangle.

Example   ξ = {integers from 1 to 9}
A = {odd numbers}
B = {multiples of 4}
P = {prime numbers}

(a) Remembering that only elements in the universal set may be used, we can list sets A, B and P:
A = {1, 3, 5, 7, 9};   B = {4, 8};   P = {2, 3, 5, 7}

(b) A and B are disjoint sets.
A∩B = { } or ∅
n(A∩B) = 0
A∪B = {1, 3, 5, 7, 9, 4, 8}
n(A∪B) = 7

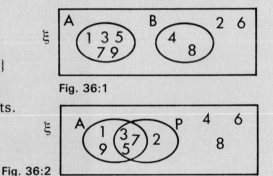

Fig. 36:1

(c) A and P are intersecting sets.
A∩P = {3, 5, 7}
A∪P = {1, 9, 3, 5, 7, 2}

Fig. 36:2

---

1 ξ = {integers from 1 to 10}
A = {multiples of 3}
B = {multiples of 5}
C = {multiples of 2}

(a) List sets A, B and C.

(b) Copy the four true statements from:
{3, 5} ⊂ A;   5 ∈ B;   {2, 4, 6} ⊂ C;   4 ∉ A;   21 ∈ ξ;   18 ∈ C;   {3, 6, 18} ⊄ A;
{5, 10, 15} = B.

2 Using the sets in question 1, draw Venn diagrams to show:
(a) ξ and A   (b) ξ, A and B   (c) ξ, B and C.

3 Use the Venn diagrams drawn in question 2 to list:
(a) B∩C   (b) B∪C   (c) A∩B.

4 ξ = {integers from 1 to 24}

List:
T = {triangular numbers};   S = {square numbers};   P = {prime numbers};
F = {factors of 24}.

5 ξ = {integers};   X = {$x: 3 \leqslant x \leqslant 7$};   Y = {$y: 6 < y < 9$}

(a) List:
   (i) $X \cap Y$ (ii) $X \cup Y$ (iii) $\xi \cap X$.

(b) Explain why you cannot list $\xi \cup X$.

6 ξ = {passengers on a bus};   W = {people going to work};   M = {males};
F = {females}

Write what you know about these people if:
(a) $n(\xi) = 24$ (b) $n(\xi \cap W) = 16$ (c) $F \cap W = \varnothing$ (d) $M \cup W = W$.

7 ξ = {pupils in 3G};   G = {girls};   L = {left-handed pupils};
H = {hockey players}

(a) Write a description of the pupils in:
   (i) $G \cap L$ (ii) $G \cup L$ (iii) $G \cap L \cap H$ (iv) $(G \cup L) \cap H$.

(b) What do you know if:
   (i) $G \supset H$ (ii) $L \not\subset G$?

B Complement

A' is the symbol for the complement of set A.

The complement of set A is the set of all the elements of ξ which are not in A.

In Figure 36:3 set A is black and set A' is green.

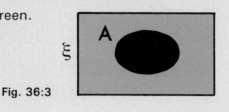

Fig. 36:3

1 For the sets drawn in Figure 36:4 list:
   (a) A   (b) A'   (c) B'   (d) C'   (e) D'   (f) E'   (g) F   (h) F'.

Fig. 36:4

2 For the sets drawn in Figure 36:4 list:
   (a) A∩B   (b) (A∩B)'   (c) A∪B   (d) (A∪B)'   (e) E∩F
   (f) (E∩F)'.

*3 $\xi = \{c, d, e, f\}$;   A = $\{c, d\}$;   B = $\{c, f\}$;   C = $\{e, f\}$

   List:
   (a) A'   (b) B'   (c) C'   (d) A∪B   (e) (A∪B)'   (f) B∩C
   (g) (B∩C)'   (h) A∩C   (i) (A∩C)'.

*4 Using the sets given in question 3 draw Venn diagrams to show:
   (a) ξ and A   (b) ξ and A and B   (c) ξ and A and C.

5 ξ = {males};   B = {burglars};   S = {successful people};
   P = {members of the police-force};   H = {happy people}

   Write a full description of the following
   people. Be careful to write *everything* that you
   know about them.

   (a) B'   (b) S'   (c) P'   (d) H'
   (e) H∩B   (f) H'∩B   (g) H∩P

6 P and Q are intersecting sets. Draw nine small Venn diagrams showing ξ, P and Q. Shade one of the following areas on each diagram:
(a) P∪Q′   (b) P′∩Q   (c) P′∪Q   (d) P′∪Q′   (e) P′∩Q′
(f) P∩Q′   (g) Q′∩Q   (h) (P∪Q)′   (i) (P∩Q)′.

7 Find two pairs in question 6 that are equal. Try to explain why they must be equal.

C   Set problems

Venn diagrams are often used to show the number of elements in a set, instead of the elements themselves. It is best to label the sets with the n( ) notation to make this clear.

Figure 36:5 illustrates the sets ξ = {1, 2, 3}; B = {1, 2}; C = {2, 3}. What does the 0 show?

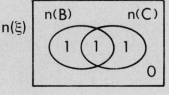

Fig. 36:5

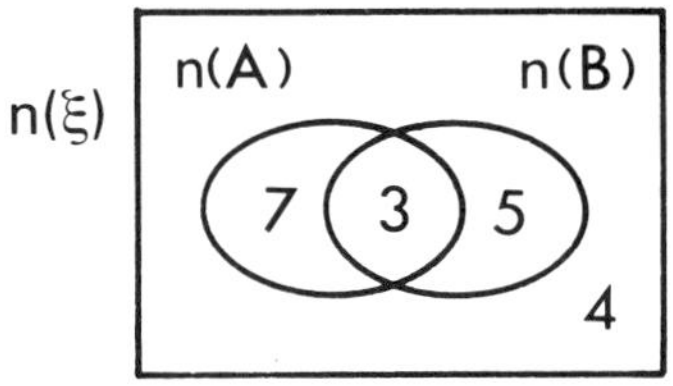

1 In Figure 36:6 what is:
(a) n(ξ)   (b) n(A)   (c) n(B)
(d) n(A∩B)   (e) n(A∪B)   (f) n(A′)
(g) n(B′)   (h) n(A∪B)′   (i) n(A∩B)′?

Fig. 36:6

2 Draw Venn diagrams to show the number of elements in the given sets if:
(a) n(ξ) = 10;   n(A) = 8;   n(B) = 6;   n(A∩B) = 4
(b) n(ξ) = 9;   n(C) = 6;   n(D) = 7;   n(C∩D) = 4
(c) n(ξ) = 20;   n(E) = 10;   n(F) = 14;   n(E∩F) = 7
(d) n(ξ) = 12;   n(G) = 10;   n(H) = 4;   n(G∪H) = 12
(e) n(ξ) = 25;   n(I) = 14;   n(J) = 6;   n(I∪J) = 19
(f) n(ξ) = 30;   n(K) = 24;   n(L) = 18;   n(K∪L) = 27.

*3 Figure 36:7 illustrates the sets:
ξ = {pupils in a classroom}
B = {pupils wearing a blazer}
G = {pupils wearing glasses}

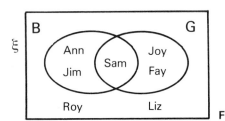

Fig. 36:7

Name the pupils:
(a) with a blazer
(b) with both blazer and glasses
(c) without blazers
(d) with a blazer or glasses or both
(e) with neither a blazer nor glasses
(f) with a blazer but not glasses
(g) with glasses but not a blazer
(h) with a blazer or glasses but not both.

*4 Choosing your answers from question 3(a) to (h), describe:
(i) B′   (ii) B∩G   (iii) B∪G   (iv) (B∪G)′.

5 Of eleven players in a team, seven like to play as forwards and six like to play as backs. Draw a Venn diagram to illustrate this.

6 Of 30 pupils, 17 like English, 12 like history and 6 like neither of these.
(a) Draw a Venn diagram to illustrate this.
(b) How many like only history?

7 A vet inspects 18 dogs. He finds that two have fleas and five have canker, while one poor thing has both. How many have neither?

8 Of 25 teachers' cars, 5 have L-plates, 12 have GB-plates and 12 have neither. How many have an L-plate but not a GB-plate?

9 Decide if the following sets are intersecting, disjoint or have one as a subset of the other, then draw a Venn diagram to illustrate them.

In each case $n(\xi) = 12$.

(a) $n(X) = 7$; $n(Y) = 4$; $n(X \cup Y) = 11$
(b) $n(X) = 8$; $n(Y) = 3$; $n(X \cup Y) = 10$
(c) $n(X) = 4$; $n(Y) = 6$; $n(X \cap Y) = 4$
(d) $n(X) = 5$; $n(Y) = 7$; $n(X \cap Y) = 4$
(e) $n(X) = 8$; $n(Y) = 2$; $n(X \cap Y) = 2$
(f) $n(X) = 5$; $n(Y) = 5$; $n(X \cup Y) = 10$

10 By shading Venn diagrams show that:
(a) $A \cup A' = \xi$ (b) $(A \cup B)' = A' \cap B'$ (c) $(A \cap B)' = A' \cup B'$.

Project

Solid symmetry

Planes of symmetry (reflection symmetry)

1 A plane of symmetry in a solid acts as a mirror. The drawings show two of the five planes of symmetry of a cuboid. Draw sketches of the other three.

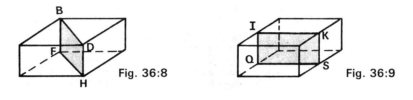

Fig. 36:8   Fig. 36:9

Axes of symmetry (rotational symmetry)

2 An axis of symmetry is a line about which a solid turns so that it fits back into a mould of itself at least once before returning to its starting position. The drawing shows one of the five axes of symmetry of a cuboid. Draw sketches of the other four.

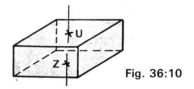

Fig. 36:10

Symmetry number

The symmetry number of a solid is the number of ways that it can be put into a mould of itself. A cuboid has symmetry number 8. Use a cuboid to demonstrate all eight ways.

Investigate the symmetries of:

(a) a cube   (b) a regular tetrahedron   (c) a cuboid of square cross-section

(d) a prism of equilateral triangle cross-section   (e) a regular hexagonal prism.

Example   Multiply $\begin{pmatrix} 2 & 4 \\ 3 & 5 \end{pmatrix}\begin{pmatrix} 5 & 2 \\ 6 & 1 \end{pmatrix}$

Each row of the first matrix multiplies each column of the second matrix in turn. The answers are placed where a line through the row crosses a line down the column.

$$\begin{pmatrix} 2 & 4 \\ 3 & 5 \end{pmatrix}\begin{pmatrix} 5 & 2 \\ 6 & 1 \end{pmatrix} = \begin{pmatrix} (2 \times 5) + (4 \times 6) & (2 \times 2) + (4 \times 1) \\ (3 \times 5) + (5 \times 6) & (3 \times 2) + (5 \times 1) \end{pmatrix} = \begin{pmatrix} 34 & 8 \\ 45 & 11 \end{pmatrix}$$

Note: If A is one matrix and B another, AB is read as 'B multiplied by A', not as 'A multiplied by B'. For most matrices AB gives a different answer to BA. We say that matrix multiplication is not commutative.

1 Multiply:

(a) $\begin{pmatrix} 2 & 3 \\ 1 & 4 \end{pmatrix}\begin{pmatrix} 3 & 2 \\ 1 & 1 \end{pmatrix}$
   (b) $\begin{pmatrix} 4 & 3 \\ 2 & 1 \end{pmatrix}\begin{pmatrix} 2 & 1 \\ 1 & 2 \end{pmatrix}$
   (c) $\begin{pmatrix} 2 & 2 \\ 0 & 4 \end{pmatrix}\begin{pmatrix} 3 & 1 \\ 4 & 0 \end{pmatrix}$

(d) $\begin{pmatrix} 2 & 3 \\ 2 & 1 \end{pmatrix}\begin{pmatrix} 3 & 1 \\ 2 & 1 \end{pmatrix}$
   (e) $\begin{pmatrix} 3 & 1 \\ 4 & 2 \end{pmatrix}\begin{pmatrix} 1 & 2 \\ 0 & 3 \end{pmatrix}$
   (f) $\begin{pmatrix} 2 & 1 \\ 3 & 2 \end{pmatrix}\begin{pmatrix} 2 & 1 \\ 3 & 2 \end{pmatrix}$

For questions 2 to 7 use the following matrices:

$A = \begin{pmatrix} 2 & 1 \\ 2 & 3 \end{pmatrix};$ $B = \begin{pmatrix} 2 & 1 \\ 1 & 2 \end{pmatrix};$ $C = \begin{pmatrix} 1 & 0 \\ 0 & 1 \end{pmatrix};$ $D = \begin{pmatrix} 4 & 1 \\ 2 & 2 \end{pmatrix};$

$E = \begin{pmatrix} -2 & 1 \\ 2 & -3 \end{pmatrix};$ $F = \begin{pmatrix} 1 & -4 \\ -2 & 0 \end{pmatrix};$ $G = \begin{pmatrix} -2 & 0 \\ 0 & -2 \end{pmatrix}$

2 Example   BA $\rightarrow \begin{pmatrix} 2 & 1 \\ 1 & 2 \end{pmatrix}\begin{pmatrix} 2 & 1 \\ 2 & 3 \end{pmatrix} = \begin{pmatrix} 6 & 5 \\ 6 & 7 \end{pmatrix}$

Find: (a) AB   (b) AC   (c) CA   (d) BC   (e) CB.

*3 Find: (a) AD   (b) DA   (c) BD   (d) DB   (e) CD   (f) DC.

*4 Find: (a) A²   (b) B²   (c) C²   (d) D².

5 Find: (a) AE   (b) EA   (c) AF   (d) FA   (e) AG
(f)   A multiplied by G.

6 Find: (a) EF   (b) FE   (c) G multiplied by E   (d) E multiplied by G
(e)   G multiplied by F   (f)   F multiplied by G.

7 Find: (a) E²   (b) F²   (c) G².

8 Example $\begin{pmatrix} 2 & 3 \\ 1 & 5 \end{pmatrix}\begin{pmatrix} x & 0 \\ 0 & y \end{pmatrix} = \begin{pmatrix} 2x & 3y \\ x & 5y \end{pmatrix}$

Find:

(a) $\begin{pmatrix} 3 & 4 \\ 2 & 5 \end{pmatrix}\begin{pmatrix} a & 0 \\ 0 & b \end{pmatrix}$ (b) $\begin{pmatrix} 2 & 4 \\ 1 & 5 \end{pmatrix}\begin{pmatrix} 0 & d \\ c & 0 \end{pmatrix}$ (c) $\begin{pmatrix} e & 0 \\ 0 & f \end{pmatrix}\begin{pmatrix} 3 & 4 \\ 2 & 5 \end{pmatrix}$

9 Find the value of each letter if:

(a) $\begin{pmatrix} 3 & 4 \\ 2 & 5 \end{pmatrix}\begin{pmatrix} m & 0 \\ 0 & n \end{pmatrix} = \begin{pmatrix} 9 & 8 \\ p & q \end{pmatrix}$ (b) $\begin{pmatrix} 3 & 5 \\ 2 & 3 \end{pmatrix}\begin{pmatrix} p & 0 \\ 0 & q \end{pmatrix} = \begin{pmatrix} r & 10 \\ 8 & s \end{pmatrix}$

(c) $\begin{pmatrix} 2 & 4 \\ 3 & 5 \end{pmatrix}\begin{pmatrix} 0 & c \\ b & 0 \end{pmatrix} = \begin{pmatrix} 8 & f \\ e & -6 \end{pmatrix}$ (d) $\begin{pmatrix} 2 & 3 \\ 4 & 5 \end{pmatrix}\begin{pmatrix} a & 2 \\ 3 & c \end{pmatrix} = \begin{pmatrix} 15 & 16 \\ b & d \end{pmatrix}$

(e) $\begin{pmatrix} 3 & 2 \\ -4 & 2 \end{pmatrix}\begin{pmatrix} a & 3 \\ a & b \end{pmatrix} = \begin{pmatrix} -10 & 3 \\ 4 & c \end{pmatrix}$ (f) $\begin{pmatrix} 3 & 2 \\ 1 & a \end{pmatrix}\begin{pmatrix} a & c \\ a & c \end{pmatrix} = \begin{pmatrix} 5 & 0 \\ b & d \end{pmatrix}$

---

10 (a) Matrix M = $\begin{pmatrix} 2 & 4 & 4 \\ 3 & 3 & 2 \end{pmatrix}$ can be shown on a graph by using each column as a pair of co-ordinates, i.e. (2, 3), (4, 3) and (4, 2).

Using axes from -4 to 4 each, plot and join these co-ordinates.

(b) If A = $\begin{pmatrix} -1 & 0 \\ 0 & -1 \end{pmatrix}$ then

$\begin{pmatrix} -1 & 0 \\ 0 & -1 \end{pmatrix}\begin{pmatrix} 2 & 4 & 4 \\ 3 & 3 & 2 \end{pmatrix} = \begin{pmatrix} -2 & -4 & -4 \\ -3 & -3 & -2 \end{pmatrix}$.

Plot and join on the grid used for (a) the co-ordinates of the product matrix, $(-2, -3)$, etc.

(c) B = $\begin{pmatrix} 2 & 0 \\ 0 & 2 \end{pmatrix}$; C = $\begin{pmatrix} 1 & 0 \\ 0 & -1 \end{pmatrix}$; D = $\begin{pmatrix} -2 & 0 \\ 0 & -2 \end{pmatrix}$; E = $\begin{pmatrix} 1 & 2 \\ 0 & 1 \end{pmatrix}$

Work out:
(i) BM   (ii) CM   (iii) DM   (iv) EM.

(d) Draw one set of axes from -8 to 10 each. Draw the triangle given by the matrix M, then draw the transformed triangles given by your answers to (c), (i) to (iv). Label each triangle.

(e) Describe fully the transformations of triangle M.

38 Factorisation: expansion; common factors

A Expansion

For Discussion

Multiplication of one bracket

$3(a + b) = 3a + 3b$

$4(a - 3) = 4a - 12$

$-2(a + 3) = -2a - 6$

$a + 3(b + 2) = a + 3b + 6$

$a(b + 2) = ab + 2a$

$2a(a + 3) = 2a^2 + 6a$

$-3(a - 3) = -3a + 9$

$a - 3(b - 2) = a - 3b + 6$

Multiplication of two brackets

Multiply each term in the second bracket by each term in the first bracket.

$(a + 2)(b + 3) = a(b + 3) + 2(b + 3)$
$= ab + 3a + 2b + 6$

$(a - 2)(b + 3) = a(b + 3) - 2(b + 3)$
$= ab + 3a - 2b - 6$

$(c + 4)(c - 3) = c(c - 3) + 4(c - 3)$
$= c^2 - 3c + 4c - 12$
$= c^2 + c - 12$

$(2d - 3)(3d - 2) = 2d(3d - 2) - 3(3d - 2)$
$= 6d^2 - 4d - 9d + 6$
$= 6d^2 - 13d + 6$

1 Remove the brackets and simplify:
(a) $2(a + 3)$ (b) $3(b - 4)$ (c) $-3(c + 2)$
(d) $-3(c - 3)$ (e) $5(3 + e)$ (f) $3(8 - f)$
(g) $g(3 - g)$ (h) $d(h - g)$ (i) $4a(b - 2)$.

2 Remove the brackets and simplify:
(a) $p(q - r)$ (b) $2(b - 4)$ (c) $d(d - f)$
(d) $3a(2 - a)$ (e) $-2(3 - b)$ (f) $-3a(a - 4)$
(g) $-a(a - b)$ (h) $-4a(a + 4)$ (i) $3m(2m - 4)$.

3 Expand:
(a) $(a + 2)(a + 3)$ (b) $(a + 3)(a - 4)$ (c) $(p - 3)(q - 4)$
(d) $(m - 4)(n - 5)$ (e) $(a + 4)(b - 5)$ (f) $(p + 4)(p - 4)$
(g) $(a + 5)(a - 5)$ (h) $(d - 6)(d - 2)$ (i) $(y - 2)(y + 3)$.

4 Expand:
(a) $(2a + 3)(a + 4)$ (b) $(2b + 4)(3b - 2)$ (c) $(3a - 2)(2b + 4)$
(d) $(3a - c)(2b - d)$ (e) $(2a - 3b)(2c - 2d)$ (f) $(2a - 3b)(2a + 3b)$
(g) $(3c + 2d)(2c - 3d)$ (h) $(a + 3)^2$ (i) $(c - 4)^2$.

5 Without showing any working, write down the expansion of:
(a) $(a + 7)(a + 1)$ (b) $(a + 2)(a + 6)$ (c) $(a - 3)(a - 4)$
(d) $(a + 5)^2$ (e) $(a - 5)^2$ (f) $(d + 3)(d - 2)$
(g) $(a + 4)(a - 4)$ (h) $(2a + 3)(3a + 4)$ (i) $(3b - 2)(2b + 4)$
(j) $(2p + 3)^2$ (k) $(3d - c)(2b + a)$ (l) $(5a + 2d)(3a - 8d)$.

B Common factors

For Discussion

$4a - 4b = 4(a - b)$ $ac + ad = a(c + d)$

$6c - 9d = 3(2c - 3d)$ $3a + ac = a(3 + c)$

$12a + 9b - 6c = 3(4a + 3b - 2c)$ $4a + ab - ac = a(4 + b - c)$

1 Factorise:
(a) $3a + 3b$ (b) $4m - 4n$ (c) $ab - ac$
(d) $ab + 2b$ (e) $6cd + 8d$ (f) $ab + bc + 4b$
(g) $20 - 5a + 10b$ (h) $m^2 - mn$ (i) $ax^2 + bx^2$.

2 Factorise:
(a) $5x^2 + 5y^2$ (b) $pa - pb$ (c) $cx^2 - cy^2$
(d) $t^2 - at$ (e) $bd + d^2$ (f) $2d^2 - 2d$
(g) $2ac - c^2 + 3c$ (h) $-15x + 20y$ (i) $-6a - 15b$.

3 Factorise:
(a) $4ab - 6a^2b^2$ (b) $5a^2c - 6ac$ (c) $4ab + 12bc - 16bd$
(d) $a^2 + ax^2$ (e) $a^2x + ax^2$ (f) $ay^2 + dy^2$
(g) $4c^2d + 6b^2c - 2bc^2$ (h) $12a^2b - 18ab^2$ (i) $abc - bcd$.

4 Factorise these where possible. When an expression will not factorise, write 'No factors'.
(a) $20a - 35b$ (b) $4a - 6b + 12c$ (c) $3ab - 6cd$
(d) $a^2b - ab$ (e) $2ab + ac + a^2$ (f) $4ab - a^2b^2$
(g) $4ad + 8bd - 7c^2$ (h) $5a^2b - 15a^2b^2 + 5ab^2$
(i) $2abc^2 + 3b^2cd - 6bcd^2$

A Graphs of quadratic functions

To complete this exercise you will need access to a computer, a printer and a program which will draw graphs of quadratic functions. A **quadratic equation** is an equation in which 2 is the highest power of the letter involved, i.e. $y = x^2 + 3x - 2$ is a quadratic but $y = x^3 + 3x - 2$ is not.

For each question, superimpose all the graphs on one pair of axes. You should take, or obtain, a print for each question and on each print label each line drawn.

1 Using axes $-4 \leqslant x \leqslant 4$ and $-2 \leqslant y \leqslant 18$, generate the graph of:

   (a) $y = x^2$ (b) $y = 2x^2$ (c) $y = 3x^2$ (d) $y = 0.5x^2$.

   Write down what you notice about the shape of a graph and the coefficient of x^2 in its equation.

   3 is the coefficient of $3x^2$.

2 Using axes $-4 \leqslant x \leqslant 4$ and $-18 \leqslant y \leqslant 2$, generate the graph of:

   (a) $y = -x^2$ (You may have to key $y = -1 * x \wedge 2$)
   (b) $y = -2x^2$ (c) $y = -3x^2$ (d) $y = -0.5x^2$

   Write down the differences between these graphs and the ones in question 1.

3 Using axes $-4 \leqslant x \leqslant 4$ and $-6 \leqslant y \leqslant 12$, generate the graph of:

   (a) $y = x^2 - 4$ (b) $y = x^2 - 2$ (c) $y = x^2 + 1$ (d) $y = x^2 + 6$.

   In an equation the number on its own is the **constant** of the equation, i.e. in $y = 2x^2 + 6$, $+6$ is the constant. Write down what you observe about where each graph cuts the y-axis and the constant of its equation. Why is this so? (**Hint:** what is the value of x on the y-axis?)

4 Using axes $-4 \leqslant x \leqslant 4$ and $-8 \leqslant y \leqslant 8$, generate the graph of:

   (a) $y = -x^2 + 6$ (b) $y = -x^2 - 1$ (c) $y = -2x^2 + 4$
   (d) $y = -2x^2 + 3$.

   Use these graphs to check your observations about question 3.

For the remainder of the exercise use the axes $-4 \leqslant x \leqslant 4$ and $-3 \leqslant y \leqslant 16$.

5 Generate the graph of:
  (a) $y = x^2 + 3x$ (b) $y = x^2 + 2x$ (c) $y = x^2 - 2x$ (d) $y = x^2 - 3x$.

In the equation $y = 2x^2 + 3x + 4$, $+3$ is the coefficient of x. Write down what you observe about the position of a graph and the coefficient of x of its equation.

The graphs all go through the point (0,0) because the equations have no real constants.

6 Generate the graph of:
  (a) $y = x^2 + 3x + 4$ (b) $y = x^2 + 2x + 4$ (c) $y = x^2 - 2x + 4$
  (d) $y = x^2 - 3x + 4$.

Use these graphs to check your observations about question 5.

7 Generate the graphs of:
  (a) $y = x^2 + 3x$ (b) $y = 2x^2 + 3x$ (c) $y = x^2 - 3x$ (d) $y = 2x^2 - 3x$.

Look at the width of each graph where it cuts the y-axis and compare this with the coefficient of x divided by the coefficient of x^2 for its equation. Check your observations by looking at the graphs of questions 1 to 6.

8 Generate the graph of:
  (a) $y = x^2 - 3x + 4$ (b) $y = 2x^2 - 3x + 4$ (c) $y = 3x^2 - 3x + 4$.

Use these graphs to check your observations in question 7.

B Curve sketching

For Discussion

There is enough information in exercise 39A to enable you to sketch the curve of a quadratic equation. There are further techniques which you may meet in the future.

To sketch the graph of the equation follow these steps illustrated in Figures 39:1 and 39:2.

Fig. 39:1

① Decide which way up the curve needs to be drawn

② Draw axes and mark where the equation cuts the y-axis, i.e. $+4$.

③ Work out the width of the equation at this point, i.e. $-4 \div +2 = -2$ and mark this point ($-$ to the right of the y-axis and $+$ to the left).

④ Decide on the slope of the graph and sketch the curve so that it passes through your marked points.

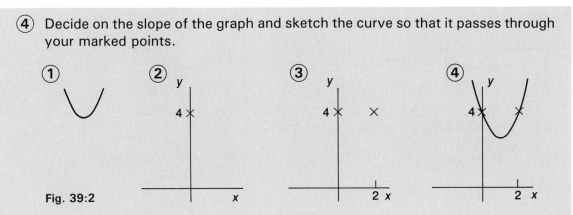

Fig. 39:2

1 Sketch the graph of:
(a) $y + 2x^2 - 2x - 2$ (b) $y = 2x^2 - 4x + 5$ (c) $y = 2x^2 + 4x + 2$
(d) $y = 2x^2 + 6x$.

2 Check the accuracy of your sketches for question 1 on a computer.

3 Make up equations of your own. Sketch the graphs of these equations and then check your answers using a computer.

C   Graphs of reciprocal functions

For Discussion

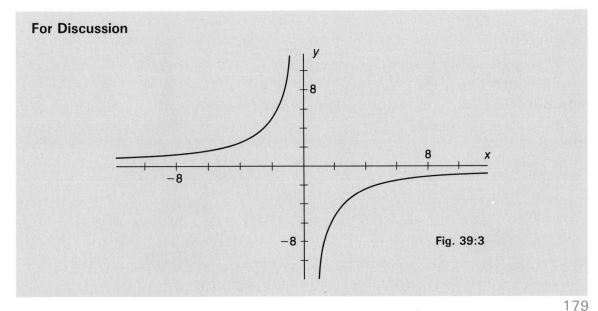

Fig. 39:3

1 Using axes $-10 \leqslant x \leqslant 10$ and $-10 \leqslant y \leqslant 10$, generate the graph of:

(a) $y = \dfrac{10}{x}$　　(b) $y = \dfrac{10}{-x}$　　(c) $y = \dfrac{-10}{x}$　　(d) $y = \dfrac{-10}{-x}$.

Write down what you observe about the graphs of these equations.

2 Using axes of your own, generate the graph of:

(a) $y = \dfrac{8}{x}$　　(b) $y = \dfrac{4}{x}$.

3 Make up equations similar to the ones in questions 1 and 2. Sketch the graphs of these equations and check your answers using a computer.

A   Tangent

For Discussion

The result of dividing the side opposite angle θ in Figure 40:1 by the length of the side adjacent (not the hypotenuse) to the angle θ is called the tangent of the angle.

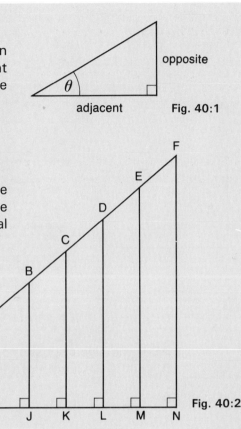

Fig. 40:1

In short: $\dfrac{o}{a} = \tan \theta$ and therefore

$o = a \times \tan \theta$.

Measure Figure 40:2 accurately to find the lengths required in the first two columns of the table. Then use a calculator to find the decimal fraction for the third column, correct to 2 d.p.

Fig. 40:2

Angle Q is 40° in these right-angled triangles.

Opposite	Adjacent	Opposite / Adjacent
AI =	QI =	
BJ =	QJ =	
CK =	QK =	
DL =	QL =	
EM =	QM =	
FN =	QN =	

Scientific calculators are programmed to give the value of $\dfrac{o}{a}$ for any required angle in a right-angled triangle.

Key in 40 $\boxed{\text{TAN}}$ to find the tangent of an angle of 40°.
Compare the calculator value with your answers in the table.

Write the values of tan θ for values of θ from 0° to 90° every 10°.
Illustrate your values with a graph.

Your calculator can also give you the angle when you key in the value of $\dfrac{o}{a}$. The keys to use vary, but often the $\boxed{\text{INV}}$ or 2nd function key is needed together with the $\boxed{\text{TAN}}$ key. It may be marked $\boxed{\text{ARCTAN}}$ or $\boxed{\text{TAN}^{-1}}$.

Check that you can find the tangent of an angle, then use the $\boxed{\text{ARCTAN}}$ key to return to the angle.

Figure 40:3 illustrates how sides o and a move as the triangle positions vary.

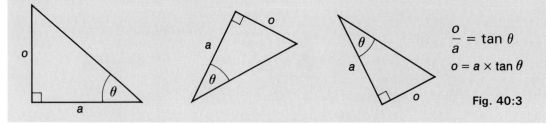

$$\dfrac{o}{a} = \tan \theta$$
$$o = a \times \tan \theta$$

Fig. 40:3

1 **Example** Calculate AB in Figure 40:4.

AB is the side opposite to the angle 35°.
6.4 cm is the length of the adjacent side.

Fig. 40:4

$$\dfrac{o}{a} = \tan \theta \;\rightarrow\; o = a \times \tan \theta$$

AB = 6.4 × tan 35°

Key: 6.4 $\boxed{\times}$ 35 $\boxed{\text{TAN}}$ $\boxed{=}$, giving 4.48 cm as the length of AB.

Calculate, correct to 3 significant figures, the length of side x in each of the triangles drawn in Figure 40:5.

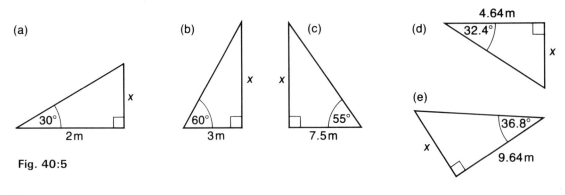

(a)

(b)

(c)

(d)

(e)

Fig. 40:5

2 Example Calculate the length of side x in Figure 40:6.

Because x is opposite the unknown angle, not the 35° angle, we need to first calculate the angle α.

$\alpha = 90° - 35° = 55°$.

Now $x = 6 \times \tan 55°$, giving $x = 8.57$ m to 3 s.f.

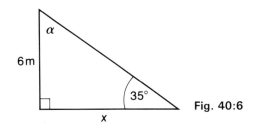

Fig. 40:6

Calculate the length of side x in each triangle in Figure 40:7.

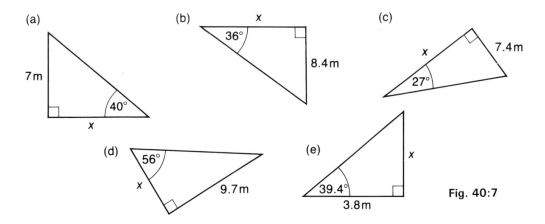

(a)

(b)

(c)

(d)

(e)

Fig. 40:7

3 Example Calculate the size of angle θ in Figure 40:8.

$$\frac{3.8}{4.6} = \tan \theta$$

Key: 3.8 $\boxed{\div}$ 4.6 $\boxed{=}$ $\boxed{\text{ARCTAN}}$

Answer: $\theta = 39.6°$ to the nearest 0.1°.

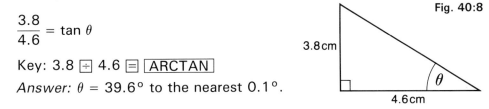

Fig. 40:8

3.8 cm

4.6 cm

θ

Calculate the angle θ in each of the triangles in Figure 40:9. (Give your answers to the nearest 0.1°.)

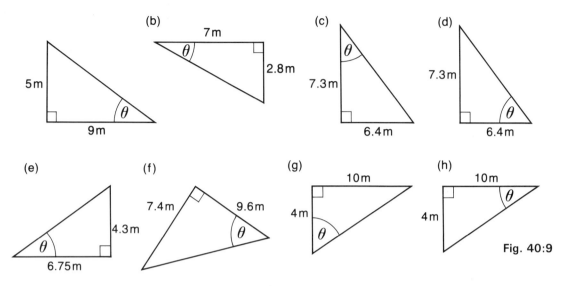

For questions 4 to 10, sketch diagrams to help you to solve the problems.

4 A mast throws a shadow 36 m long on level ground when the altitude of the sun is 60°. Find the height of the mast.

5 From a point 120 m away from the bottom of a vertical cliff, the angle of elevation of its top is 42°. Find the height of the cliff.

6 A ladder leans against a wall so that its inclination to the ground is 63°. The foot of the ladder is 2 m out from the wall. How far up the wall does the ladder reach?

7 Figure 40:10 shows a sketch of a garage roof. Find the height of the apex of the roof above the garage walls.

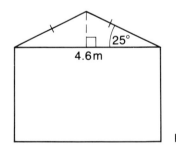

Fig. 40:10

8 The gradient of a hill is 1 in 5. What is the angle of slope?

9 The gradient of a hill is 1 in 4. What is the angle of slope?

10 June travels 14 km north and then 8 km east. What is then her bearing from her starting point?

B Sines and cosines

For Discussion

In any right-angled triangle, the **sine** of an angle is the answer to

opposite ÷ hypotenuse

and the **cosine** of an angle is the answer to

adjacent ÷ hypotenuse.

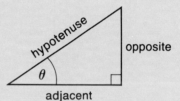

Fig. 40:11

In short: $\dfrac{o}{h} = \sin \theta$ and $\dfrac{a}{h} = \cos \theta$

$o = h \times \sin \theta$ $a = h \times \cos \theta$

A mnemonic which may help you remember the tangent, sine and cosine ratios is:

One Ancient Teacher Of History Swore At His Class

1 Example Calculate the lengths of sides p and q in Figure 40:12.

$o = h \times \sin \theta$
$p = 10 \times \sin 30°$
Key: 10 ⊠ 30 [SIN] ▣
Answer: p is 5 m.

$a = h \times \cos \theta$
$q = 10 \times \cos 30°$
Key: 10 ⊠ 30 [COS] ▣
Answer: q is 8.66 m.

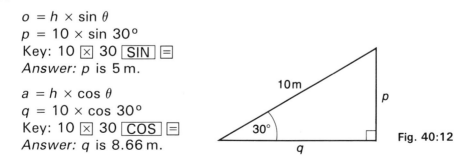

Fig. 40:12

Calculate, correct to 3 s.f., the lengths of the lettered sides in Figure 40:13.

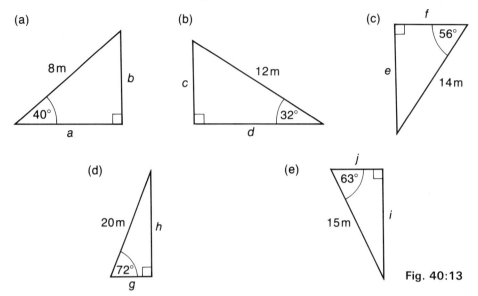

(a)   8m   b   40°   a

(b)   12m   c   32°   d

(c)   f   56°   e   14m

(d)   20m   h   72°   g

(e)   j   63°   15m   i

Fig. 40:13

2 Example   Calculate angles θ and α in Figure 40:14.

$$\frac{o}{h} = \sin \theta$$

$$\frac{7}{9} = \sin \theta$$

Key: 7 ÷ 9 = ARCSIN
Answer: $\theta = 51.1°$ to the nearest 0.1°
$\alpha = 90° - 51.1° = 38.9°$

Or

$$\frac{a}{h} = \cos \alpha$$

$$\frac{7}{9} = \cos \alpha$$

Key: 7 ÷ 9 = ARCCOS
Answer: $\alpha = 38.9°$ to the nearest 0.1°.
$\theta = 90° - 38.9° = 51.1°$

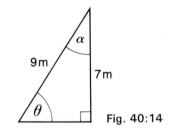

9m α 7m θ Fig. 40:14

Calculate the sizes of the angles θ and α in Figure 40:15.

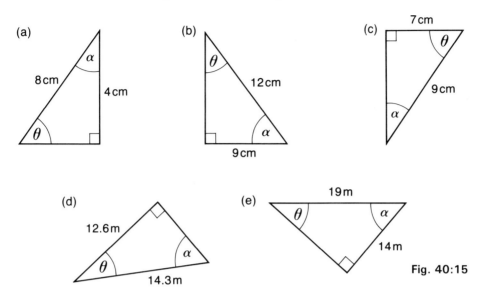

Fig. 40:15

3 Draw accurate diagrams for Figure 40:15 parts (a), (b) and (c). Measure the angles in your diagrams with a protractor and compare your results with your calculated answers.

4 Completely solve the triangles in Figure 40:16.

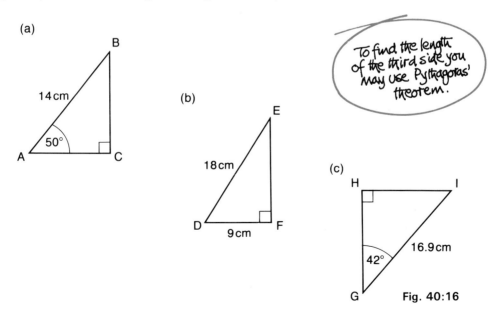

To find the length of the third side you may use Pythagoras' theorem.

Fig. 40:16

5 **Example**   Calculate the hypotenuse in Figure 40:17.

$$\frac{a}{h} = \cos\theta \;\rightarrow\; \frac{a}{\cos\theta} = h$$

$$\frac{8}{\cos 40^\circ} = h$$

Key: 8 ÷ 40° [COS] =
Answer: $h = 10.44$ cm

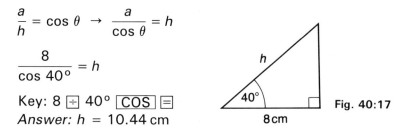

Fig. 40:17

Find the lengths of the hypotenuses in Figure 40:18.

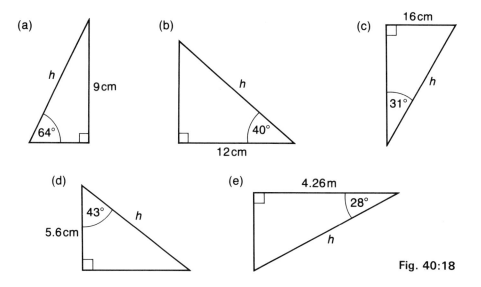

Fig. 40:18

6 A ladder 6 metres long just reaches the top of a wall when it makes an angle of 62° with the ground. How high is the wall?

7 A kite flies on a 34 metre string at 71° to the ground. Find its height.

8 A ski-lift 420 metres long slopes at an angle of 66°. To what height does it rise?

9 Find, to the nearest cm, the length of a guy-rope pegged 7 metres from the base of a pole if it makes an angle of 63° to the horizontal.

10 A 12 m long conveyor slopes at 40° to the ground. How high does it reach?

11 Use a computer or calculator graph program to investigate trigonometrical graphs, e.g. $y = \sin x$, $y = \cos x$, $y = \tan x$, $y = \sin^2 x + \cos^2 x$, etc.!

For Discussion

The scores in a test taken by 50 pupils were:

39 14 6 21 33 45 21 17 27 45 34 13 22 4 16 43 29 30 22 32 35
14 23 7 23 13 28 43 16 34 31 17 45 43 17 17 8 26 27 36 32 24
24 19 25 12 26 9 25 37

Class interval	Tally	Frequency	Cumulative frequency
1–10	⍿	5	5
11–20	⍿ ⍿ II	12	5 + 12 = 17
21–30	⍿ ⍿ ⍿ II	17	17 + 17 = 34
31–40	⍿ ⍿	10	34 + 10 = 44
41–50	⍿ I	6	44 + 6 = 50

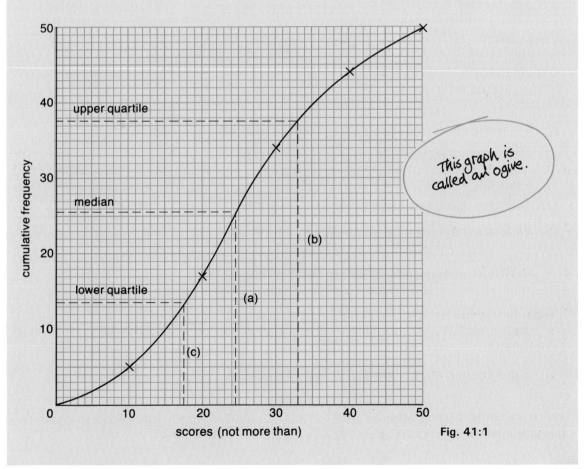

This graph is called an ogive.

Fig. 41:1

The median is between the 25th and 26th pupil, which corresponds to 24.5 marks.

The median mark for the test was approximately 24.5.

The upper quartile is at $\frac{3}{4} \times 50 = 37.5$, so between the 37th and 38th pupil, which corresponds to 33 marks.

Three-quarters of the pupils scored 33 or less.
One-quarter of the pupils scored more than 33.

The lower quartile is at $\frac{1}{4} \times 50 = 12.5$, so between the 12th and 13th pupil, which corresponds to 17.5 marks.

One-quarter of the pupils scored 17.5 or less.
Three-quarters of the pupils scored more than 17.5 marks.

The inter-quartile range is $33 - 17.5 = 15.5$ marks.

Half of the pupils scored between 17.5 and 33 marks which is a range of 15.5 marks.

1 Copy and complete this table for the scores in a test taken by two classes in a school.

Class interval	1–10	11–20	21–30	31–40	41–50
Frequency	5	14	26	11	4
Cumulative frequency	5	19			

Draw a cumulative frequency curve (**ogive**) to illustrate the table.

(a) Use your curve to estimate the median mark.

(b) Estimate the upper quartile mark.

(c) Estimate the lower quartile mark.

(d) Estimate the inter-quartile range.

See the statements printed in green in the 'For Discussion' section for examples.

(e) Write down statements to explain the values of the median, the upper quartile, the lower quartile and the inter-quartile range.

2 Students in a hostel are grouped by age as follows:

Age group	18–19	20–21	22–23	24–25	26–27
Number in group	10	12	24	14	6

Copy the table, adding another row for the cumulative frequency. Draw an ogive to illustrate the table.

Use your curve to find:
(a) the median age of the students
(b) the inter-quartile range.

3 In a class experiment, 30 pupils had to pick up as many peas as possible in two minutes using a straw. The results were:

8 11 30 34 21 27 28 38 17 29 36 25 12 26 24 33 14 33 24 41
37 35 27 47 13 22 39 32 4 23

Construct a frequency table for these results (as in the For Discussion section) using class intervals of 1–10, 11–20, etc.
Draw an ogive for your results.

(a) Estimate the median number of peas picked up.
(b) Estimate how many pupils got within three peas of this median.
(c) Check your answer to (b) by consulting the given data.
(d) Why could your answer to (b) be different from the actual answer?

4 Fifty pupils were asked to guess the weight of a bottle in a competition. The guesses were:

120 131 150 143 132 163 152 148 152 147 166 130 124 156 147
139 146 135 140 155 151 165 125 142 134 141 153 145 162 149
177 146 158 157 138 153 126 151 138 137 136 174 144 148 145
170 164 133 154 159

Construct a frequency table using class intervals of 120–129, 130–139, etc. Draw the ogive for these results and use your curve to estimate:

(a) the median weight   (b) the upper quartile weight
(c) the lower quartile weight   (d) the inter-quartile range.

5 In a survey of 170 families in a village it was found that the number of children per family was:

Number of children	0	1	2	3	4	5	6
Frequency	24	38	60	26	11	7	4

Draw a cumulative frequency curve to illustrate these results and use your curve to estimate the median number of children per family and the inter-quartile range.

6 Construct a table similar to the one in question 5 for members of your class. Use your results to draw a cumulative frequency curve and hence find the median number of children per family. Find also the mean value and the modal value.

Paper 1

1 ξ = {integers from 1 to 18};   P = {prime numbers};   F = {factors of 18};
T = {triangular numbers};   R = {rectangular numbers};   S = {square numbers}

List sets P, F, T, R and S.

2 What scale factor was used to enlarge the object in
Figure P1?

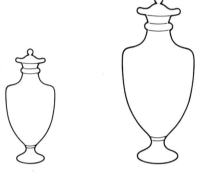

Fig. P1

3 Figure P2 shows a modulo 5 clock. To which
number will the hand be pointing after turning
through 48 divisions from 0 in a clockwise
direction?

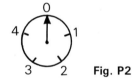

Fig. P2

*4 Construct a rectangle ABCD with AB = 3 cm and BC = 2 cm. Enlarge your rectangle by scale
factor 2, using A as centre.

*5 Calculate:
(a) $\dfrac{3}{8} + \dfrac{5}{6}$ (b) $15 \times \dfrac{4}{5}$ (c) $7.18 \div 0.4$ (d) $2.2 \div 0.05$

6 Construct three copies of the rectangle ABCD with AB = 3 cm and BC = 2 cm.

Using one rectangle for each part enlarge ABCD by scale factor 2 using as centre:
(i) A   (ii) the centre of the rectangle (where the diagonals cross)
(iii) a point 1 cm from A on the line BA produced (made longer).

7 Showing all working find:
(a) $4\frac{3}{4} - 1\frac{7}{16}$ (b) $15 \times \frac{4}{5}$ (c) $7.18 \div 0.4$ (d) $1.25 \div 0.08$

8 Figure P3 shows plans and elevations of five wooden blocks. Describe each block as clearly as possible, then draw a 3D sketch of it.

(a)　　　　　(b)　　　　　(c)　　　　　(d)　　　　　(e)

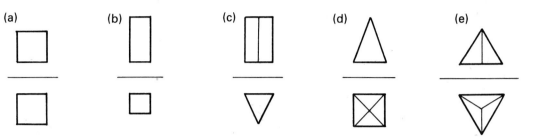

Fig. P3　(Elevations above lines, plans below.)

Paper 2

1 Write three numbers that multiply to make 7.

2 Write as the product of prime factors:
(a) 42　　(b) 75.

3 Write the first six rows of Pascal's triangle, starting with 1.

4 Find, for 1, 3, 4, 4 and 8:
(a) the mean　　(b) the median　　(c) the mode.

*5 Using the formula: The circumference of a circle is about 3.1 multiplied by the diameter, calculate to the nearest centimetre the circumference of a circle of radius 7 cm.

6 Find the sum of each of the first six rows of Pascal's triangle, then without writing any more rows deduce the sum of the tenth row.

7 The hour hand of a clock describes a circle of radius 10 cm. Taking $\pi = 3.14$ find how far the tip of the hand travels in:
(a) one revolution　　(b) one day　　(c) one hour, correct to 1 d.p.

8 A running track has two 83-metre straights joined by two semi-circles of internal diameter 14 metres.

Taking π as $3\frac{1}{7}$ calculate the length of the track's:
(a) inside edge　　(b) outside edge if there are seven 1 metre wide lanes.

9 Use brackets and $+$, $-$, $\times$ and $\div$ signs to make the following correct.

Remember that the order of working signs is BODMAS, that is Brackets, Of, Divide, Multiply, Add, Subtract.

(a) $2 * 2 * 2 * 2 = 8$ (b) $3 * 3 * 3 * 3 = 7$ (c) $4 * 4 * 4 * 4 = 6$
(d) $5 * 5 * 5 * 5 = 5$

Paper 3

1 What is the H.C.F. of:
(a) 8 and 10   (b) 10 and 18   (c) 5 and 6   (d) 6, 8 and 12?

2 What is the L.C.M. of:
(a) 4 and 6   (b) 5 and 7   (c) 8 and 10   (d) 12 and 15?

3 A right-angled triangle has sides of lengths 3 cm, 4 cm and 5 cm. State what these lengths become if the triangle is enlarged by scale factor:
(a) 2   (b) $\frac{1}{4}$.

*4 For 1, 3, 5, 5, 8 and 8 state:
(a) the mean   (b) the modes   (c) the median.

*5 What simple fraction is:
(a) 25%   (b) 75%   (c) 10%   (d) 20%   (e) $66\frac{2}{3}$%?

*6 What is the time 144 hours after 1300? Give your answer as an a.m. or p.m. time.

*7 Example   Find 15% of £12.

$$\frac{15}{100} \times £12 \rightarrow \frac{^3\cancel{15}}{\cancel{100}_{20_{10}}} \times £\cancel{12}^6 = \frac{£18}{10} = £1.80$$

Note: It was better to leave $\frac{18}{10}$ rather than cancel it to $\frac{9}{5}$ as division by 10 is easy.

Find 15% of:
(a) £6   (b) £14   (c) £20   (d) £65.

8 A metal plate is a square of side 16.7 cm with a square hole of side 5.9 cm inside it. Calculate the area of metal on one side of the plate.

9 State the H.C.F. and the L.C.M. of $2ax^2$ and $6a^2$.

10 Sketch a hexagonal prism, then calculate its volume in mm^3 if the hexagon has an area of 91 mm^2 and the prism is 91 mm long.

194

11 Find x if:

(a) $3x + 7 - x = 5$ (b) $\dfrac{8}{1 - x} = 4.$

Paper 4

1 Calculate: (a) $\frac{5}{9} \times \frac{2}{5}$ (b) $5\frac{1}{4} \times \frac{6}{7}$ (c) $\frac{3}{8} \div \frac{9}{4}.$

2 Write as the product of prime factors:
(a) 20 (b) 30 (c) 48 (d) 56 (e) 81.

3 Divide 20 by 7, giving the answer correct to one place of decimals.

4 Find 8% of 48, giving your answer as a decimal fraction.

*5 What do we usually call the parallelogram with:
(a) all its sides equal, but no right angles
(b) all its sides equal and all angles right angles?

*6 Find the volume of a cuboid (box) 8 cm long, 5 cm wide and 3 cm deep.

7 Find: (a) $2\frac{1}{4} \div 1\frac{1}{8}$ (b) $\frac{14}{15} \div 1\frac{2}{5}.$

8 For Figure P4:

(a) calculate the area of the right-angled triangle

(b) express the triangle's area as a fraction of the rectangle's area, as simply as possible

(c) change your answer to (b) to a percentage.

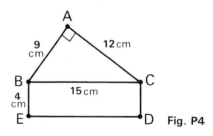

Fig. P4

9 (a) Draw up the route matrix for Figure P4, taking A, B, C, D and E as the nodes.

(b) How many nodes, arcs and regions in the diagram?

10 In Figure P4, calculate the vertical height of the triangle.

11 $P = 4(1 - \frac{1}{3} + \frac{1}{5} - \frac{1}{7} + \ldots).$

(a) Copy the series. Continue it for four more terms.

(b) Calculate the value of P given by the series as far as $\frac{1}{7}$.

(c) Using a calculator or a computer calculate the values of P as the series lengthens. Find the average of each consecutive pair of values and comment on your results.

Paper 5

1 Figure P5 shows a distance/time graph for a journey.

(a) Where and when does the journey start?

(b) Where and when does the journey finish?

(c) How many kilometres long is the total journey?

(d) State the average speeds from the start to A, A to B, and B to C.

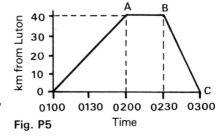

Fig. P5

2 (a) Increase 27 in the ratio 5:3.
(b) Divide £20 in the ratio 5:3.

*3 Calculate:
(a) 13.6 − 7.58   (b) 2.3 × 0.19   (c) 51.24 ÷ 0.2

*4 (a) Cancel $\frac{21}{28}$ to a simpler fraction.

(b) Add $1\frac{3}{4}$ to $2\frac{3}{8}$.

(c) **Example** $2\frac{1}{2} \div 6 \rightarrow \frac{5}{2} \times \frac{1}{6} = \frac{5}{12}$

Find $3\frac{1}{4} \div 5$.

*5 Write in standard form:
(a) 5300   (b) 91 000   (c) 724.6

6 How much fertiliser will be needed for 12 hectares if 9 kg are sufficient for 15 hectares?

7 If $p = 7.206$, $q = 0.3$ and $r = 0.15$, find:
(a) $p - q$ (b) pq (c) qr (d) $q - r$ (e) $r \div q$ (f) $p \div q$
(g) $q \div r$ (h) $p \div r$.

8 How many seven-eighths make a whole one?

9 The leader of a desert patrol logged their journey from base as:

Bearing Distance

060°   6 km
140°   8 km
250°   4 km

Draw a plan of the journey, using a scale of 1 cm to represent 1 km

From the last position the leader planned to return directly to base. Use your plan to find:

(a) the bearing the patrol had to follow   (b) the distance they still have to travel.

Paper 6

1 Find:
(a) $\frac{2}{3} \times \frac{3}{4}$ (b) $2\frac{3}{4} \times 5\frac{1}{3}$ (c) $\frac{2}{3} + \frac{3}{4}$ (d) $2\frac{3}{4} + 5\frac{1}{3}$.

2 (a) Increase 12 in the ratio 4:3.
(b) Decrease 12 in the ratio 4:3.

3 Write the family names of the polygons with the following number of sides.
(a) 3   (b) 4   (c) 5   (d) 6   (e) 8   (f) 10

4   A •₃   B •   C •

(a) Copy the above nodes then draw the two-way network for the route matrix on the right.

(b) The order of node A is 3. Write by nodes B and C their orders.

(c) How many arcs and how many regions in your network?

		to		
		A	B	C
f	A	0	2	1
r	B	2	0	2
o				
m	C	1	2	0

*5 Figures P6, P7 and P8 show the average April rainfall in three countries. Describe the rainfall pattern in each country.

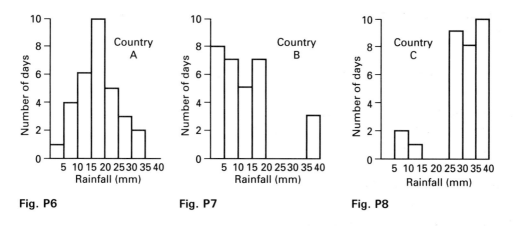

Fig. P6   Fig. P7   Fig. P8

6 Simplify:
(a) 36:20   (b) $\frac{138}{276}$ (c) $4\frac{3}{7} + 12\frac{4}{5}$ (d) $2\frac{2}{9} \div 5$.

7 Calculate the volume of air in a closed box made from 5 mm-thick plastic if its external dimensions are 20 cm by 15 cm by 11 cm.

Paper 7

1 Find:

(a) $\frac{7}{8} + \frac{1}{3}$ (b) $\frac{7}{8} - \frac{1}{3}$ (c) $4\frac{1}{2} + 2\frac{3}{8}$ (d) $4\frac{1}{2} - 2\frac{3}{5}$

2 Example {factors of 24} = {1, 2, 3, 4, 6, 8, 12, 24}

(a) List {factors of 30}.

(b) What is the Highest Common Factor of 24 and 30?

3 What is the Lowest Common Multiple (the lowest number that is a multiple of both numbers) of:

(a) 7 and 10   (b) 6 and 10   (c) 5 and 10?

4 Using the axes shown in Figure P9, draw a journey graph to show a girl leaving home at 0 hours at an average speed of 2 km/h for 2 hours, then stopping for 2 hours before returning home again at 2 km/h.

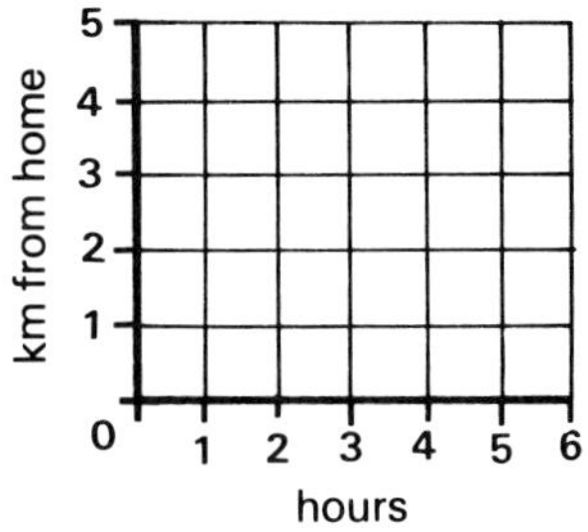

Fig. P9

5 Referring to Figure P10, state as a column matrix:

(a) vector $\underset{\sim}{a}$ (b) vector $\underset{\sim}{b}$ (c) vector $\underset{\sim}{c}$

(d) vector $\underset{\sim}{d}$.

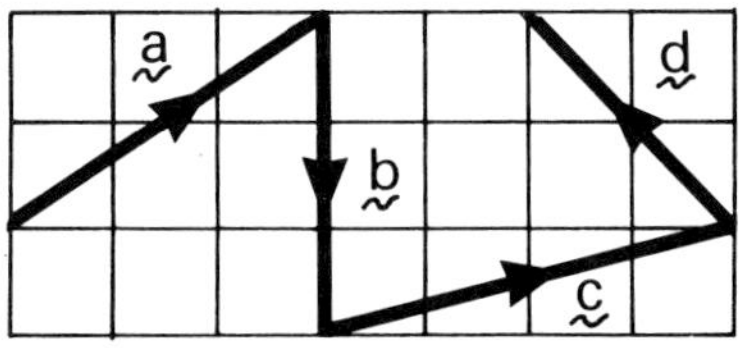

Fig. P10

6 Example Figure P11 shows vector $\underset{\sim}{x}$.

Remembering the arrows, draw, the correct length and direction, vector:

(a) $2\underset{\sim}{x}$ (b) $-\underset{\sim}{x}$ (c) $-2\underset{\sim}{x}$.

Fig. P11

*7 Find three-quarters of £64.

8 Find:

(a) $\frac{2}{5}$ as a percentage   (b) 12% as a simplified fraction   (c) $\frac{3}{8}$ of 28

(d) 4% of 16 as a decimal fraction   (e) $3.2 \div 0.05$

(f) 5% of 12 as a common fraction.

9 Find the H.C.F. and the L.C.M. of:

(a) 54 and 252   (b) x^3y^2z and xy^3.

Paper 8

1 Example In Figure P12, $\underset{\sim}{r}$ is the resultant vector of $\underset{\sim}{a}$ and $\underset{\sim}{b}$.

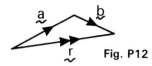

Fig. P12

If $\underset{\sim}{a} = \begin{pmatrix} 2 \\ 2 \end{pmatrix}$ and $\underset{\sim}{b} = \begin{pmatrix} 2 \\ -1 \end{pmatrix}$ then

$$\underset{\sim}{r} = \begin{pmatrix} 2 \\ 2 \end{pmatrix} + \begin{pmatrix} 2 \\ -1 \end{pmatrix} = \begin{pmatrix} 4 \\ 1 \end{pmatrix}.$$

Find the resultant vector of:

(a) $\begin{pmatrix} 1 \\ -1 \end{pmatrix}$ and $\begin{pmatrix} -2 \\ -1 \end{pmatrix}$ (b) $\begin{pmatrix} 3 \\ 0 \end{pmatrix}$ and $\begin{pmatrix} -4 \\ 2 \end{pmatrix}$

2 Use area formulae to find the areas of the triangle, parallelogram and trapezium in Figure P13.

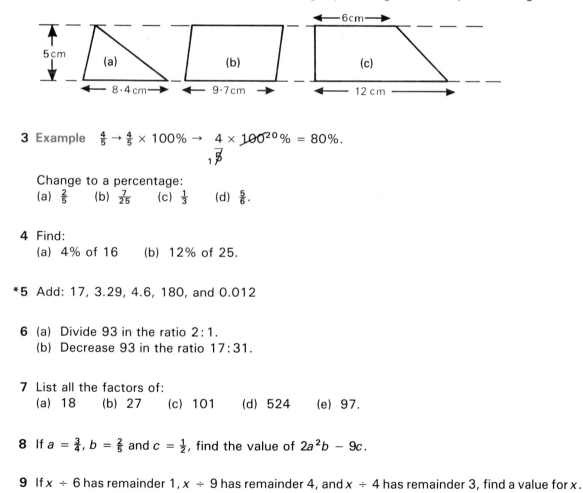

3 Example $\frac{4}{5} \rightarrow \frac{4}{5} \times 100\% \rightarrow 4 \times \frac{\overset{20}{\cancel{100}}}{\cancel{5}_1} \% = 80\%.$

Change to a percentage:
(a) $\frac{2}{5}$ (b) $\frac{7}{25}$ (c) $\frac{1}{3}$ (d) $\frac{5}{6}$.

4 Find:
(a) 4% of 16   (b) 12% of 25.

*5 Add: 17, 3.29, 4.6, 180, and 0.012

6 (a) Divide 93 in the ratio 2 : 1.
(b) Decrease 93 in the ratio 17 : 31.

7 List all the factors of:
(a) 18   (b) 27   (c) 101   (d) 524   (e) 97.

8 If $a = \frac{3}{4}$, $b = \frac{2}{5}$ and $c = \frac{1}{2}$, find the value of $2a^2b - 9c$.

9 If $x \div 6$ has remainder 1, $x \div 9$ has remainder 4, and $x \div 4$ has remainder 3, find a value for x.

Paper 9

1 Find:
   (a) 7% of 25   (b) $\frac{3}{5}$ as a percentage
   (c) the new price of a £7000 car after an 8% price rise.

2 By what must $\frac{3}{4}$ be multiplied to give the answer 1?

*3 (a) State the formula for:
       (i) the circumference of a circle of diameter d
       (ii) the area of a circle of radius r.

   (b) Taking $\pi = 3.1$ calculate the circumference and the area of a circle of diameter 12 cm.

*4 Calculate the area of each shape in Figure P14.

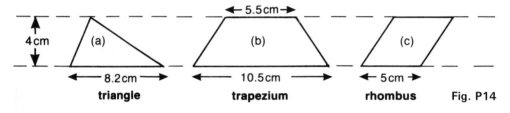

| triangle | trapezium | rhombus | Fig. P14 |

*5 What is the usual name for a circular prism?

*6 Divide 45 in the ratio 2:1.

*7 To decrease in the ratio 5:7 multiply by $\frac{5}{7}$.
   (a) Decrease 14 in the ratio 5:7.
   (b) Decrease 24 in the ratio 5:8.
   (c) Decrease 14 in the ratio 4:5.
   (d) Increase 10 in the ratio 3:2.

8 A sweet, as shown in Figure P15, consists of a core of liquorice surrounded by nougat. The inner core is a cylinder of diameter 10 mm and the whole sweet has a diameter of 14 mm and a height of 10 mm.

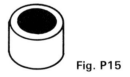

Fig. P15

Calculate, taking π as 3.14 or using the π key on your calculator:
   (a) the area of the circle of liquorice on one end
   (b) the area of the complete circular end of the sweet
   (c) the circumference of one end of the sweet
   (d) the volume of the sweet
   (e) the volume of the nougat.

The volume of a prism is its cross-section area times its height.

Paper 10

1 Show clear compass constructions for an angle of:
   (a) 60°   (b) 30°   (c) 90°.

2 A car covers 100 km at 40 km/h, then 80 km at 60 km/h. At what time did it arrive at its destination if it started at 2245 hours?

3 By what must $\frac{2}{3}$ be multiplied to give the answer 1?

*4 (a) A child scores 8 out of 10 in a test. What percentage score is this?
   (b) Express as a percentage:
      (i) 8 out of 25   (ii) 4 out of 12.

*5 Find:
   (a) 4% of 75   (b) 10% of £15   (c) 12% of 5 as a decimal fraction.

*6 A shopkeeper sells goods for 50% profit on his cost. What would he charge for an article that cost him:
   (a) £10   (b) £6.60   (c) £45?

*7 If $a = 2$ what is the value of:
   (a) $3a$ (b) $2a + 1$ (c) a^2 (d) $2a^2$ (e) $4 - 3a$?

*8 If $b = -2$ what is the value of:
   (a) $3b$ (b) $1 - b$ (c) b^2 (d) $b - 4$ (e) $\dfrac{b}{2}$?

9 If $s = 6$ and $t = 2$ state the value of:
   (a) st (b) $s - t$ (c) $s^2 - t^2$ (d) $2s^2$ (e) $s \div t$ (f) st^2.

10 Calculate the average speed for the whole journey in question 2, correct to 1 km/h.

11 For the prism in Figure P16:
   (a) find the area of the shaded cross-section
   (b) find its volume
   (c) draw, full size, a net of the prism.

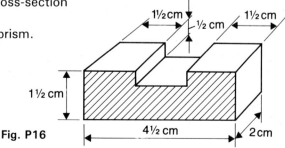

Fig. P16

12 In Figure P17, F is the centre of the circle, DEFC is a rectangle and diameter AB is 43.6 mm long. How long is CE?

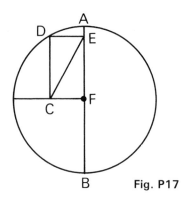

Fig. P17

Paper 11

1 Find:
(a) $4.02 \div 0.2$ (b) $3\frac{1}{5} \div 2\frac{2}{3}$.

2 The temperature rises from 18°C to 27°C. What percentage rise is this?

3 Find the mean of the first five numbers in the Fibonacci sequence that starts 1, 1, 2.

4 How far does a 10p piece roll in one full turn, correct to the nearest millimetre?

5 What is the probability that next year's Derby winner was born on a Monday?

*6 Copy Figure P18 four times. Illustrate the following rotations, one on each diagram.

(a) 90° clockwise about (1, 3).
(b) 180° about (3, 3).
(c) 90° anticlockwise about (4, 3).
(d) 180° about (2, 4).

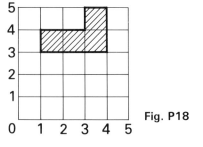

Fig. P18

7 Figure P19 shows a method for erecting a perpendicular at A on line XY. Construct Figure P19, making XY = 6 cm and XA = 2cm.

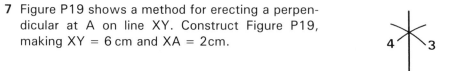

Fig. P19

202

8 Draw a circle, centre O, with radius 3 cm. Draw a straight line OTA where OT = 3 cm and OA = 5 cm. Use the method of Figure P19 to construct a perpendicular to OTA at T.

9 A is on a bearing of 107° from B. What is the bearing of B from A? (Draw a sketch to illustrate your answer.)

10 (a) Figures P20 and P21 show the ages of the population of two countries. Compare them.

Fig. P20   Fig. P21

(b) Draw a pie chart for a country which has 5 m age 0–14, 3 m age 15–40, 2.5 m age 41–65, 1.5 m age 65 + .

Paper 12

1 Jane works 40 hours one week. She is paid £6.50 an hour for the first 30 hours, then at time-and-a-half for the last 10 hours.
(a) What is her overtime pay per hour?
(b) What is her total pay for the week?

2 When income tax (PAYE) is at 25% how much tax will be paid on earnings of £50?

3 A man earns £150 one week. Of this he is allowed to earn £30 free of tax, then he has to pay tax at 25% on the rest.

(a) How much tax will he pay?
(b) What will he have left of his £150 pay after paying tax?

4 How many:
(a) metres in 1 km   (b) centimetres in 1 km   (c) metres in 6.25 km?

5 Simplify:

(a) $\begin{pmatrix} 3 & -1 & 2 \\ -4 & 0 & -1 \end{pmatrix} + \begin{pmatrix} -1 & 2 & -4 \\ 1 & 3 & -1 \end{pmatrix}$

(b) $\begin{pmatrix} 3 & -1 & 2 \\ -4 & 0 & -1 \end{pmatrix} - \begin{pmatrix} -1 & 2 & -4 \\ 1 & 3 & -1 \end{pmatrix}$

6 Find the value of x if:
(a) $2x = 35$ (b) $3x + 7 = 11$.

*7 Draw a sketch to show a point X on a bearing of 270° from another point Y. Mark X, Y and the 270° angle.

8 Find:

(a) $3\frac{3}{4} - 1\frac{9}{10}$ (b) $2\frac{1}{4} \div 18$ (c) $1\frac{1}{5} \div 2\frac{2}{5}$

9 A plant grows from 2 cm to 3.6 cm. What percentage increase is this?

10 $f(x): x \rightarrow x^2 - 1$; $g(x): x \rightarrow 3 - 2x^2$

Find:

(a) $f(-1)$ (b) $g(-2)$ (c) $g(f(1))$ (d) $g(f(2))$.

Paper 13

1 If normal pay is £4.50 an hour, what is the pay for an hour at time-and-a-half?

2 How much is the tax at 25% on earnings of £60?

*3 In Figure P22:

(a) e and i are adjacent angles on a straight line. If $i:e = 2:1$, how many degrees is angle e?

(b) If the diagram is one corner of a regular polygon, with e the exterior angle and $i:e = 2:1$, how many sides has the polygon?

Fig. P22

*4 A plant grows from 10 mm to 13 mm. What percentage increase is this?

*5 Find:

(a) 3.65×2.8 (b) $4\frac{1}{4} + 2\frac{3}{5}$ (c) $17.6 \div 0.08$

*6 What number is:

(a) $2 \times 2 \times 3 \times 3 \times 5$ (b) $2 \times 3 \times 5 \times 5$ (c) $2 \times 5 \times 7 \times 7$?

*7 List all the factors of 100.

8 Anne is paid £4.50 per hour for a 30-hour week. One week she works 35 hours (the five hours overtime being paid at time-and-a-half). She is allowed to earn £48.75 free of tax, paying tax at 25% on the remainder. Her National Insurance contribution is £9.30.

Calculate:

(a) her gross income (before any deductions)   (b) her taxable income

(c) the tax she must pay   (d) her final nett (take-home) pay.

9 A regular polygon has exterior and interior angles in the ratio 2 : 7.

Calculate:
(a) an exterior angle   (b) an interior angle   (c) the interior angle sum
(d) the total number of diagonals possible.

10 Frank drives 30 miles at an average speed of 60 m.p.h. then 30 miles at an average speed of 30 m.p.h.

Calculate:
(a) how long the journey took
(b) his average speed for the whole journey.

11 △ABC has AB = 8 cm, BC = 5 cm and CA = 4 cm. △XYZ is similar to △ABC with XY = 12 cm and XY > YZ > XZ. Calculate the lengths YZ and ZX.

Paper 14

1 Write the formula for:
(a) the area of a triangle   (b) the volume of a prism.

2 $s = 7.19$; $t = 10.098$; $u = 2.7$
(a) Write s correct to 1 decimal place.
(b) Write t correct to 2 decimal places.
(c) Write u correct to the nearest unit.
(d) Find:
     (i) $t - s$ (ii) ut to 3 d.p.   (iii) $t \div u$.

3 Copy the flag and point O shown in Figure P23, using the same size and position. Then show the flag after a rotation of 270° clockwise about O.

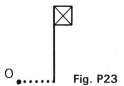

Fig. P23

4 Draw accurately an isosceles triangle of sides 5 cm, 4 cm and 4 cm. Make measurements to calculate its area correct to 1 d.p.

5 Using only a ruler and compasses construct △LMN with LM = 40 mm, ∠L = 120° and LN = 35 mm. Measure NM.

*6 Write in algebra shorthand:
(a) $e + e$ (b) $e \times e$ (c) $3 \times d \times d \times e$.

*7 Find the value of the expressions in parts (a), (b) and (c) of question 6 if $e = 5$ and $d = 2$.

*8 The average of three numbers is 4. Two of the numbers are 2 and 6. What is the third?

9 All the gold mined before 1980 would make only a cube of side about 16 metres.

One gram of gold can be beaten into a sheet of area 3000 cm².

1 cm³ of gold has a mass of 19.3 g.

In 1980 gold cost about $20 a gram and $2.35 = £1.

Find:

(a) the value in 1980 of 1 kg of gold in $ and in £ to the nearest £1

(b) the mass of the cube of gold in tonnes to the nearest thousand

(c) the area the gold could cover in km² to the nearest thousand.

Paper 15

1 Draw, using a protractor for the angles, triangle ABC with AB = 7 cm, $\angle A = 42°$ and $\angle C = 68°$. (Hint: Calculate $\angle B$ first.) Measure AC.

2 Draw all the quadrilaterals with special names which have at least one line of symmetry. Mark every line of symmetry and write the name of the quadrilateral underneath.

3 Write correct to 3 significant figures:
(a) 0.014226   (b) 1250.381

4 You may find it helpful to refer to the revision notes for angles (in the Summaries of Books 1 and 2) when answering this question.

For Figure P24:

(a) Name three pairs of adjacent angles on a straight line.

(b) Name a pair of vertically opposite angles.

(c) What kind of angles are the pair:
(i) c and e (ii) c and d (iii) a and e?

(d) If $a = 70°$ calculate the sizes of b, c, d and e.

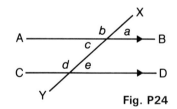

Fig. P24

5 State the order of rotational symmetry for:
(a) a square   (b) a kite   (c) an isosceles trapezium   (d) a rhombus
(e) a parallelogram.

6 Change to metres:
(a) 6 km   (b) 3.4 km   (c) 4.006 km   (d) 34 cm.

*7 If Indira earns £470 each month, how much will she earn in a year?

8 On squared paper draw a horizontal axis showing 'minutes from zero hour' from 0 to 12 and a vertical axis showing 'cm from home' from 0 to 10.

(a) Draw lines to show:
(i) a snail leaving home at zero hour (0 min), travelling at 1 cm/min
(ii) another snail coming towards the first at $1\frac{1}{2}$ cm/min, 8 cm from home 5 min after zero hour.

(b) About how long after zero hour do the two snails meet?

9 How many sides has a polygon with an angle sum of 1800°?

10 A metal alloy is made of three metals P, Q and R in the ratio 9:7:4. If the mass of metal P in a bar of this alloy is 32.67 kg, what is the mass of metal R in it?

Paper 16

1 Draw axes, x from -4 to 4, and y from -6 to 6. Draw and label the graphs of:
(a) $x = -3$ (b) $y = -x$ (c) $y = x + 1$ (d) $y = 3x$.

2 Figure P25 shows vector $\underset{\sim}{a}$.

Copy it, the same size, then draw vectors:
(a) $-\underset{\sim}{a}$ (b) $2\underset{\sim}{a}$ (c) $\frac{1}{2}\underset{\sim}{a}$.

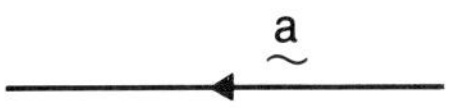

Fig. P25

3 Solve:
(a) $3m + 7 = 13$ (b) $6d - 17 = 19$ (c) $4m + 23 = 7$.

4 Work in binary:
(a) $1101 + 1001$ (b) 101×101 (c) $10110 - 1011$.

5 Increase 12 in the ratio $11:8$.

*6 In Figure P26, $\underset{\sim}{d}$ is the vector $\begin{pmatrix} 2 \\ 4 \end{pmatrix}$; $\underset{\sim}{r} = \begin{pmatrix} -1 \\ 3 \end{pmatrix}$.

$\underset{\sim}{r}$ is the resultant of $\underset{\sim}{d}$ and $\underset{\sim}{e}$.

(a) State the vector $\underset{\sim}{e}$ as a column matrix.

(b) Check that $\underset{\sim}{d} + \underset{\sim}{e} = \underset{\sim}{r}$,

that is that $\begin{pmatrix} 2 \\ 4 \end{pmatrix} + \underset{\sim}{e} = \begin{pmatrix} -1 \\ 3 \end{pmatrix}$.

7 Referring to Figure P26:

   (a) State as column matrices vectors d̰ and ḛ, and their resultant r̰.

   (b) State as column matrices the vectors:
      (i) −d̰   (ii) 2ḛ   (iii) the resultant of −d̰ and 2ḛ.

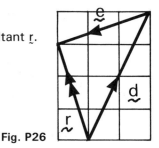

Fig. P26

8 Using only a ruler and a pair of compasses construct △PQR with PQ = 4.5 cm, ∠P = 90° and ∠Q = 30°. Measure the hypotenuse.

9 A man earns £9200 in 8 months. What is his annual salary?

10 Figure P27 represents the cross-section of a pipe, the sides being 0.5 cm thick.

   (a) Calculate the shaded area.

   (b) What is the volume of material used if the pipe is 6 metres long? Give your answer in cm³.

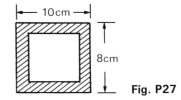

Fig. P27

11 Given that r and h are lengths:

   (a) explain why the formula $F = 2\pi r(r + h)$ must give an area

   (b) explain why the formula $G = \pi(r + h^2)$ cannot be correct.

Paper 17

1 Two angles of a quadrilateral are 80° and 40°. Find the other two angles if one is twice the other.

2 Write in cm:
   (a) 3.6 m   (b) 4.26 m   (c) 0.75 m   (d) 0.06 m.

3 Write in kg:
   (a) 1400 g   (b) 2003 g   (c) 32 g   (d) 400 g   (e) 4 g.

4 A triangle has sides 6 cm, 8 cm and 10 cm long. State the size of a second triangle if the ratio of the sides of the first to the second is:
   (a) 1 : 2   (b) 2 : 1   (c) 2 : 3.

5 Find the area of each shape in Figure P28.

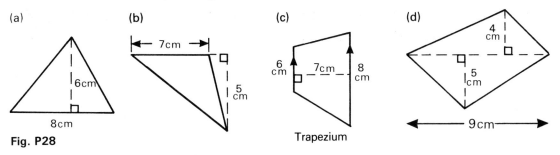

Fig. P28

Trapezium

*6 Example   To increase 25 in the ratio 7:5.

$$^5\!\!\!\not{25} \times 7 = 35$$
$$\overline{\not{5}}_1$$

Example   To decrease 36 in the ratio 5:12.

$$^3\!\!\!\not{36} \times \frac{5}{\not{12}_1} = 15$$

(a) Increase 49 in the ratio 9:7.
(b) Decrease 32 in the ratio 3:8.
(c) Decrease 18 in the ratio 5:9.
(d) Increase 108 in the ratio 11:9.

7 Remove brackets and simplify:
(a) $6(3a - 4b) - 3(5a + 3b)$ (b) $4a(3a - 5b) - 3b(2a + 4b)$.

8 If $a = 3\frac{3}{4}$, $b = 3\frac{1}{2}$ and $c = \frac{7}{12}$, find:
(a) ac (b) $b \div c$ (c) $b - c$.

9 State the H.C.F. of:
(a) $4a^3$ and a^2 (b) $4a^3b^2$ and $6a^2c^2$.

10 A0 paper has area $1\,\text{m}^2$, with sides in the ratio $\sqrt{2}:1$. Calculate its width to the nearest millimetre.

Paper 18

1 Simplify:
(a) $3t - 2 + 5t + t^2 + 1$ (b) $2k \times 3k^2$ (c) $2x^2y \div xy$.

2 Copy and complete the journey graph shown in Figure P29 to illustrate a group of cyclists who leave home at 8 a.m. and cycle 10 km in the first hour. In the next hour they manage another 20 km and then rest for 30 minutes. They then head for home and cover 5 km in $\frac{1}{2}$ h.

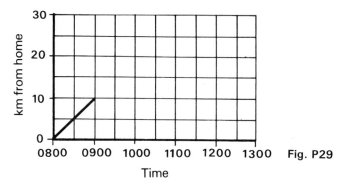

Fig. P29

(a) How far are they now from home?
(b) If they are to reach home by 1 p.m. how fast must they now cycle?

*3 **Example**   {factors of 15} = {1, 3, 5, 15}

List all the factors of:
(a) 18   (b) 27   (c) 41   (d) 63   (e) 29.

*4 Which of the numbers in question 3 (a) to (e) are prime?

*5 Change to millimetres:
(a) 1 cm   (b) 4.2 cm   (c) 0.4 cm   (d) 1 m.

*6 Write as ordinary numbers:
(a) 2.4×10^2 (b) 4.613×10^4 (c) 3.02×10^1

7 Write in litres:
(a) 1600 ml   (b) 600 ml   (c) 42 ml   (d) 2000 cm^3 (e) 500 cm^3.

8 Find the H.C.F. of:
(a) 8 and 12   (b) 12 and 56   (c) 36 and 96   (d) 128 and 496.

9 List all possible integral values of x if:
(a) $2 < x < 5$ (b) $-3 \leqslant x < 0$.

10 Solve:
(a) $4a + 5 = 3a + 9$ (b) $5b - 6 = 2b + 3$ (c) $7c + 6 = c + 48$ (d) $3d - 12 = d - 20$.

11 Sketch axes from -4 to 4 each, then shade the region
$\{(x, y): \; -1 \leqslant x \leqslant 3: \; 1 \leqslant y \leqslant 4\}$.

Paper 19

1 Write in metres:

(a) 2 km   (b) 3.4 km   (c) 4.006 km   (d) 200 cm   (e) 308 cm   (f) 56 cm.

2 Example $8a - (3a - 2d) \rightarrow 8a - 3a + 2d \rightarrow 5a + 2d$.

Remove the brackets and simplify:

(a) $6a + (2a + 3d)$ (b) $7a - (5d - 3a)$ (c) $7b + (3a - 5b)$
(d) $4a - (3a - 4b)$ (e) $7a - (4a + 3b)$.

3 Solve: (a) $2a + 6 = 18$ (b) $5a - 9 = 6$ (c) $4a + 18 = 6$ (d) $3a + 47 = 11$.

4 Using $c = 2\pi r$ or $c = \pi d$ and taking π as 3.14, find the circumference of:

(a) a plate of radius 15 cm   (b) the end of a pencil of diameter 8 mm
(c) the end of a rod of radius 3.4 cm.

5 What is the mode of: (a) 2, 4, 6, 5, 2, 4, 3, 4, 1, 0   (b) a, b, c, d, b, c, d, a, b?

*6 Calculate: (a) 23.6×4.2 (b) 0.78×26 (c) 3.14×2.4 (d) 0.075×2.3

*7 Example $4(2a - 3b + 2) \rightarrow 8a - 12b + 8$

Remove the brackets from: (a) $3(2a - 6)$ (b) $-4(3a - 2b)$.

8 Use surface area formulae to find the surface areas of the solids in Figure P30. All measurements are in centimetres.

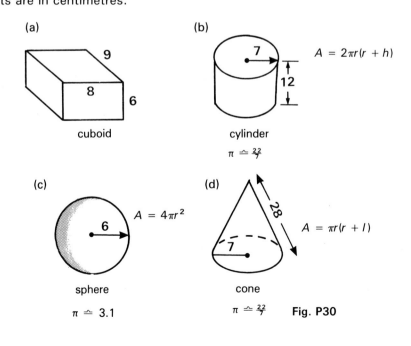

(a) cuboid

(b) cylinder $\pi \fallingdotseq \frac{22}{7}$ $A = 2\pi r(r + h)$

(c) sphere $\pi \fallingdotseq 3.1$ $A = 4\pi r^2$

(d) cone $\pi \fallingdotseq \frac{22}{7}$ $A = \pi r(r + l)$

Fig. P30

9 Figure P31 shows a tetrahedral die, its four faces being numbered 1, 2, 3 and 4.

Two such dice are thrown and the two scores added. Copy and complete the table to show all possible results.

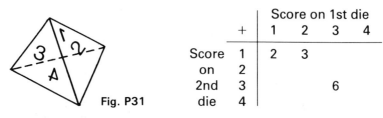

Fig. P31

+	Score on 1st die			
	1	2	3	4
Score 1	2	3		
on 2				
2nd 3			6	
die 4				

Use your completed table to find the probability that the total score from the throw of two dice will be:

(a) 6   (b) 5   (c) 4   (d) 8   (e) 10   (f) 1.

Paper 20

1 Copy Figures P32 and P33.
By dividing them into triangles and rectangles calculate their areas.

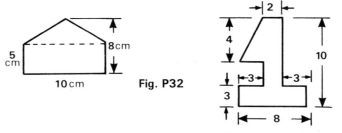

Fig. P32

Dimensions are in cm   **Fig. P33**

2 Find the mean, mode(s) and median of:
(a) 0, 1, 1, 2, 3, 4, 6, 9, 9   (b) 5, 4, 1, 3, 4, 2, 6, 9   (c) 3, 4, 4, 7, 8, 9.

*3 For each diagram in Figure P34:
(a) state the name of the pair of marked angles   (b) state the size of the lettered angle.

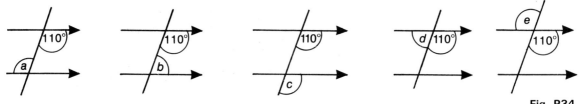

Fig. P34

*4 Change to grams: (a) 2 kg   (b) 2.4 kg   (c) 0.6 kg   (d) 2 kg 48 g.

*5 Which of the networks shown in Figures P35 and P36 is traversable; that is, can be drawn with one stroke without lifting the pencil or going over a line more than once?

Fig. P35   Fig. P36

*6 (a) Draw a compass and mark on it the points: N, NE, E, SE, S, SW, W, NW.
   (b) By each marked point write its three-figure bearing.

7 Using axes −3 to 3 each, draw the graph of :   (a) $y = 2x + 3$ (b) $y = -2x + 2$.

8 In a car rally 8 out of the 36 starters failed to finish. What percentage finished?

9 Remove the brackets and simplify:
   (a) $(3a - 2d) - (4d + 2a)$ (b) $3(3a - 2b) - 4(3b - a)$
   (c) $-4(2a - 3b) + 9(3a - 5b + 2c)$ (d) $5(2b - 3c) - (-3b + 4c)$.

Paper 21

1 A tourist received DM4.60 for each pound she changed. How much did she receive for:
   (a) £10   (b) £50   (c) £120?

2 Draw Figure P37 to the sizes, given, then enlarge it by rays by a scale factor of:
   (a) 2   (b) $\frac{1}{2}$ (c) −1.

Find the areas of the enlarged shapes.

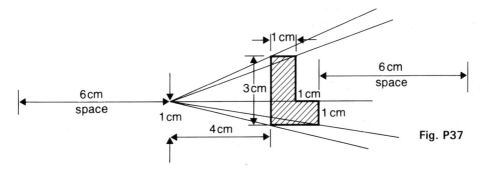

Fig. P37

3 Solve simultaneously by substitution: $y = x - 1$ and $2x + y = 8$.

*4 Find the value of the letter in each of the following equations.
  (a) $2 + x = 7$ (b) $2 + x = 1$ (c) $3 + a = 1$ (d) $2 + m = 0$

*5 Find:
  (a) $4\,\text{min}\,32\,\text{s} + 3\,\text{min}\,41\,\text{s}$ (b) $7\,\text{h}\,28\,\text{min} + 3\,\text{h}\,32\,\text{min}$ (c) $7\,\text{h} - 3\,\text{h}\,42\,\text{min}$
  (d) $5\,\text{h}\,16\,\text{min} - 2\,\text{h}\,32\,\text{min}$.

6 Find the value of the letter in each of the following equations.
  (a) $2 + x = 1$ (b) $1 + \frac{1}{2}m = 0$ (c) $1 - b = 2$ (d) $2 + 2a = 0$ (e) $2 - 2a = 2$
  (f) $3k - 6 = 9$ (g) $6 - 3p = 9$ (h) $\frac{x}{3} = 2$ (i) $\frac{2a}{5} = -4$ (j) $\frac{3}{n} = -1$

7 A car bought for £8000 has lost £1250 in value in one year. What percentage of the *original* price is it now worth?

8 Figure P38 shows the cross-section of a steel girder.

  (a) If the girder is 5 m long what is its volume in cm^3?

  (b) What is its mass in kg if 1 cm^3 of steel has a mass of 7.5 g?

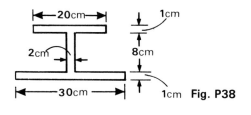

Fig. P38

9 Using $\pi = 3.14$ find correct to 2 d.p. the perimeter and area of the shape in Figure P39.

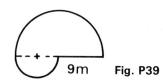

9m Fig. P39

Paper 22

1 Work out which is the better buy:
  (a) oranges at 12p each **or** 3 for 34p
  (b) oranges at 4 for 46p **or** 10 for £1.10
  (c) 1 kg of beef for £2.68 **or** 5 kg for £13.

2 Calculate the area of each shape in Figure P40. All measurements are in centimetres.

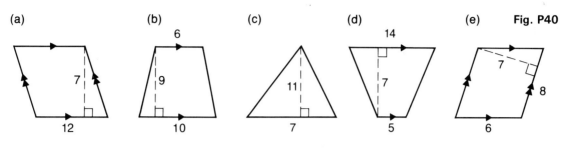

(a) (b) (c) (d) (e) **Fig. P40**

*3 Find the sizes of angles *a* to *e* in Figure P41.

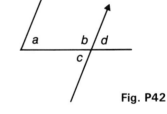

Fig. P41

4 In Figure P42 name the angle pair:
(a) *c* and *d*   (b) *a* and *d*   (c) *a* and *c*
(d) *a* and *b*.

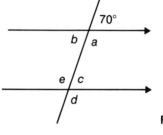

Fig. P42

5 My bicycle, which has only one gear, has a gear wheel of 40 teeth driving another with 10 teeth.

(a) How many times does the road wheel turn for each turn of the pedals?

(b) How far will the cycle travel in 100 turns of the pedals if the road wheel is 60 cm in diameter? Answer in km correct to 3 d.p. Take $\pi = 3.14$.

6 Investigate the patterns made by the numbers in Pascal's triangle when it is written in different modulos. Modulo 2 is a good one to start with. The first five rows will then be:

```
        1
       1 1
      1 0 1
     1 1 1 1
    1 0 0 0 1
```

see
'Modular arithmetic'
on p. 237.

Paper 23

1 (a) Add:
   (i) 23.6 + 148.5 + 207 + 6.84   (ii) 6.4 + 5 + 0.36 + 8.6

   (b) Subtract:
   (i) 13.6 from 34.05   (ii) 50.6 from 2000

   (c) Multiply:
   (i) 6.002 by 8.7   (ii) 143 by 5.7

   (d) Divide:
   (i) 255.06 by 13   (ii) 2550.6 by 1.3

2 What is the percentage loss when a bicycle bought for £120 is sold for £30?

Use the formula:

Loss % = (Loss/Original) × 100%.

3 How many three-quarters make a whole?

*4 Find the L.C.M. (the lowest number which is a multiple of each number) of:
   (a) 3 and 5   (b) 4 and 6   (c) 6 and 12   (d) 4, 6 and 9.

5 Find the L.C.M. of:
   (a) 2, 5 and 8   (b) 6, 14 and 42   (c) 4, 12 and 15.

6 Simplify:
   (a) $2a^3 \times 3a^2$ (b) $4b^2 \times 6c^3$ (c) $32a^5b^6 \div 8a^3b^8$.

7 Remove the brackets from:
   (a) $5a - (2a + 3b)$ (b) $6m + (3a - 2m)$ (c) $8a - (-4a)$.

8 A train travelling at 50 m.p.h. takes 3 hours less to travel between two towns than a train which averages 20 m.p.h. What is the distance between the towns?

9 Write your answers to question 1 (a) to (d) in standard form.

10 Simplify:
   (a) $n^5 \div n^2$ (b) $16a^3 \div 8a^2$ (c) $24b^6c^7 \div 16b^3c^4$ (d) $3a^3 \times 4a^3$
   (e) $6a^2b \times 4a^3b^2$ (f) $4a^3b^2c \times 5c^2d$.

Paper 24

1 Copy Figure P43 on 2 mm graph paper, with scales of 1 cm to 10 m.p.h. and 1 cm to 10 km/h.

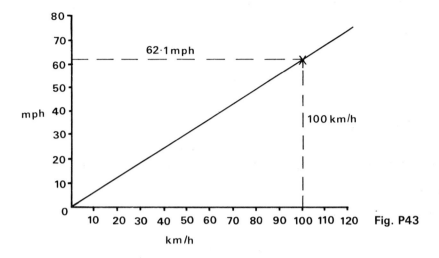

Fig. P43

(a) Use your graph to convert to km/h:
   (i) 40 m.p.h.   (ii) 30 m.p.h.   (iii) 50 m.p.h.

(b) Use your graph to convert to m.p.h.:
   (i) 40 km/h   (ii) 110 km/h.

2 (a) Find the exterior angle of a regular octagon.

(b) Use your answer to part (a) to find:
   (i) the interior angle of a regular octagon
   (ii) the sum of the interior angles of an octagon.

3 Remove the brackets and simplify:
   (a) $5a - (3b + 2a)$ (b) $4b - (3b - 2a)$ (c) $4a - (3a + 2b)$
   (d) $6a + (8c - 2a)$ (e) $2(a - 3b)$ (f) $6a - 3(a + 2)$.

4 What must $1\frac{1}{2}$ be multiplied by to give 1?

*5 How much will a woman earn in a 40-hour week if she is paid £3.20 per hour?

6 A flag pole is 14 m long measured from ground level. If $\frac{1}{8}$ of it is below ground, how long is the pole?

7 Solve by substitution:
   (a) $x = 2$; $2x + 3y = 13$ (b) $y = x - 3$; $3x + y = 13$.

8 In this multiplication, even numbers are written E and odd numbers are written O. What was the original question? (Zero counts as even, i.e. E).

$$
\begin{array}{r}
\text{E O O} \\
\text{O O} \times \\
\hline
\text{E E O} \\
\text{O O E O E} \\
\hline
\text{E E E O O}
\end{array}
$$

Paper 25

1 Solve: (a) $4f - 8 = 12 + 2f$ (b) $2t - 12 = t - 5$ (c) $6 + f = 8 - f$.

2 Solve simultaneously:
(a) $3x + 2y = 12$
    $4x - 2y = 2$ Add
(b) $3x + 4y = 16$
    $x + 4y = 8$ Subtract

3 Remove the brackets and simplify: (a) $4a - (2a - 2)$ (b) $9a + (3a - 4)$.

4 Find:
(a) $\frac{3}{4} + \frac{2}{3}$ (b) $\frac{5}{6} + 1\frac{2}{3}$ (c) $\frac{5}{7} - \frac{1}{2}$ (d) $2\frac{1}{3} - 1\frac{3}{4}$ (e) $\frac{4}{5} \times \frac{5}{6}$ (f) $\frac{9}{10} \times \frac{2}{3}$

(g) $3\frac{3}{4} \times 2\frac{2}{5}$ (h) $\frac{2}{3} \div \frac{4}{5}$ (i) $\frac{9}{10} \div \frac{3}{5}$ (j) $4\frac{1}{6} \div 1\frac{2}{3}$

*5 What would you have to pay for each article in Figure P44?

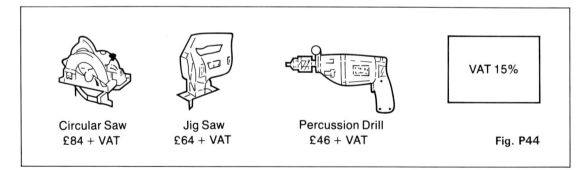

| Circular Saw | Jig Saw | Percussion Drill | VAT 15% |
| £84 + VAT | £64 + VAT | £46 + VAT | Fig. P44 |

*6 Eight boys share £15.76 equally between them. How much do they each receive?

7 A shop buys batteries in boxes of two dozen for £11.52 and sells them at 60p each. What is the percentage profit on the cost price?

8 Figure P45 is the design for a fish-plate. The semi-circular arcs are each of radius 12 cm and the distance between their centres is 21 cm. Taking $\pi = 3.14$ calculate:
(a) the perimeter of the plate
(b) the area of one side of the plate.

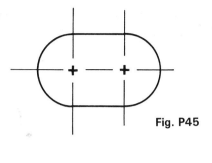

Fig. P45

9 Find the total surface area of each solid shown in Figure P46.

(a)

(b)

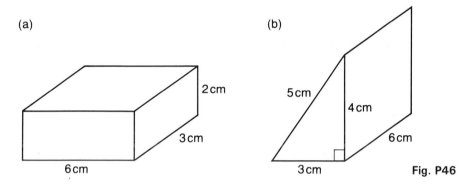

2 cm

3 cm

6 cm

5 cm

4 cm

6 cm

3 cm

Fig. P46

10 Find the volume of each solid shown in Figure P46.

Paper 26

1 Simplify:
(a) $a^4 \times a^3$ (b) $a^8 \div a^2$ (c) $3a^2 \times 4a^3$ (d) $8a^6 \div 2a^3$.

2 The membership of a youth club increases from 280 to 294. What is the percentage change? Use the formula:
Change percent equals change over original times a hundred.

3 A number is chosen at random from 1 to 12. State the probability that it is:
(a) 7   (b) an even number   (c) an odd number
(d) a prime number   (e) less than 13.

4 In Figure P47, $\overrightarrow{AB} = \begin{pmatrix} 2 \\ -1 \end{pmatrix}$ and $\overrightarrow{BC} = \begin{pmatrix} 0 \\ -3 \end{pmatrix}$.

Write vectors $\overrightarrow{CD}$ to $\overrightarrow{IJ}$ in the same way.

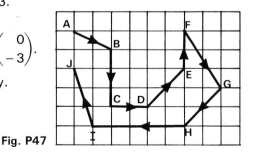

Fig. P47

*5 Calculate:
  (a) $13.7 + 0.64 + 18 + 273$ (b) $4000 - 27.38$

*6 Find the surface area of a sphere of radius $10\frac{1}{2}$ cm.
  Use the formula:
  Surface area of a sphere $= 4 \times \frac{22}{7} \times$ radius $\times$ radius.

7 Solve simultaneously:
  (a) $2x + 3y = 9$ (b) $2x + 3y = 14$
       $2x - 5y = 1$ $3x - 5y = 2$

8 A shop sells newspapers for 35% more than it pays for them. What is the selling price each for newspapers bought by the shop at £4.80 per quire (24 newspapers)?

9 How many three-eighths in a whole one?

10 Replace the stars in the statement $\frac{*}{*} = \frac{*}{*}$ using the numbers 2, 3, 4 and 6 in as many ways as you can. (Repetitions of numbers are allowed.)

Paper 27

1 (a) Increase 36 by 25%.   (b) Decrease 420 by 10%.

2 For 4, 2, 9, 8, 6, 4, 3, and 8 find:
  (a) the mean   (b) the modes   (c) the median.

3 If 3 is added to a number and the result is divided by 4 then the answer is 12. Find the number.

4 Find the volume of each solid shown in Figure P48.

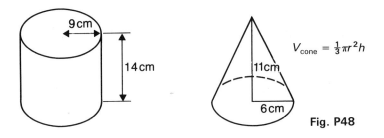

Fig. P48

*5 Write in figures:
   (a) sixty thousand   (b) twenty thousand and sixty
   (c) three million, fifty thousand and six.

*6 Find the lettered angles in Figure P49.

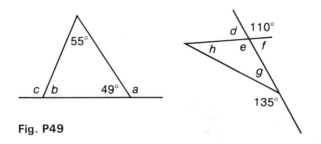

Fig. P49

*7 A train leaves a station at 1422 and arrives at its destination at 1613. How long does the journey take?

8 If $C°$ Celsius is the same temperature as $F°$ Fahrenheit then $C = \frac{5}{9}(F - 32)$.

   (a) Find the Celsius temperature that is the same as 61°F.

   (b) Find the Fahrenheit temperature that is the same as 14°C.

9 Make:
   (a) d the subject of $c = \pi d$ (b) b the subject of $a = \frac{1}{2}bh$
   (c) s the subject of $v = s^3$ (d) r the subject of $a = \pi r^2$.

Paper 28

1 A piece of wood was $36\frac{3}{8}$ inches long before $2\frac{9}{16}$ inches were cut off. How long is the remaining piece?

2 An aeroplane takes $1\frac{1}{4}$ hours to fly 400 miles. How far will it fly in 5 hours at the same average speed?

*3 Using the twenty-four hour clock write down the time twenty-six minutes after fifteen fifty-five.

*4 An orchard contains 35 rows of apple trees with 36 trees in each row. How many trees are there?

*5 Using only the figure 2 and as many signs as you like, write as many expressions as you can that equal 4.

6 A ladder 6 metres long leans against a house wall with its foot 1.5 m away from the base of the wall.

Represent this with a diagram, then calculate the vertical height of the top of the ladder correct to 1 d.p.

7 How far will the aeroplane in question 2 fly in $1\frac{3}{4}$ hours at the same average speed?

8 A girl planted out some sweet peas. The birds ate an eighth of them and slugs ate a fifth of them. There were then 54 plants left. How many did the girl plant?

9 Figure P50 represents a rectangular-based pyramid. DC = 8 cm, BC = 6 cm and AC = AE = 13 cm. Use Pythagoras' Theorem to help you calculate:
(a) EC   (b) OC
(c) AO, the perpendicular height of the pyramid.

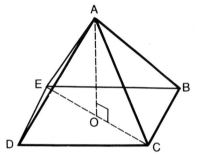

Fig. P50

10 Mike is 12 and his father is 36. Write an equation to find out in how many years Mike will be half as old as his father.

11 Arrange in decreasing order of size 2^{12}, 4^{10}, 8^6.

Paper 29

1 Share £36 between two people so that one has five times as much as the other.

*2 The cost of hiring a coach is £72. How much does each passenger pay if the cost is shared equally between:
(a) 30 passengers   (b) 50 passengers?

*3 Use brackets and signs to make the following true:
(a) 5 5 5 5 = 5   (b) 6 6 6 6 = 4   (c) 7 7 7 7 = 3
(d) 8 8 8 8 = 2   (e) 9 9 9 9 = 1

*4 Carrot fly affects 25% of my carrot crop. What is the probability that a carrot pulled at random will:
(a) have been attacked   (b) have not been attacked?

5 Find the volume of:

   (a) a cone of base radius 6 cm, height 10.5 cm (take $\pi = \frac{22}{7}$)

   (b) a square-based pyramid, side of base 12 cm, height 10.5 cm.

6 Share £56 between David, Mary and Jan so that Mary has twice as much as David, and Jan has twice as much as Mary.

7 Draw a sketch of the following triangles, then construct them accurately using a ruler and a protractor.

   (a) △ABC; AB = 5 cm, ∠A = 70°, AC = 4 cm.
      Measure BC.

   (b) △DEF; DE = 5 cm, ∠D = 85°, ∠F = 40°.
      Measure EF.

8 By what must $1\frac{1}{2}$ be multiplied to give the answer 2?

9 Figure P51 shows the design for a metal block.

   (a) Taking $\pi = 3\frac{1}{7}$ find the volume of the block.

   (b) Find the mass of the block in kg if the metal used has a density of 7.5 g/cm³.

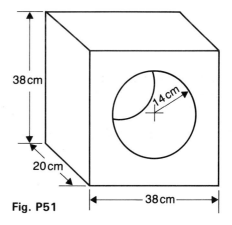

Fig. P51

Paper 30

1 Which special quadrilaterals have point symmetry, rotational symmetry order 2, and two lines of symmetry?

*2 (a) The train indicator says that the Swansea train is running 46 minutes late. If it was due to arrive at 1938 at what time is it now expected?

   (b) If the 1158 train was 17 minutes late when did it arrive?

*3 Copy Figure P52.

Using the digits 1 to 8, place a different digit in each of the circles so that numbers that differ by one (such as 2 and 3) do not lie in a pair of circles connected by a straight line.

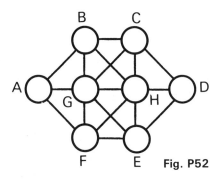

Fig. P52

4 (a) Make r the subject of $a = \pi r l$.
(b) Make b the subject of $A = \frac{1}{2}(a + b)h$.

5 Find the angles of a triangle in which two angles are equal and the third is 15° greater.

6 All the labels on 20 tins of cat food are missing. I know that there were three tins of fish and twelve tins of beef. If I pick one tin what is the probability that it will be:
(a) fish   (b) beef   (c) neither fish nor beef?

7 Each stage of a five-stage rocket has an 80% chance of success. What is the percentage chance of a successful launch into orbit?

8 Investigate the following subtraction method. Explain the method used and say how useful you think it is.
(a) $263 - 185 = 100 - 20 - 2 = 78$
(b) $469 - 178 = 300 - 10 + 1 = 291$
(c) $1901 - 727 = 1000 + 200 - 20 - 6 = 1174$

9 The net in Figure P53 will fold to make an open cube. It uses five squares, so in theory it should be possible to cut three open-cube nets from a 5 by 3 rectangle of squares. Is it?

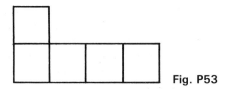

Fig. P53

Glossary

If you cannot remember what a word means, or cannot find a particular topic in the book, this glossary should help you. To save space, words that are listed alphabetically in the Summaries of Books 1 and 2 are not included in this glossary.

Note When you are told to 'see ANGLES', for example, without a number in brackets, this refers you to the heading in the Summaries of Books 1 and 2.

When you are told to 'see CHANGE OF SUBJECT (31)', for example, this refers you to the heading in the Summaries of Book 3 and to chapter 31 of this book where more information may be found.

Words in italics, like *digit*, may themselves be looked up in this glossary.

A

Adjacent	Next to: see ANGLES.
Allied	Joined to: see ANGLES.
Alternate	On opposites sides: see ANGLES.
Apex	The top point, especially of a triangle.
Arc	Part of the circumference of a circle.
	A line joining two *nodes*: see NETWORKS.

B

Binary	See BASES.

C

Cardinal bearing	A bearing that uses N, S, E and W. See BEARINGS.
Change of subject	See CHANGE OF SUBJECT (31).
Chord	A straight line joining two points on the circumference of a circle.
Circumcircle	See CONSTRUCTIONS.
Coefficient	The *constant* multiplying an algebraic term, e.g. in $3x^2$ the coefficient of x^2 is 3.
Column matrix	A *matrix* with only one column of figures, e.g. the vector $\begin{pmatrix} 2 \\ 3 \end{pmatrix}$.
Commutative	Interchangeable. Addition of numbers is commutative as $3 + 4 = 4 + 3$. Subtraction of numbers is not, as $6 - 2 \neq 2 - 6$.
Complement	One of two parts that make up a whole. Complementary angles add up to $90°$. Complement of a set: see SETS (36).
Concave	'With a cave'; a concave polygon has at least one angle pointing inwards ('re-entrant').
Cone	A *pyramid* with a circular base.
Congruent	Exactly the same in both shape and size.
Consecutive	Following one after another; 5, 7, 9 and 11 are consecutive odd numbers.
Constant	Unchanging: a constant term in an algebraic expression will be the same for all values of the letters, e.g. the 3 in $y = x + 3$.
Construct	Draw accurately, usually using only a ruler and a pair of compasses.

Convex	'Pointing outwards'; the opposite of *concave*.
Correlation	Connecting together: positive correlation means that as one set of data increases in value, the second increases too; negative correlation means that as one set of data increases, the second decreases: see SCATTER GRAPHS (8).
Corresponding	In the same position: see ANGLES; SIMILARITY.
Cubic	In the shape of, or involving, a cube. 1 cm³ (one cubic centimetre) is the volume of a cube of side 1 cm. It is also the volume of anything with the same volume as this cube.
Cuboid	A solid with six rectangular faces, like a brick. If all the rectangles are squares it is called a cube.

D

Decimal places	The numbers of figures after the decimal point: see APPROXIMATIONS.
Decision tree	A flowchart used to identify objects: see DECISION TREES (8).
Deduce	To reach a conclusion by reasoning.
Denary	Based on ten.
Denominator	The bottom number in a fraction; it tells into how many parts the whole has been divided.
Diagonal	A line joining corners of a polygon: see POLYGON (15).
Difference	The result of a subtraction.
Digit	One of the figures in a number.
Digit-sum	Used in this course for the result of continually adding the *digits* of a number until a single digit results: see DIVISIBILITY.
Disjoint	Not connected: see SETS.
Distance/time graph	See DISTANCE/TIME GRAPHS (7).
Domain	The set of numbers, or the *region*, from which you start: see MAPPINGS.

E

Enlargement	See ENLARGEMENT (1).
Exclusive events	See PROBABILITY (25).
Exterior angle	The angle between a *produced* side of a polygon and the *adjacent* side: see POLYGONS (15).

F

Factorise	Split into expressions that multiply together to make the whole.
Factors	Numbers or expressions that multiply by others to make the whole: e.g. 5 and 10 are factors of 100. See PRIME FACTORS (3).
Frequency	How often something occurs. See FREQUENCY TABLES (19).
Function	See MAPPINGS.

H

Hatch	To define an area by drawing a set of parallel sloping lines on it.
H.C.F./Highest Common Factor	See PRIME FACTORS (3).
Hexadecimal	Base sixteen; uses the letters *a* to *f* to represent 10 to 15. Used in 'machine code' programming of computers.
Hypotenuse	The longest side in a right-angled triangle: see PYTHAGORAS' THEOREM (32).

I

Image	The result of a *transformation*. Also the result of a mapping see MAPPINGS.
Improper fraction	A top-heavy fraction, like $\frac{13}{2}$.
Incircle	See CONSTRUCTIONS.
Inclusive	'Including everything', e.g. (integers from 1 to 3 inclusive) = {1, 2, 3}.
Independent events	See PROBABILITY (25).
Index/Indices	The raised figure (figures) that give the *power*, e.g. the 2 in x^2.
Inequality	See INEQUALITIES (22A).
Infinite	Without ending.
Integer	A +ve or -ve whole number, not a fraction, e.g. -3, 8, 170.
Interior angle	The angle made inside a polygon by two *adjacent* sides: see POLYGONS (15).
Interquartile range	The spread of the middle 50% of a set of data: see STATISTICS (19).
Intersection	The crossing point of two lines. See also SETS.

K

Kite	See QUADRILATERALS.

L

L.C.M./Lowest Common Multiple	See PRIME FACTORS (3).
Litre	The metric unit for capacity: see METRIC SYSTEM.
Locus (plural loci)	The path made by a moving point: see CONSTRUCTIONS (17).
Loss/Loss %	The opposite of *profit*. A car bought for £8000 and sold for £2000 is sold at a loss of £6000 or $\frac{6000}{8000} \times 100\% = 75\%$.

M

Magnitude	Size; the magnitude (length) of a vector is called its *modulus*.
Matrix	A table of figures; plural is 'matrices'.
Mixed number	A number consisting of an integer and a fraction, like $3\frac{3}{4}$.
Modulus	See VECTORS (9).
Multiple	A number made by multiplying one integer by another. See PRIME FACTORS (3).
Multiplying factor	See PROPORTION (6).

N

Natural numbers	Numbers used for counting.
Node	See NETWORKS.
Null set	A set with no elements, e.g. {prime even numbers greater than 2}.
Numerator	The top number in a fraction.

O

Ordered pair	An alternative name for co-ordinates.

P

Parallelogram	See QUADRILATERALS.

Pentagon	A five-sided polygon.
Percentage error	An indication of the seriousness of an arithmetical error. Found by the formula (Error/True) × 100%.
Perpendicular	At right angles.
Perpendicular bisector	A line which crosses the midpoint of another line at right angles: see CONSTRUCTIONS.
Pictogram	A chart showing information by means of picture symbols that represent a certain amount.
Point symmetry	See POINT SYMMETRY (34).
Possibility space	The complete set of possible outcomes in a probability question.
Power	The result of multiplying a number by itself a number of times. It can be shown using an *index*, e.g. as 5^3.
Prime factor	A number which is both prime and a *factor* of the given number: see PRIME FACTORS (3).
Produce	To make a line longer; e.g. 'Produce AB to C' means lengthen line AB from end B.
Product	The result of a multiplication.
Profit	The gain made when something is sold for more than was paid for it. Percentage profit is usually found from the formula: (Profit/Cost price) × 100%.
Pyramid	A solid with a polygon as its base and triangular sides meeting at a common *vertex*.

Q

Quotient	The result of a division.

R

Range	In statistics the amount by which the largest item exceeds the smallest; see also *interquartile range*. For range in algebra, see MAPPINGS.
Reciprocal of *x*	The result of dividing 1 by *x*: see FRACTIONS (5).
Rectangular numbers	Numbers which are not prime (except 1).
Recur	To repeat, as in recurring decimals, the repeating figure(s) being indicated with a dot (or two dots).
Reflex	An angle more than 180°. If a reflex angle is intended then it will be written as 'Angle ABC reflex'.
Region	A special area of a diagram, especially of a graph or network. See NETWORKS; GRAPHS; GRAPH REGIONS (23).
Resultant	See VECTORS (9).
Rhombus	See QUADRILATERALS.
Rotation	A turn about a fixed point: see ROTATIONS (13).
Rotational symmetry	See ROTATIONS (13).
Route matrix	See NETWORKS.

S

Scale factor	See ENLARGEMENT (1).
Scatter graph	A graph to investigate for *correlation* between two sets of data. See SCATTER GRAPHS (8).

Sequence	A set of numbers or terms connected by a fixed rule, e.g. 1, 4, 7, 10, 13, . . . $3n - 2$.
Significant figures	See SIGNIFICANT FIGURES (16).
Simplify	To make easier; usually in algebraic simplification you have to multiply out brackets and collect like terms.
Simultaneous	At the same time: see SIMULTANEOUS EQUATIONS (26, 29).
Slope	See DISTANCE/TIME GRAPHS (7) and SLOPING LINE GRAPHS (18, 23).
Solve	To find the numerical value of the letter(s).
Sphere	The mathematical name for a ball.
Standard form	The method of writing a number as a number between 1 and 10 multiplied by a *power* of ten, e.g. 2.5×10^{-3} is the standard form method of writing 0.0025. Many scientific calculators use standard form to display large and small numbers, 0.000 000 6 showing as 6 -07. Computers usually show this as 6E $- 7$: see STANDARD FORM (2).
Subset	Part of another set: see SETS.
Sum	The result of an addition.

T

Tangent	In geometry, a straight line which touches, but does not cross, a curve. See TANGENTS TO CIRCLES (28).
Tonne	A metric unit of mass (or weight), equal to 1000 kg.
Transformation	Any operation which changes the size, shape or position of a figure, including: Topological transformation; Reflection; *Translation*; *Rotation*.
Translate	To slide a shape: see VECTORS.
Transpose/Transposition	See CHANGE OF SUBJECT (31).
Trapezium	See QUADRILATERALS.
Traversability	See NETWORKS.
Trial and improvement	Finding an answer by guessing, then trying to improve on your guess.

U

Union	See SETS (36).
Universal set	See SETS (36).

V

Variable	A letter which may stand for various numbers.
Venn diagram	See SETS (36).
Vertex	A corner of a shape.

Y

$y = mx + c$	The 'general equation' of all straight line graphs. See SLOPING LINE GRAPHS (18, 23).

Notes: (a) Topics are given in alphabetical order.

(b) The numbers in brackets refer to chapters in *this* book (summarised on page 242 to 249) where further information may be found.

Algebra (14, 20, 22, 26, 29, 31, 33)

Algebra is frequently revised as new work is developed. See the given chapters for examples and notes. Refer also to the following notes under the headings Equations, Graphs, and Mappings.

Angles (15)

In Figure S1: angle *a* is **acute**
angle *b* is **obtuse**
angle *r* is **reflex**.

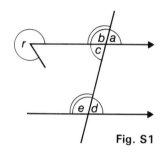

Fig. S1

$a + b = 180°$ (Adjacent ∠s on a straight line)
$a = c$ (Vertically opposite ∠s)
$a = d$ (Corresponding ∠s)
$c = d$ (Alternate ∠s)
$c + e = 180°$ (Allied ∠s)

Hints: **Adjacent** ⇒ next-door
Corresponding ⇒ in the same position
Alternate ⇒ on opposite sides (Z angles)
Allied ⇒ joined together.

Note: All angles that add up to 180° are said to be **supplementary**.

Approximations (16)

Rounding and **decimal places** are reviewed in exercise 16A.

Examples 697 is 700 to the nearest ten.
3.95 is 4.0 to one decimal place.

Exercise 16B introduces **significant figures**.

Areas (10, 21, 27)

The area of a rectangle is the length of its base multiplied by its height.

The area of a triangle is half the length of its base multiplied by its height.

Bases

Denary: Our usual number system; called **Base Ten** because it uses ten figures (0 to 9).

Binary: The number system used by microchips; called **Base Two** because it uses two figures (0 and 1).

The column headings in binary rise in powers of 2:

2^4 2^3 2^2 1^1 2^0 →   16s   8s   4s   2s   1s

Binary arithmetic ✕

Exactly the same rules apply as for normal (denary) arithmetic, but remember that $1 + 1 = 10$ and $1 + 1 + 1 = 11$, where 10 (or ^{10}) means *two* and 11 (or ^{11}) means *three*.

Addition

```
  1 1 1
+ 1 0 1
-------
1 1 0 0
-------
  1 1
```

Subtraction

Decomposition method

```
  1̶ ¹0̶ ¹0 1
-     1 1 1
-----------
        1 0
```

Note: The 1 you take (leaving 1̶) becomes ^{10} in the next column. Taking 1 from ^{10} leaves $^10̸$

Equal addition method

```
  1 ¹0 ¹0 1
- 1¹0̸ 1 1 1
-----------
        1 0
```

Multiplication

(a) $1011 \times 100 = 101\ 100$ ('add 0s' as in denary)

(b)
```
        1 1 1
    ×   1 1 1
    ---------
        1 1 1
      1 1 1 0
    1 1 1 0 0
    ---------
  1 1 0 0 0 1
      1 0 1
        1
```

Note: In the 4s column, $1 + 1 + 1 + 1$ gives 100. Carry the 1 to the 16s column and the 0 to the 8s column. The $1 + 1 + 0$ in the 8s column then gives another carry 1 in the 16s column.

Division

```
            1 0 1 1
1 1 ) 1 0 0 0 0 1
    - 1 1
    -------
      1 0 0
    -   1 1
    -------
        1 1
      - 1 1
```

Bicimals

Bicimals are the binary equivalent of decimals:

$0.1_{binary} = \frac{1}{2}$; $0.01_{binary} = \frac{1}{4}$

Bearings

In Figure S2: B is 045° or NE from A;
                 A is 225° or SW from B. ✓

When asked for a bearing *from* a point, imagine yourself at that point, mark a North line, then turn clockwise.

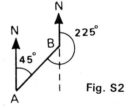

Fig. S2

If you are given the bearing of A from B and have to find the bearing of B from A (called the **back-bearing**), you can either find it from a diagram like Figure R2, or add 180° to the angle given then subtract 360° if the answer is more than 360°.

Examples   A is 080° from B, so B is 080° + 180° = 260° from A.

               C is 250° from D, so D is 250° + 180° = 430° → 430° − 360° = 70° from C.

Circles (10C, 28)

The circumference of a circle is $\pi \times d$, where d is the diameter.
The area of a circle is $\pi \times r^2$, where r is the radius.

In these examples, centres are marked •₁ •₂ in order of use and arcs are marked ⌒₁ ⌒₂ to link with the numbered centres. Lines are marked ₃ in order of drawing.

All **angle constructions** are based on two basic methods:
An angle of 60° (Figure S3) and the **bisection of an angle** (Figure S4).

To construct an angle of 30° bisect a 60° angle.

To construct an angle of 90° either draw a 60° angle followed by a 30° angle (Figure S5a) or bisect an angle of 180° (Figure S5b).

To construct an angle of 45° bisect a 90° angle.

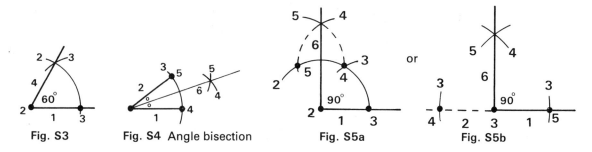

Fig. S3   Fig. S4 Angle bisection   Fig. S5a   Fig. S5b

Figure S6 shows the construction of the **perpendicular bisector of a line.**

Figure S7 shows how to construct a **triangle given its three sides**. Note the arcs at the apex.

Figure S8 shows the construction of the **incentre and incircle of a triangle** by bisecting its angles.

Figure S9 shows the construction of the **circumcentre and circumcircle of a triangle** by perpendicularly bisecting its sides.

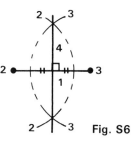

Fig. S6

Perpendicular bisector

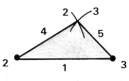

Fig. S7 △ given 3 sides

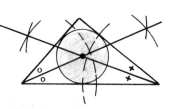

Fig. S8 Incircle of △

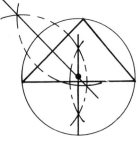

Fig. S9 Circumcircle of △

Conversion graphs

Figure S10 shows a conversion graph. It enables rapid conversion (change) from speed in km/h to speed in m.p.h.

Given that 8 km is about 5 miles we can plot (8, 5) and (16, 10). We know that 0 km = 0 miles, giving point (0, 0). Join the points. The dotted line shows that 12 km/h is about $7\frac{1}{2}$ m.p.h. *or* $7\frac{1}{2}$ m.p.h. is about 12 km/h.

Conversion graphs need not be straight lines, though for most of the examples you are likely to meet they will be.

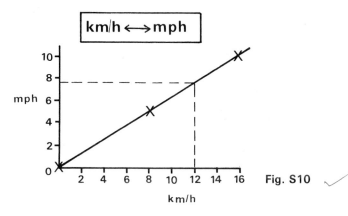

Fig. S10

Decimal fraction arithmetic (30)

The following methods may be used instead of using a calculator.

Addition and Subtraction
As for integers; keep points in line; all units figures in the same column.

Multiplication
Ignore the points and any zeros at the start or finish of the numbers. Then restore any final zeros and insert a point with the same number of figures after it as the total number of figures after the points in the question.

Example

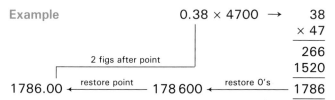

$$0.38 \times 4700 \rightarrow \begin{array}{r} 38 \\ \times\ 47 \\ \hline 266 \\ 1520 \\ \hline 1786 \end{array}$$

178 600 $\xleftarrow{\text{restore 0's}}$ 1786

1786.00 $\xleftarrow{\text{restore point}}$ 178 600

2 figs after point

Division
Division by an integer is done by the usual method. Division by a decimal is done by multiplying both the divisor and the dividend by the power of 10 that makes the divisor into an integer. Once this has been done the answer to the division is the required answer. No further change in the position of the point is required.

Example   18.324 ÷ 0.09 $\xrightarrow{\text{multiply both by 100}}$ 1832.4 ÷ 9 = 203.6

Directed numbers (35, 37)

Positive (plus) numbers are more than zero. They need no sign.

Negative (minus) numbers are below zero. They need a $-$ sign.

The sign $+$ is used both to show a number is more than zero and also to mean the operation of addition. The sign $-$ is used both to show a number is below zero and also to mean the operation of subtraction. This can be rather confusing!

Like signs multiply to make a plus: $\quad - - \rightarrow +; \quad - \times - \rightarrow +$

Unlike signs multiply to make a minus: $\quad - + \rightarrow -; \quad + - \rightarrow -; \quad - \times + \rightarrow -; \quad + \times - \rightarrow -$

Examples If $a = -2$, $b = -3$, and $c = 4$ then:

(i) $a + b = -2 + -3 \rightarrow -2 - 3 = -5$

> **Note:** $-2 - 3$ can be thought of as 'take away 2 then take away 3', or as 'start at -2 then go down 3'.

> **Note:** $-2 - 3$ does not become $+$ because the two minus signs are not *multiplied* together. Two minuses do *not* make a plus, but minus times a minus *does* make a plus.

(ii) $a - b = -2 - -3 \rightarrow -2 + 3 = 1$

> **Note:** $-2 + 3$ can be thought of as 'take away 2 then add 3', or as 'start at -2 then go up 3'.

(iii) $bc = -3 \times 4 = -12$

(iv) $ab = -2 \times -3 = 6$

(v) $\dfrac{c}{a} = \dfrac{4}{-2} = -2; \quad \dfrac{a}{b} = \dfrac{-2}{-3} = \tfrac{2}{3}$

> **Note:** The same sign rules apply for division as for multiplication.

Divisibility

In this section, 'divides' means 'divides exactly'. People often mean this when they use the word divide, e.g. the correct answer to 'Will 13 divide by 2?' is 'Yes', but the questioner probably means 'Is the answer to $13 \div 2$ an integer?'

Digit-sum means the single figure obtained by repeatedly adding the digits of a number, e.g. the digit-sum of 156 is $1 + 5 + 6 = 12 \rightarrow 1 + 2 = 3$.

Divisibility rules

A number divides by:	2	3	5	6	9	10
if its 'digit-sum' is:	anything	3, 6 or 9	anything	3, 6 or 9	9	anything
and its last figure is:	even	anything	0 or 5	even	anything	0

Also: A number divides by 4 if its last two digits divide by 4.

A number divides by 8 if its last three digits divide by 8.

Equations (22B, 26, 29, 31)

See Graphs (below) for equations of lines.

Equations with only one letter-term are best solved by inspection.

Example   To solve $7 - 4x = 10$.

$4x$ must be -3, for $7 - -3 = 10$.
If four x's make -3 then one x must be a quarter of -3, giving the answer
$x = -\frac{3}{4}$.

Example   To solve $\dfrac{16}{x + 1} = 1$.

$x + 1$ must be 16, for $\frac{16}{16} = 1$.
If $x + 1$ is 16, then $x = 15$.

Fibonacci's sequence

A sequence is a set of numbers where a new number is found by applying some rule to the previous numbers.

Fibonacci's sequence usually starts with two 1s. The rule is 'Add the last two numbers'. Hence:
1, 1, 2, 3, 5, 8, 13, . . .

Fractions (common) (5, 30)

Fraction → Decimal: $\frac{3}{5} \to 3 \div 5 \to 5\overline{)3.0}\;\;(0.6)$

Hence $\frac{3}{5} = 0.6$

Decimal → Fraction: 0.375 $\xrightarrow[\text{thousandths column}]{\text{last fig. is in}}$ $\dfrac{375}{1000} \to \dfrac{3}{8}$

Addition and Subtraction: Work whole number part first.

Examples $6\frac{3}{8} + 1\frac{1}{4} = 7\frac{3}{8} + \frac{2}{8} = 7\frac{5}{8}$

$4\frac{1}{3} - 2\frac{2}{5} = 2\frac{5}{15} - \frac{6}{15} = 2 - \frac{1}{15} = 1\frac{14}{15}$

Multiplication and Division: See the Summaries of Book 3.

Graphs (7, 18, 23, 26A)

In Figure S11 the region hatched is
$\{(x, y): -2 < x < 0\} \cap \{(x, y): -2 < y < 2\}$
That is, where the region with x co-ordinates between -2 and 0 intersects the region with y co-ordinates between -2 and 2. This region can also be written as
$\{(x, y): -2 < x < 0; -2 < y < 2\}$

Fig. S11

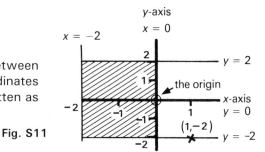

235

Mappings (Functions)

A mapping transforms (changes) one thing into another according to a given rule.

Example $f : x \rightarrow x^2$ (Read this: A function of x is: x maps onto (becomes) x^2.)
It can also be written as $f(x) = x^2$.

Using this function, $3 \rightarrow 3^2$, or $f(3) = 9$. Similarly $f(4) = 16$.
$\{3, 4\}$ is called the **domain** and $\{9, 16\}$ is called the **range**.

Matrices (35, 37)

See the Summaries of Book 3 for notes, and Networks (page 000) for **route matrix**.

Mean/Median/Mode (12, 19)

The **mean** is the average resulting when the total amount is shared out equally.

The **mode** is the most frequent item. There may be more than one mode.

The **median** is the middle item when the data is arranged in order. For an even number of items the median is taken as the mean of the two middle items.

Metric system

1000 kg = 1 tonne; 1000 cm³ = 1 litre; 10 000 m² = 1 hectare

When changing from one metric unit to another, the figure in the units column is rewritten in the correct column of the new unit, and noughts are never inserted or removed from between the given figures.

Example 108.9 mm → ? metres

The 8 units are 8 mm. As 8 mm is $\dfrac{8}{1000}$ metre, the 8 is rewritten in the $\dfrac{1}{1000}$s column, giving 108.9 mm = 0.1089 metre.

Example 3.06 cm → 0.0306 m

$$3\,\text{cm} = \frac{3}{100}\,\text{m}$$

Example 0.003 06 m → 0.000 003 06 km

$$0\,\text{m} = \frac{0}{1000}\,\text{km}$$

When changing square or cubic units, change as follows:
$5\,\text{m}^2 = 5\,\text{m} \times 1\,\text{m} = 500\,\text{cm} \times 100\,\text{cm} = 50\,000\,\text{cm}^2$
$568\,\text{cm}^2 = 568\,\text{cm} \times 1\,\text{cm} = 5.68\,\text{m} \times 0.01\,\text{m} = 0.0568\,\text{m}^2$

Modular arithmetic

Example   In Modulo 4 only four numbers exist: 0, 1, 2 and 3. There are no fractions, negatives, etc.

Figure S12 sho s the mod 4 clock. After 3 the clock returns to 0, so 4, 8 and 16 are all 0 (mod 4). 18 is 4 complete turns with 2 left over, so 18 → 2 (mod 4).

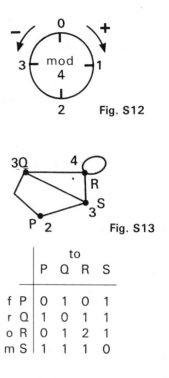

Fig. S12

Networks

Figure S13 shows a two-way network. Q is a **node** of order 3 (3 **arcs** leave it). Order-2 nodes, like P, only exist if specially marked. Figure S13 has 4 nodes (*N*), 6 arcs (*A*) and **4 regions** (*R*). Note that the loop counts as one arc and the regions include the outside of the network.

For all networks $N + R = A + 2$ (Euler's (pronounced 'Oiler') Theorem).

A **route matrix** describes a network by stating how many ways there are of passing from one node directly to another. This is route matrix for Figure S13.

Fig. S13

		to			
		P	Q	R	S
f	P	0	1	0	1
r	Q	1	0	1	1
o	R	0	1	2	1
m	S	1	1	1	0

A two-way route matrix is always symmetrical about the leading (\) diagonal. Note that the loop at R is shown as a 2, clockwise and anticlockwise.

Figure S14 shows a one-way network and its matrix. Note that a one-way matrix is not symmetrical. When drawing a one-way network from a matrix be careful that you do not draw a new arc if you can put a second arrow on an existing one. Figure S15 illustrates this.

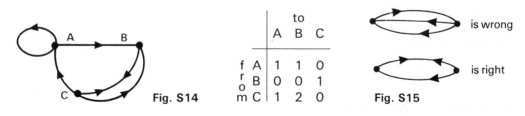

		to		
		A	B	C
f	A	1	1	0
r	B	0	0	1
o	C	1	2	0
m				

Fig. S14   Fig. S15

is wrong

is right

A network is **traversable** (can be drawn with one continuous line) if it has two odd nodes or no odd nodes. An odd node must be either a start or a finish. An even node may be both the start and the finish, or an intermediate point.

Pascal's triangle

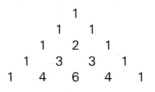

Percentages (11)

Fraction to percentage: $\frac{2}{15} \rightarrow \frac{2}{\underset{3}{\cancel{15}}} \times \cancel{100}^{20}\% = \frac{40}{3}\% = 13\frac{1}{3}\%$

Percentage of an amount: To find 35% of £45.

$$35\% \Rightarrow \frac{35}{100}; \text{ of } \Rightarrow \text{multiply}$$

$$35\% \text{ of } £45 \rightarrow \frac{\overset{7}{\cancel{35}}}{\underset{4\,20}{\cancel{100}}} \times £\cancel{45}^{9} = \frac{£63}{4} = £15.75$$

Pie-chart

A pie-chart shows statistical data as slices of a circular 'pie'. Each section, or **sector**, is a certain fraction of the 360° in the complete circle.

Example   To show 40% in favour, 60% against.
Use 40% of 360° = 144° and 60% of 360° = 216°.

Polygons (12)

Pentagon (5 sides); Hexagon (6 sides); Heptagon (7 sides); Octagon (8 sides); Nonagon (9 sides); Decagon (10 sides).

Prime numbers (3A)

Primes have only two factors, 1 and themselves. Some primes are: 2, 3, 5, 7 and 11.

Prisms (21, 24)

A prism is a solid with a constant cross-section (the same shape all through it). The two end faces are parallel, and if slices parallel to the end faces are taken from one end of the prism to the other then each slice is identical.

Some common examples are:
a domino (a rectangular prism); an unsharpened pencil (probably a hexagonal prism); a Toblerone box (a triangular prism); a stick of chalk (a circular prism, or a cylinder).

The volume of a prism is the area of its cross-section multiplied by the perpendicular distance between the end faces (its length or its height for a *right* prism).

Figure S16 shows a right prism and a *skew* prism.

Right prism   Skew prism

Fig. S16

Probability (4, 25)

The probability of an outcome is a fraction between 0 (impossible) and 1 (certain). If all outcomes are equally likely then the probability of a certain outcome is the fraction:

$$\frac{\text{number of ways the outcome can happen}}{\text{number of possible outcomes}}$$

Quadrilaterals

The properties of special quadrilaterals can be observed from a careful sketch. See Figure S17.

Remember: A parallelogram has no axes of symmetry.

Remember: The diagonals of a kite, a rhombus, and a square cross at right angles.

Remember: The angle sum of all quadrilaterals is 360°.

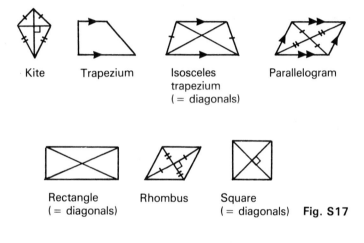

| Kite | Trapezium | Isosceles trapezium (= diagonals) | Parallelogram |

| Rectangle (= diagonals) | Rhombus | Square (= diagonals) | **Fig. S17** |

Ratio (6, 27)

Example   In Figure S18 the distances of A and B from C are in the ratio 3 : 4. If AC = 15 km find BC.

A ——————— C ——————— B   **Fig. S18**

AC : BC = 3 : 4 = 15 km : n
The 3 is increased five times to give 15; increase the 4 five times to give n = 20 km.

Alternatively use the multiplying factor $\frac{4}{3}$ as explained in chapter 6.

Beware: It is tempting, but wrong, to use an addition approach. For instance, in the above example to say that as 3 + 12 = 15, then the answer is 4 + 12 = 16.

Example   Divide £16 in the ratio 3 : 5.

Ratio 3 : 5 gives 3 + 5 = 8 parts.
£16 in 8 parts gives £2 per part, so 3 parts = £6 and 5 parts = £10.

S

Reflection

Figure S19 illustrates the transformation of reflection.

An **object** point and its **image** are the same distance from the mirror, and the line joining them crosses the mirror line at right angles.

Note: When reflecting a shape, reflect each of its corners in turn.

Note: If the mirror line is sloping, turn your paper until the mirror line is upright. Our eyes are accustomed to left/right symmetry.

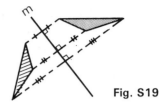

Fig. S19

Similarity (27)

Similar figures have the same shape but are of different sizes. Their corresponding sides are in the same ratio. See Figure S20.

Figures that have the same shape and are of the same size are said to be **congruent**.

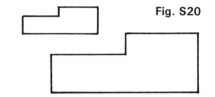

Fig. S20

Statistical diagrams (8)

Pictogram See Figure S21.

Clerical/shop	🧍🧍🧍🧍🧍
Engineering/ industrial	🧍🧍🧍
Welfare/social	🧍🧍🧍🧍
Forces/police/ fire service	🧍🧍🧍
Newspapers/ radio etc.	🧍🧍
Catering/ hotels	🧍🧍

🧍 represents 50 school leavers   **Fig. S21**

The data is represented by drawings, each standing for a certain amount.

Bar chart: See Figure 12:1 on page 59.

Note: Sometimes you will see a bar chart with the vertical axis labelled 'frequency' called a **histogram**. This is not correct. In a histogram it is the area of the bars that represents the frequency; the vertical axis may be labelled 'frequency density' and/or a key to the area representation given.

Proportionate bar chart See Figure S22.
This joins all the bars of a bar chart together end to end.

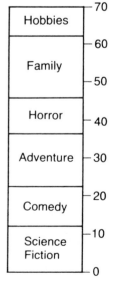

Fig. S22 Favourite TV programmes

240

Line graph (frequency polygon)   See Figure S23.

Points are usually joined with straight lines but sometimes with a curve. Intermediate points do not always have any meaning.

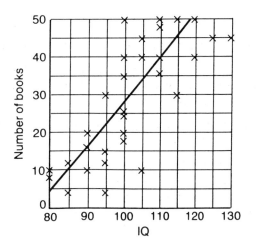

Fig. S23

Pie chart   See Figure S24.

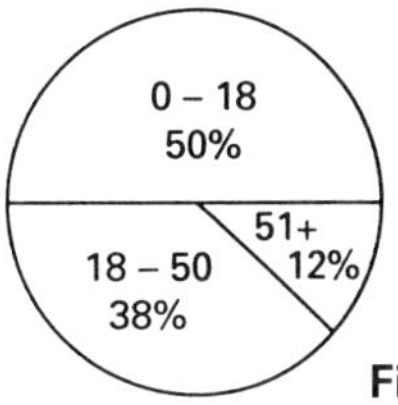

Fig. S24

The data are divided up between the 360° that make the circle. For example 5 out of a total of 30 would be represented by $\frac{5}{30} \times 360° = 60°$.

Scatter graph   See page 244.

This is useful to seek for connections between two sets of data, for example any connection between results in Science and Maths.

Cumulative frequency curve   See page 189.

This shows how the data builds up. The shape of the curve gives a good idea of the spread of the data.

Triangular numbers

.   .·.   .·.·.   .·.·.·.
1   3   6   10   etc.

Vectors (9)

A vector is a line with both length and direction. It may be described by a column matrix showing how far right (+) or left (−) and up (+) or down (−) the vector translates a point. See Figures S25 and S26.

Fig. S25

Fig. S26

In Figure S27 the hatched square is **translated** to the shaded square by the vector $\binom{3}{1}$. Each corner moves forward 3 and up 1.

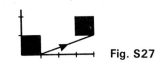

Fig. S27

Summaries: Book 3

Note: Only 'key facts' are given in this summary. The numbers in brackets after the headings refer you to the book chapters where fuller details may be found.

Enlargement (1)

A transformation in which a shape is enlarged by a given **scale factor** from a given centre. If the scale factor is less than 1 then the enlarged shape is smaller!

Figure S28 shows various enlargements. In each case the hatched triangle ABC is transformed into the shaded triangle A'B'C'.

Note: The sides of the object and image triangles are parallel.

Note: If the scale factor is negative then the image is inverted and on the opposite side of the centre of enlargement.

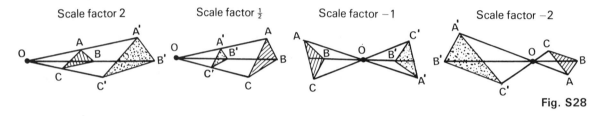

Scale factor 2   Scale factor ½   Scale factor −1   Scale factor −2

Fig. S28

Standard form (2)

Numbers written in the form $a \times 10^n$, where a is a number from 1 to $9.\dot{9}$, and n is a positive or negative integer, are in **standard form**.

Examples   76 000 $\longrightarrow$ 7.6×10^4
0.005 26 $\longrightarrow$ 5.26×10^{-3}

The **index** (raised figure) tells you how many columns the figures should be moved to convert from standard form to an ordinary number. Move the figures to the left for a positive index, and to the right for a negative index.

Prime factors: H.C.F.; L.C.M. (3)

To write a number as a product of _prime factors_.

Example $162 = 2 \times 81 = 2 \times 3 \times 27 = 2 \times 3 \times 3 \times 9 = 2 \times 3 \times 3 \times 3 \times 3$

See exercise 3A, questions 3 and 4, for further examples.

To find the H.C.F. (Highest Common Factor) of a set of numbers

A factor divides exactly into a number; the highest number that is a factor of each of a set of numbers is called their Highest Common Factor (H.C.F. for short).

For small numbers the H.C.F. can easily be found mentally, e.g. the H.C.F. of 12, 15 and 18 is 3. For larger numbers a prime factor method is useful: see exercise 3B, question 7.

To find the L.C.M. (Lowest Common Multiple) of a set of numbers

A multiple is made by multiplying a number by an integer. The lowest number that is a multiple of each of a set of numbers is called their Lowest Common Multiple (L.C.M. for short).

For small numbers the L.C.M. can easily be found mentally, e.g. the L.C.M. of 6, 8 and 12 is 24. For larger numbers a prime factor method is useful, see exercise 3C, question 5.

Do not confuse H.C.F. with L.C.M.! Remember what a factor is and what a multiple is. For a given set of different numbers their H.C.F. is always smaller than their L.C.M.

For applications to algebra see exercise 3A, questions 6 and 8; exercise 3B, questions 8 and 9; exercise 3C, question 6.

Fractions: Multiplication and division (5)

Mixed numbers must be changed to top-heavy fractions before multiplying or dividing them by other fractions.

To multiply: Cancel if possible, then multiply together the top numbers and the bottom numbers. See exercise 5A for examples.

To divide: Change the sign to multiply and invert (turn upside-down) the following fraction. Then proceed as for multiplication. See exercise 5B for examples.

Proportion: Multiplying factors (6)

If a plant usually produces 4 flowers per stem, then the proportion of flowers to stems is 4 to 1, or 4 : 1. Proportion examples usually involve increasing or decreasing amounts in the same ratio.

To change an amount in the ratio $x:y$ multiply it by $\dfrac{x}{y}$.

See chapter 6 for more notes and examples.

Distance/time graphs (7)

Time is always on the bottom (horizontal) axis. The vertical axis is used for distance. Be sure to state the units being used, and from where the distance is measured.

The slope of a distance/time graph gives the speed. The steeper the slope the faster the speed.

The journey line in Figure S29 shows that 50 km were travelled in 2 hours, so the average speed is 25 km/h (or 25 km h^{-1}).

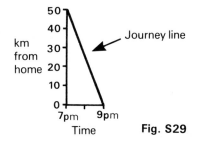

Fig. S29

Scatter graphs (8)

A graph that illustrates any connection between two sets of data. See Figure S30.

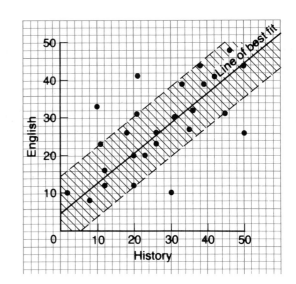

Fig. S30

Vectors (9)

Vectors can be described as a matrix, e.g. $\begin{pmatrix} -3 \\ 1 \end{pmatrix}$ (see under 'Vectors' in the Summaries of Books 1 and 2), or by their end letters, $\overrightarrow{AB}$, or by a single letter distinguished by a wavy line, a̰, or (in print) by being darker, **a**.

Figure S31 shows some examples. Note that all parallel vectors can use the same letter, and that non-parallel vectors must use different letters.

Fig. S31

Areas (10)

Learn: The area of a parallelogram is its base times its height.

Learn: The area of a trapezium is half the sum of the parallel sides times the perpendicular distance between them.

Learn: The area of a circle is π times the square of the radius.

Percentages (11)

Learn: One as a percentage of another equals one over the other times a hundred.

Example   16 as a percentage of 25 $= \dfrac{16 \times \cancel{100}^{4}}{{}_{1}\cancel{25}} = 64\%$

Be very careful that you do not confuse '16 as a percentage of 25' with 'Find 16 percent of 25'. 16% means $\frac{16}{100}$, so 16% of 25 is $\dfrac{\cancel{16}^{4} \times \cancel{25}^{1}}{{}_{1}{}_{4}\cancel{100}} = 4.$

It would be helpful if questioners always said 'Find 16 out of 25 as a percentage' when they want the answer 64%.

Learn: **Change percent equals change over original times a hundred.**

'Change' can be any difference between two quantities, for instance an increase, a decrease, a profit, a loss, or an error.

Example   A boy counts 86 sheep when really there are 90. What is his percentage error?

The error (the 'change') is 4; the original is 90.

$$\text{Percentage error} = \frac{4}{9\!\!\!/0} \times 10\!\!\!/0 = 4\tfrac{4}{9}\%$$

For further examples see exercise 11B, questions 1 and 2.

Learn: **To increase by $r\%$ multiply by** $\dfrac{100 + r}{100}$ (or $(100 + r)\%$).

Learn: **To decrease by $r\%$ multiply by** $\dfrac{100 - r}{100}$ (or $(100 - r)\%$).

Example   To increase 18 by 45% work out $18 \times \tfrac{145}{100}$ or 18×1.45

Example   To decrease 18 by 45% work out $18 \times \tfrac{55}{100}$ or 18×0.55

Some calculators will work out the answer to the above two examples by:

18 ⊞ 45 ⅐   and   18 ⊟ 45 ⅐   or   18 ⊠ 45 ⅐ ⊞   and   18 ⊠ 45 ⅐ ⊟
(You may need to press ⊜ after these sequences.)

Rotations and rotational symmetry (13)

Rotations are best observed by practical work: either by using a tracing or by actually rotating the question diagram.

If a shape rotates through $x°$ then the corresponding sides of the object and image are at $x°$ to each other (or are parallel if $x = 180$).

The **order of rotational symmetry** is the number of times a shape fits into a tracing of itself in one full turn. (Some mathematicians do not consider a shape to have rotational symmetry if it only fits into the tracing once, as in the case of a trapezium.)

Algebraic multiplication and division (14)

Deal with any integers; then the letters in alphabetical order.

To multiply: add the indices.

To divide: subtract the indices.

See exercise 14B for examples.

Polygons (15)

The exterior angles total 360° in all polygons. See Figure S32.

The interior angles of an *n*-sided polygon total $(n - 2) \times 180°$. See Figure S33.

If a polygon has *n* sides then $(n - 3)$ diagonals may be drawn from one vertex. See Figure S34.

If a polygon has *n* sides then $\dfrac{n(n - 3)}{2}$ diagonals may be drawn.

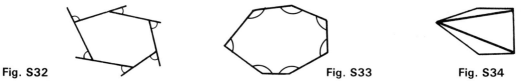

Fig. S32   Fig. S33   Fig. S34

Significant figures (16)

This is like decimal place approximation, but all figures are counted except zeros between the decimal point and the first non-zero digit, and place-value zeros before the point.

Examples   3075 is 3100 to two significant figures.
                  0.0503 is 0.050 to two significant figures.

Note: Always make sure that the number is approximately (about) the same size after the approximation as it was originally. For example, 1236.8 correct to 2 significant figures is 1200, not 12.

Constructions (17)

Constructing triangles: Draw a sketch first to work out the best method. Leave in your construction lines in test.

To drop a perpendicular: A perpendicular from A to BC starts at point A and meets line BC at right angles. See Figure S35 and the introduction to exercise 17A.

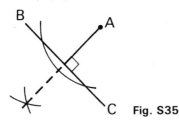

Sloping line graphs (18, 23)

To plot the graph of $y + 2x = 3$.

Choose three values for *x*, including 0, and find *y* for each:

e.g. If $x = 0$ then $y + 0 = 3$ so $y = 3$. Plot $(0, 3)$.
     If $x = 2$ then $y + 4 = 3$ so $y = -1$. Plot $(2, -1)$.
     If $x = -1$, then $y - 2 = 3$, so $y = 5$. Plot $(-1, 5)$.
See Figure S36.

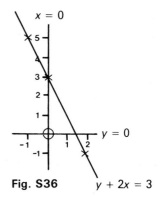

Fig. S35

Fig. S36 $y + 2x = 3$

Frequency tables (19)

These simplify the arithmetic when there is a large amount of data. 'Frequency' means how often something happens. The data is collected together, e.g. if the data consists of marks you count how many score 5, how many score 6, etc. See chapter 19, question 2 for an example.

Expansion of brackets (20)

A number or term written immediately in front of a bracket multiplies every term in that bracket.

Beware of minus signs!

For examples see chapter 20.

Inequalities (22A)

If $A = \{x: -2 < x \leqslant 2; x \text{ integral}\}$ then $A = \{-1, 0, 1, 2\}$.

Algebraic inequalities can be solved exactly as if they were equations (unless they involve division by a possibly negative letter).

Example   Solve $3x - 2 > 5$.

   If $3x - 2 > 5$ then $3x > 7$, giving $x > 2\frac{1}{3}$.

Equations (22B)

When there is more than one letter-term the 'changing sides' or 'balance' method must be used.

Example   Solve $4x - 1 = 3x + 5$.

   $4x - 1 = 3x + 5 \rightarrow 4x - 3x - 1 = 5 \rightarrow x - 1 = 5 \rightarrow x = 6$.

Graph regions (22, 23)

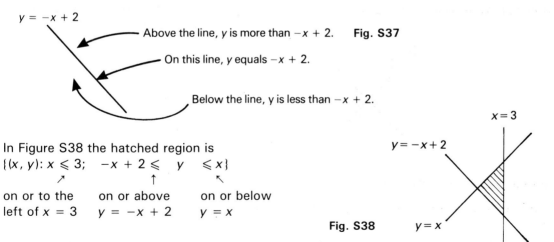

$y = -x + 2$

Above the line, y is more than $-x + 2$.   **Fig. S37**

On this line, y equals $-x + 2$.

Below the line, y is less than $-x + 2$.

In Figure S38 the hatched region is
$\{(x, y): x \leqslant 3; \quad -x + 2 \leqslant \quad y \quad \leqslant x\}$

on or to the   on or above   on or below
left of $x = 3$ $y = -x + 2$ $y = x$

$x = 3$

$y = -x + 2$

Fig. S38 $y = x$

Volumes (24)

The volume of a prism is found by multiplying its cross-section area by its length (or height).

A cylinder is a prism with a circular cross-section. Its volume is $\pi r^2 h$.

Probability: exclusive, independent and non-independent outcomes (25)

Outcomes of events can be exclusive, independent, or non-independent.

Exclusive – only one of the outcomes is possible in any one trial.

Independent and non-independent – all outcomes are possible in any one trial. If non-independent, one successful outcome affects the probability of the others.

Exclusive: $P(A \text{ or } B) = P(A) + P(B)$

Independent: $P(A \text{ and } B) = P(A) \times P(B)$

Non-independent: as independent, but consider the change to $P(B)$ when A occurs.

See chapter 25 for a fuller explanation. It is a difficult topic!

Simultaneous equations (26, 29)

If there is one unknown quantity you only need one equation to find out what it is, e.g. $3x = 12$ tells you that $x = 4$. If there are two unknowns then you need two equations; solving them **simultaneously** ('at the same time') means finding the values that make both equations true, e.g. if $y = 2x$ and $x + y = 6$, then the only possible answer for both to be true is $x = 2$ and $y = 4$.

Four methods are possible:

(a) Draw intersecting graphs. See exercise 26A, For Discussion Part One.

(b) Substitute for one letter in one equation its value in the other equation. This is a good method when one equation is in the form $y = \dots$ or $x = \dots$. See exercise 26B, introduction and question 4.

(c) Add or subtract the equations to eliminate one of the letter-terms (having multiplied as necessary to make one letter-term the same in both). See exercise 29A, question 5; exercise 29B, questions 2, 3 and 4.

(d) Use matrices. This is ideal for solution by computers. It will be taught to you in Book 4.

Similar shapes (27)

Similar shapes have the same size angles and their sides are in the same ratio. The transformation of enlargement produces similar shapes.

Tangents to circles (28)

Figure S39 illustrates the construction of a tangent at a point on a circle.

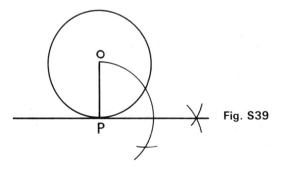

Fig. S39

Figure S40 illustrates the construction of the two tangents from a point to a circle.

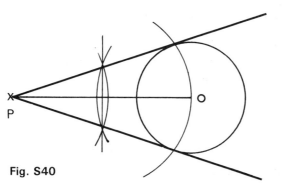

Fig. S40

Note the equalities shown in Figure S41, and that the tangent meets the radius at 90°.

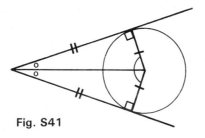

Fig. S41

Change of subject (31)

This is like solving equations, except that you have to find one letter in terms of the others. Most students find the flow-diagram method is easiest, although it cannot be used if the subject letter appears more than once in the equation. See the examples in Chapter 31.

Pythagoras' Theorem (32)

In a right-angled triangle the square on the hypotenuse is equal to the sum of the squares on the other two sides.

For examples see the introduction to chapter 32.

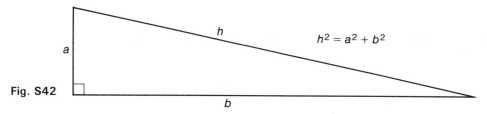

$$h^2 = a^2 + b^2$$

Fig. S42

Point symmetry (34)

If a figure has point symmetry it looks the same when turned upside-down. See the introduction to chapter 34 for a fuller explanation.